IMPROVING THE HEALTH
OF THE NATION

RE

COLIN FRANCOME has had articles published in many of the major British journals including *British Medical Journal, Lancet, British Journal of Criminology* and *Political Quarterly*. He is the editor of the health series for Middlesex University Press and is well known for his book *Abortion Freedom* and as main author of *Caesarean Birth in Britain*.

DAVID F. MARKS is Professor of Psychology and Director of the Health Research Centre at Middlesex University. He has taught or conducted research at universities in England, Italy, Norway, New Zealand, Spain and the USA. He has authored over 250 research publications, including nine books. His research interests include the study of cognitive and social processes, especially in relation to health, health behaviour and healthcare. From 1992 to 1994 he served as chair of the Special Group in Health Psychology of the British Psychological Society. He is the editor of the *Journal of Health Psychology*.

IMPROVING THE HEALTH OF THE NATION

THE FAILURE OF THE GOVERNMENT'S
HEALTH REFORMS

Dr Colin Francome
&
Professor David Marks

Foreword by Professor Harry Keen,
NHS Support Federation

MIDDLESEX UNIVERSITY PRESS

First published in 1996 by Middlesex University Press.
Middlesex University Press is an imprint of Middlesex University Services Limited,
Bounds Green Road, London N11 2NQ.

ISBN 1 898253 05 6

A CIP catalogue record for this book is available from the British Library.

Design by Tim McPhee.
Production in association with Book Production Consultants plc, 25–27 High
Street, Chesterton, Cambridge CB4 IND, UK.

Typeset in Sabon.
Printed and bound by Cambridge University Press, Cambridge, UK.

CONTENTS

To Sid and Hazel Francome,
Victor and Mary Marks.
With love and appreciation.

FOREWORD: HEALTH SERVICES FOR THE NATION – PUBLIC OR PRIVATE CONCERN?

You may question the democratic legitimacy of the Thatcher government's disintegrative attack on the NHS, known as 'the reforms'. Concocted in secret, without benefit of electoral mandate or the inconvenience of consultation, and ignoring the outmoded extravagance of consent, the reforms implacably imposed a new ideological mould upon the NHS. The dizzying successes of the British free-market economy were to replace the old-fashioned notions of public service and social purpose upon which the NHS had been founded.

Democratically illegitimate though it was, the NHS Act became the law of the land in 1990 and has been ruthlessly applied to the dismantling of the NHS ever since. Some of the worst commercial practices are now applied to the operation of this once proud public service. Brought in from the commercial sector, a veritable army of managers and market bureaucrats – each with their squadron of administrative, secretarial and technical staff – have striven to outdo each other in presentational glitz, to deflect real public inquiry and to renew their short-term contracts.

The public feels that it is being conned. The political salesmen offered them 'increased patient freedom of choice'. Instead they experienced more restrictions upon freedom of medical referral than ever before. The 1948 NHS enabled any doctor to refer any patient to any centre for care. From 1990, that happened no longer. The patient now goes where the health contract has been let. Many patients have been transferred from one hospital to another, not for their health but to meet a contract.

The profession feels it has been conned. Many doctors were galled by the offer that 'money will follow patients'. They thought that by working harder and better they would attract more patients and improve the income of their hospitals (and perhaps their own as well). This too was false. Money did not follow patients; patients followed contracts. Far from working harder for their hospitals, many specialists found themselves standing idle when the hospital contracts for the year had run out after nine months. Patients waiting for operations outside, empty operating theatres inside, surgeons twiddling their thumbs? The market has fallen down badly in providing local care at the time of need.

The private sector has cashed in. Those patients who can afford it – and those who if the pain is bad enough or the risk frightening enough will sell up or borrow money – buy their items of care on the private health care market, ironically often from NHS doctors, even in the local NHS hospital. Cash up front has opened the door. Once upon a time the NHS was equally available to all in need regardless of ability to pay; now equity of access to care has been abandoned as a basic concept. GP fundholder patients get greater resourcing and faster tracking than ordinary NHS patients, and the NHS sells off its 'unused capacity' to the private payer at the expense of the ordinary NHS patient.

Freedom from bureaucracy was the promise. The reality has been the greatest explosion in managerial and administrative numbers and the greatest diversion of resources from patient care in the history of the NHS. The NHS, previously administered by a small number of dedicated people, required management reinforcement. Even in his wildest dreams, however, Sir Roy Griffiths – its managerial re-engineer – could not have foreseen (or approved) the deluge of well over twenty thousand new managers, plus four or five times that number of support staff, at a conservatively estimated additional cost of £2 billion a year, in largest part not to run the health care but to run the market. A new corpus of arrogant, technically and professionally ignorant, financially astute and well-rewarded management has been installed, convinced that the NHS is 'full of waste' and with their jobs on the line to clean it all up. Financial competition setting hospital against hospital, doctor against doctor, clinic against clinic, is proving to be a very expensive business, diverting vast sums of badly needed money away from patient care and into commercial management culture.

In the US the market prevails. On average, an American citizen spends over three times as much per year on health care as a UK citizen. Americans make a lot more doctor visits and get a lot more operations each year but the national health indices are indifferent. Markets can only work where money is made. In health care, money is spent and the best outcome is obtained where attention is directed to spending that money wisely and well.

Markets in health are at best an irrelevance, at worst an obscenity. They are costly, ineffective, inequitable, unsocial. They impose constraints of commercial confidentiality on professional freedom of communication and on the use of public money. Teaching and research impede the generation of finance and so must be under downward pressure in a market-orientated structure – unless they too are commercialised. Democratic accountability is foreign to commercial management; the quangoisation of public services is the commercial substitute for democracy.

The private takeover has now extended to the heartlands of the NHS. The Private Finance Initiative effectively puts all new capital-requiring NHS developments (of structures or services) or replacements out to private tender. Only those least profitable, 'down-market' areas of medicine which fail to attract the interest of private investment will be considered for public funding from a Treasury that is increasingly revenue limited.

We are clearly very close to a moment of irreversible decision about the future of the NHS. Will there be a rebirth of public concern and enthusiasm for this extraordinarily successful and cost-effective public possession founded on social purpose; or will we convert to an alien, new free-market philosophy in health, here of unproven quality and effectiveness and of highly dubious success elsewhere? There may be time to put this decision to the test of public opinion in an election choice. There may not.

Professor Harry Keen,
NHS Support Federation

ACKNOWLEDGEMENTS

Professor Kevin Gournay wrote much of the material on mental health in Chapter 7. Kay Caldwell collaborated with Colin Francome on the research into hip replacements. Iain Crinson collaborated with Colin Francome on the research into accident and emergency units. Caryl Bryant and Marie Dunne collaborated with Colin Francome on the research into kidney replacements. The contribution of all these to this book is gratefully acknowledged.

Thanks also to Julia Schofield, Karin Pappenheim, Julia Clark, Katy Jones, Mildred Gordon MP, Professor Edmund Penning-Rowsell, Professor Susanne MacGregor, Paul Moynagh, Dr Marion Newman, Robert Wharton, Angela Baird, Kit McCarthy Ross Taylor, Michael Walker, Paul Evans, Karin Pappenheim, Joan Walsh and Katy Jones.

| CHAPTER ONE |

INTRODUCTION

*It is the growth in inequality in the 1980s and
1990s that has led to Britain falling down the
international league table of health.*

The overall health of British people is a cause for great concern.
Fundamental changes are needed both in the organisation of society
and in the delivery of health care. These are the major conclusions of
our review of the effects of the government's health changes. The
statistical evidence shows that even in the period before the
introduction of the NHS reforms Britain had been falling behind other
countries in the attempt to improve the health of society. In 1970 life
expectancy had been about the same in both Britain and Japan, 72
years. However, during the period 1970–90 life expectancy in Japan
increased by 6.9 years to become the highest in the world. In contrast,
the improvement in Britain over the same period was only 3.9 years
and the country's position within the life expectancy league table of
countries belonging to the Organisation of Economic Co-operation
and Development fell from tenth to seventeenth.[1] In fact in his 1991
annual report the Chief Medical Officer at the Department of Health
drew attention to what appeared to be a rise in national mortality rates
for men and women aged 15–45 years from 1985.[2]

The British government's response to the evident need to improve
Britain's health was to introduce a series of 'reforms'. The White Paper,
Working for Patients, was published in January 1989 and there were
fine words from the Prime Minister, Margaret Thatcher, in the
Foreword:[3]

> The National Health Service at its best is without equal.
> Time and again, the nation has seen just how much we
> owe to those who work in it. A skilled and dedicated staff
> – backed by enormously increased resources – have
> coped superbly with the growing demands of modern

1 Wilkinson, 1994, p. 22.
2 Department of Health, 1991.
3 Department of Health, 1989.

medicine and increasing numbers of patients. There is a great deal of which we can all feel very proud. The National Health Service will continue to be available to all, regardless of income, and to be financed mainly out of general taxation. But major tasks now face us: to bring all parts of the National Health Service up to the very high standard of the best, while maintaining the principles on which it was founded; and to prepare for the needs of the future. We aim to extend patient choice, to delegate responsibility to where the services are provided and to secure the best value for money. All the proposals in this paper put the needs of patients first.

The government reforms were introduced in 1991. The main features were the introduction of a split between purchasers and providers. The former health authorities became purchasers of care on behalf of their local population. There was the introduction of General Practitioner fundholding whereby some doctors could buy a range of services for their patients. In addition hospitals were taken from the direct control of the local authorities and became trusts with their own boards of directors.

The government believed that the introduction of more financial awareness into the health service would lead to improvements in health. To monitor these it set out specific targets in the document *The Health of the Nation*, published in 1992. This was proposed as a strategy for health in England, and similar documents were prepared for Wales and Scotland. In the report the government argued that 'Many people die prematurely or suffer debilitating ill health from conditions which are to a large extent preventable'.[4] It maintained that the government's overall goal was to add years to life and life to years. It proposed to increase the number of years lived free from ill health and to minimise the adverse effects of illness and disability.

However, despite the statements predicting improvements, there was opposition to the reforms from the medical profession, which had a number of concerns about the changes, as we shall see. These began before the introduction of the reforms, and continued as the effects of the changes became evident. In July 1993 the chairman of the British Medical Association asked the government to stop and take stock of the reforms. He said that, as the country as a whole was running a

4 Department of Health, 1992, p. 11.

budget deficit of £50 billion, the medical profession could not expect it simply to dole out more money to the health service. However, he continued:[5]

> The government could put the changes on hold. I would love to see the internal market overhauled. A more feasible option might be to give all general practitioners a budget but make sure that they had strong links with the commissioning authorities...The government at the moment is hearing only the good news about the reforms. It needs our help to discover what is really going on.

He continued by saying that he was preparing a dossier to send to the government.

On 11 April 1994 the following report appeared on page 2 of the *Guardian*:

> The NHS market has become an 'uncontrolled monster', the chairman of the British Medical Association ruling council warned yesterday. Ministers responsible for imposing the system without trials and without consulting the health professions had been 'criminally irresponsible', said Dr Sandy Macara who was setting out a plan to restore sanity to the situation. He said three years of the system had offered no evidence of benefit to patients to justify the trauma and upheaval of mindless change.

Dr Macara went on to say that a doctor who gave a patient an untested and untried drug without proper study and trial would be rightly criticised, but this was effectively what the government had done. He noted that some fundholders had been winners in the system, as had a proportion of the early trusts and managers who had been earning good salaries. In respect of the latter he pointed to the fact that the share of NHS funds spent on administration had risen from 4 per cent in the mid 1980s to 11 per cent in 1993.

At their annual conference in June 1994 Britain's senior hospital doctors showed their frustration with the government health changes. The *British Medical Journal* pointed out that the underlying concern amongst consultants was the maintenance of professional standards. Chris Bayliss, a consultant radiologist in Exeter, commented: 'Our

5 Smith, R., 1993b, p. 83.

professional standards, morals and ethics are being continually undermined. Our goodwill is running out.'[6]

This kind of frustration with the NHS changes is in contrast with the rosy picture painted by the then Prime Minister and shows the need to analyse the changes.

As we have indicated, Britain's health statistics in terms of length of life, infant and perinatal mortality are inferior to those of many other countries. In this book we analyse the reasons for this and make suggestions as to how Britain's overall health can be improved.

It is interesting to see that in this regard there is a manifest desire amongst the British people to ensure that health is given a prominent position. Wherever cutbacks in services have been threatened, local people have worked to maintain them. We were invited to carry out a survey in Barnet to find out the attitudes of the local people to the closure of the accident and emergency unit and the removal of acute beds from Edgware hospital. Out of a random sample of two hundred people we found every single person was against the closure.[7] Despite this public attitude, the local Member of Parliament voted for the closure in the House of Commons.

In the next chapter we shall see that after the formation of the National Health Service, there was a view that the British health system was the 'envy of the world'. As the country has slipped down the international league table, it has become clear that this is no longer commonly felt. We therefore make proposals about how the health of the country can be restored to equal that of other leading countries.

MAIN FEATURES OF *THE HEALTH OF THE NATION*

The report stressed that health was better than it has ever been. It drew attention to the fact that a century ago four out of ten children did not survive into adulthood and life expectancy at birth was only 44 years for men and 48 for women. These figures have increased to 73 years for men and 79 years for women.[8]

The report chose five key areas where it believed that great improvements in health could be achieved. Targets were set which, in the main, related to the year 2000 – although some were concerned with a longer period than this. The 1990 base for comparison of

6 Beecham, 1994, p. 1587.
7 Francome, 1995.
8 Department of Health, 1992, p. 9.

mortality targets was calculated as an average of the three years 1989, 1990 and 1991.

1 Coronary heart disease and stroke

The report said these areas were included because of the scope for prevention through the reduction in the prevalence of associated risk factors – unbalanced diet, smoking, raised blood pressure, alcohol misuse and lack of physical activity. Reducing these risk factors would also contribute to the prevention of many other diseases.

Targets

These are to be achieved by the year 2000, with a 1990 baseline. They are as follows:
- to reduce the death rates for both coronary heart disease and strokes in people under 65 by at least 40 per cent;
- to reduce the death rate from coronary heart disease in people aged 65–74 by at least 30 per cent;
- to reduce the death rate for stroke in people aged 65–74 by at least 40 per cent.

2 Cancers

The Health of the Nation stated that this area was selected because of the toll cancers take in terms of ill health and death and because some can be prevented by, for example, not smoking.

Targets

These are as follows:
- to reduce the death rate for breast cancer amongst those invited for screening by at least 25 per cent by the year 2000;
- to reduce the incidence of invasive cervical cancer by at least 20 per cent by the year 2000;
- to reduce the death rate for lung cancer under the age of 75 by at least 30 per cent in men and at least 15 per cent in women by the year 2010;
- to halt the year on year increase in the incidence of skin cancer by the year 2005.

3 Mental illness

The report said that this area was chosen as it affects many people and because the government believed there was much that could be achieved by an improvement in services.

Targets
These are:
- to improve significantly the health and social functioning of mentally ill people by the year 2000;
- to reduce the overall suicide rate by at least 15 per cent (from 11.1 per 100,000 in 1990 to no more than 9.4);
- to reduce the suicide rate of severely mentally ill people by at least 33 per cent (from the estimate of 15 per cent in 1990 to no more than 10 per cent).

4 HIV/AIDS and sexual health
These areas were included because they were believed to be perhaps the greatest new threat to public health this century.

Targets
The targets in this section refer to AIDS indirectly. They are as follows:
- to reduce the incidence of gonorrhoea by at least 20 per cent by 1995, as an indicator of HIV/AIDS trends – this would mean a reduction from 61 new cases per 100,000 population in 1990 to no more than 49 new cases per 100,000;
- to reduce by at least 50 per cent the rate of conceptions amongst the under-16s by the year 2000 – this would be from 9.5 per 1,000 girls age 13–15 in 1989 to no more than 4.8.

5 Accidents
These were included as they are a substantial cause of illness and death, especially in young and elderly people. Furthermore they can often be avoided.

Targets
The targets in this section are as follows:
- to reduce the death rate for accidents among children under the age of 15 by at least 33 per cent by 2005 – this would be from 6.7 per 100,000 population in 1990 to no more that 4.5 per 100,000;
- to reduce the death rate for accidents among young people aged 15–24 by at least 25 per cent by 2005 – this would be from 23.2 per 100,000 population in 1990 to no more that 17.4 per 100,000;
- to reduce the death rate for accidents among people aged 65 and over by at least 33 per cent by 2005 – this would be from 56.7 per 100,000 population in 1990 to no more than 38 per 100,000.

In a government document outlining the strategy more fully, the Department of Health stated that the greatest advances in health would develop in three main ways:[9]
1 Encouraging people to lead healthier and safer lives and to promote the availability of affordable health choices.
2 Providing a healthier and safer environment.
3 Providing the right type of high quality services.

CRITICISMS OF THE GOVERNMENT'S HEALTH TARGETS

The seven members of our research team have been critical of many of the targets. One possibility, of course, is that by the government choosing selected targets resources may be diverted from other health areas which might well suffer. It is for this reason that we chose not only to consider the government targets, but to identify other areas, specifically kidney transplants and hip replacements, which are important to health. A second point is that the trend in a number of areas was downward anyway:
• The percentage of men smoking fell in England from 51 per cent in 1974 to 31 per cent in 1990. Over the same period women's smoking declined from 40 per cent to 28 per cent.[10]
• The death rates from coronary heart disease amongst the under-65s fell from 82 per 100,000 in 1980 to 58 in 1990.[11]
• The death rates from stroke amongst the under-65s fell from 25 per 1,000 in 1970 to 12.5 per 1,000 in 1990.[12]
• The number of cases of gonorrhoea fell from 58,000 in 1981 to 20,000 in 1991. This is a remarkable fall. Official figures for AIDS shows its incidence rose from zero notified cases in 1981 to over 1,500 in 1991. So during the period 1981–91 there was an inverse correlation between numbers of cases of AIDS and those of gonorrhoea. Future trends in gonorrhoea may continue downwards but the prediction in the official publication *Social Trends* is that the number of AIDS cases will rise to nearly 2,500 by the year 1997.[13]
• The number of deaths from accidents fell from 5,934 in 1982 to 5,217 in 1990 and 4,229 in 1992.[14]

9 Department of Health, 1993d, p. 6.
10 Department of Health, 1993d, p. 71.
11 Department of Health, 1992, p. 47.
12 Department of Health, 1992, p. 48.
13 OPCS, 1994d, p. 97.
14 Department of Transport, 1994b, p. 173.

This evidence suggests that many of the improvements that we observe may not be due to *The Health of the Nation* initiative, and in the important case of AIDS it is likely that the index will improve but that the problem will worsen.

The criticism that the government used an index that was already improving does not apply, however, to suicide. The rate for young men rose from 62 per million in 1982 to 116 per million in 1990. The women's rate was 20 per million in 1982 and showed little change rising to only 21 per million in 1990.[15] Similarly under-16 teenage pregnancy has not been falling. In fact it rose – from 7.2 per 1,000 in 1980 to 10.1 in 1990, with a small fall to 9.3 in 1991.[16] If these areas are to show improvement, then changes will be necessary.

A different criticism of some of the targets is that they are a little vague. Professor Kevin Gournay argues that this is especially the case with the government aim to 'improve significantly the health and social functioning of mentally ill people'. He points out this is difficult, if not impossible, to monitor. We know that suicide rates are difficult to measure and some may be recorded by coroner's courts as accidental deaths in order to help the deceased people's families to cope. This may be particularly the case in areas where a high proportion of people are linked with the Roman Catholic Church, as this denomination regards suicide as a mortal sin.

As regards heart disease, the targets seem a little inconsistent. For example, there are no targets for reducing cholesterol levels in England (which stand at 5.8 mmol/l for men and 5.9 mmol/l for women), but there are targets for Wales (5.0) and Ireland (5.2).[17]

Another important point is the lack of attention paid to the socio-economic differences in health. This is not surprising, for the government has been at pains to minimise the impact of reports of class differentials. When the Black Report came out in 1980, only 260 copies of the duplicated manuscript were made and major organisations did not receive copies.[18] In January 1986 the Health Education Council commissioned Margaret Whitehead to investigate changes in inequality that had occurred since 1980. Before publication of her findings in March 1987, it was announced that the Health Education Council – which had been responsible for many national health education programmes – would be closed and a new

15 Wilkinson, 1994, p. 39.
16 Francome and Walsh, 1995, p. 4.
17 Jones, 1994b.
18 Townsend and Davidson, 1992, p. 3.

organisation, the Health Education Authority, would be set up. *The Lancet* reported that Alliance MPs told the Health Minister that 'the termination of the HEC had far more to do than ministers admitted with its high-profile campaign on issues such as smoking, drinking and diet, which had offended great interests the Government preferred to keep sweet'.[19] When *The Health Divide*[20] was about to be published, the chairman of the HEC, Sir Brian Bailey, cancelled the press briefing and was quoted in the *Independent* as saying that the information on the class differences was 'political dynamite in an election year'.[21] It was then discovered that an official from the Department of Health had rung the chairman about the report the night before. It appeared that again the government was trying to restrict dissemination of knowledge about class differences in health. Baroness Seear said that, unless the report was published, 'we are bound to assume that there are things that the government do not wish the public to see.'[22] The report was in fact published, after complaints from MPs. However, the failure to stress social class in *The Health of the Nation* may be seen in the light of these apparent attempts to suppress information on the class divide in health.

Elsewhere one of us has emphasised the lack of targets relating to health differentials as a fatal flaw in the White Paper:[23]

> Social and economic improvements among those sectors of the population suffering the poorest levels of health, ie the unemployed, working class, ethnic minorities, people with disabilities and older people, will be a necessary precondition for an overall reduction in ill health.

In addition to scant attention to social class differences are the problems of the long-term sick and the elderly. The *British Medical Journal* drew attention to a statement from Parliament that the NHS has 'a responsibility to provide long term care for people who need it for reasons of ill health'.[24] The report continued that patients were being pressurised into moving out of free NHS hospitals and into private nursing homes, which drain away their life savings if they have capital of more than £3,000. (This figure has subsequently been raised.)

19 Townsend and Davidson, 1992, p. 7.
20 Whitehead, 1992.
21 Townsend and Davidson, 1992, p. 8.
22 Townsend and Davidson, 1992, p. 9.
23 Marks, 1994, p. 121.
24 Anonymous, 1994c, p. 742.

The issue came to public attention when a patient who was severely brain damaged by a stroke was discharged after eighteen months in Leeds General Infirmary to a nursing home for which his family had to pay. The Ombudsman ruled that the NHS should have continued to provide care free of charge. The NHS accepted the ruling, the man was taken back under its wing and his wife was reimbursed.

There is little in *The Health of the Nation* about the elderly, and this is a serious gap. There have been cases in which elderly people have been forced to sell their houses and use up their life savings to pay for nursing home care. This is likely to be a growing problem as we have rising numbers of elderly. We will discuss this issue when we look at the question of community care in Chapter 7 and in the final chapter.

The Health of the Nation also omitted any targets to narrow the differentials between people with different ethnic backgrounds. It merely identified people from minority ethnic populations as a special group with a number of different needs.

There are some important health problems that are not discussed in the White Paper. We have already mentioned organ transplantation and hip replacement, and there are numerous others. One is asthma. Cases have doubled over the past twenty years. Up to 10 per cent of the population is now affected by asthma and a growing body of evidence suggests that increasingly dirty air is to blame.[25] This draws attention to the need for a healthy environment, an issue which will be discussed and for which proposals will be made in the final chapter. We shall provide evidence that fundamental changes are needed in British society in order that substantial improvements in health can be achieved.

THE PARTICIPANTS IN THE NHS AND THEIR VIEW OF THE CHANGES

For this book we have carried out many surveys of the views of doctors in different positions within the NHS. We have studied the views of one group of purchasers – Directors of Public Health – twice. There are two sources of access to care in the NHS. The first is through General Practitioners (GPs) and the second is through accident and emergency units. We have published studies of the initial views of the changes for both these groups. We have updated the studies with new questions for this book, making a total of six surveys of these three groups.

---

25 Ryan and Reeves, 1994.

In addition we put further questions to other key workers within the health service. One important issue has been the growth of transplantation in recent years. Contacts with patients revealed this was an area of interest, and we therefore carried out a study of kidney transplant surgeons. Furthermore, we were concerned that some people were facing unacceptable delay for hip replacement. We therefore carried out a study of orthopaedic surgeons.

The various studies we have carried out are listed in Table 1.1 below.

Table 1.1   *Studies carried out for this research*

Year	Research	Number	Response
1990	Accident and emergency units	172	74%
1992	Directors of Public Health	150	84%
1992	General Practitioners	280	77%
1994	General Practitioners	251	72%
1994	Directors of Public Health	136	90%
1994	Kidney consultants	60	86%
1994	Orthopaedic surgeons	141	79%
1994	Accident and emergency units	119	81%
Total number of doctors consulted		1309	

In this book we shall present evidence from 1,309 consultations, which include 531 with GPs and 492 with consultants. The total does not include the many discussions we had with both consultants and GPs outside the formal surveys. The response rates for the surveys varied between 72 per cent and 90 per cent. All the rates are high and reflect both the amount of effort involved in designing the questionnaires and the fact that for each survey, except the first one of GPs and Directors of Public Health, there was three mailings.

We provide evidence that in some areas the changes have been negative in their effects, with GPs in particular being overwhelmed with paperwork and more than four out of five doctors saying they are unable to keep abreast of medical developments.

In the next chapter we consider the background to the current position. In Chapter 3 we look at the ideas behind the government changes and in Chapter 4 we consider some of the effects. In the five chapters after that we look at the relevance of the five *Health of the Nation* targets in turn and consider why, in some areas – such as suicide rates – there has been worsening of the performance indicators, and in others – such as smoking prevalence in 11–15-year-olds – no change has occurred so far. Chapter 10 considers kidney transplants and analyses our study of orthopaedic surgeons. In the final chapter we provide evidence from numerous sources to show that the growth in inequality in the 1980s and 1990s has been a major factor in preventing great improvements in health statistics. It makes proposals for changes at the personal and governmental level which, if implemented, we believe would bring improvements in the overall health of people in Britain.

CHAPTER TWO

THE POSITION IN BRITAIN BEFORE THE 1990 CHANGES

Disease must be attacked in the poorest or in the richest in the same way as the fire brigade will give full assistance to the humble cottage as readily as to the most important mansion.
Winston Churchill

The decision to have a National Health Service was taken during the Second World War. After a great deal of debate the Act setting up the service was passed in 1946 and Britain's National Health Service came into operation on 5 July 1948. It was the first health service in any Western society to provide free health care to the whole population.[1] Other countries had developed compulsory health insurances, but under these the health cover was generally confined to pensioners and to those who were insured and their dependents. Britain's introduction of the principle of universal coverage was new.[2] When the NHS came into operation 1,143 hospitals owned and run by a large variety of voluntary bodies provided 90,000 beds, and 1,545 hospitals owned by local authorities provided another 390,000 beds. These were integrated into the national service which had a total of 2,688 hospitals and 480,000 beds.[3]

At the same time the benefits of free GP care were extended to the whole population. Everyone was entitled to free care financed by the state. Furthermore, the proponents aimed to provide service of the highest quality. Aneurin Bevan told the House of Commons that the NHS was designed to 'universalise the best'.[4] It proved a popular measure and one commentator said that ten years after its inception the NHS seems to have been accepted as an altogether natural feature

....
1 Klein, 1984, p. 1.
2 Abel-Smith, 1978, p. 1.
3 Abel-Smith, 1978, p. 8.
4 Klein, 1984, p. 25.

of the British landscape.[5] It was a major development. Before we consider it more fully it is important to point out that it was a logical extension of many practices that had been growing over the years. Therefore we shall briefly consider health care before the NHS came into being.

HEALTH CARE BEFORE THE NHS

Institutional health care in this country began with the provisions for the sick and destitute made by the medieval monasteries and the earliest charity hospitals. St Bartholomew's Hospital was the first – founded in London in 1123.[6] State involvement in health began in the seventeenth century with the Elizabethan Poor Laws. These gave local authorities the power to levy rates to finance the support of disadvantaged individuals such as the lame and the blind who were unable to work.[7] In the eighteenth century there were two developments. The first was the establishment of the workhouse system, which became the main source of residential support for the impoverished sick. The second was the growth in the charity or voluntary hospital sector which went through a notable period of growth between 1750 and 1800 as Britain increased domestic productivity and foreign trade enhanced the wealth of the country. However, at this time and for a further century, hospital in-patient and out-patient care was largely provided for the urban poor only. The quality of care in hospitals was probably inferior to that received by the affluent at home, from whom doctors received the main part of their income. At the voluntary hospitals doctors received clinical experience rather than income.

There were two main initiatives in the nineteenth century. The County Asylums Act of 1808 enabled local authorities to build facilities for the mentally ill. Eventually a network of mental hospitals was constructed.[8] Secondly, an amendment made to the Poor Laws in the 1830s required the provision of wards for the sick poor. By 1864 there were around fifty thousand poor persons in such hospitals and a further eleven thousand people in voluntary hospitals.[9]

In 1867 the Metropolitan Poor Act created a common fund for the

....
5 Eckstein, 1970, p. 2.
6 Taylor, 1984, p. 4.
7 Pater, 1981.
8 Taylor, 1984, p. 4.
9 Abel-Smith, 1964.

foundation and support of fever and mental hospitals in London. The stimulus for the development came in part from the increased recognition of the infectious origins of most fevers and of the advantage of isolating those affected from the rest of the population. It has been argued that this represented 'an important stepping stone on the way to the eventual creation of the NHS'.[10]

In 1875 the Disraeli government introduced a Public Health Act which promoted the development of clean water, adequate drainage and sanitation. However, health was still generally poor and during the Boer War, for example, almost half the eligible population was found to be unfit for military service. This shocked people and was a factor in the setting up of the School Medical Service in 1907.[11]

At the end of the nineteenth century there was an expansion in the number of hospital beds in both the public and the private sector. Demand increased because of the rising population and the improving standards in Poor Law facilities. The total number of beds available in public infectious hospitals and workhouse institutions rose from 83,000 in 1891 to 154,000 in 1911. This was a rise of 85 per cent. The voluntary sector also expanded at the end of the century, increasing from 29,000 in 1891 to 43,000 in 1901. In fact one US medical historian has commented that to a considerable extent Britain was a welfare society, if not a welfare state, even before 1900. He suggested that this was related to two aspects of nineteenth-century Britain: Benthamite collectivism and Protestant philanthropy. A large percentage of Nonconformists with money followed the advice of the founder of Methodism, John Wesley: 'gain all you can; save all you can; give all you can'. A large part of what they gave went into hospital building – although even Wesley conceded that the state of these hospitals was often appalling.[12]

The distinction between medical specialists and GPs developed around the turn of the century. The income of the GPs came from fees paid directly by private patients and from payments made by the many friendly societies, which provided insurance cover for the cost of GP services and prescribed medicines. GPs were anxious to ensure that access to hospital care should be obtained by way of referrals from them.[13]

....
10 Taylor, 1984, p. 4.
11 Eckstein, 1970, p. 85.
12 Eckstein, 1970, pp. 15–18.
13 Taylor, 1984, p. 4.

National Insurance Act 1911
This Act came into operation in 1912. It was an important development, requiring lower paid workers to be insured for basic GP and pharmaceutical care. Their dependents were not included in this cover. This system was administered through county or county borough insurance committees which were the forerunner of today's Family Practitioner Service administrative structure. It did not cover children, wives who did not work, the self-employed or many old people and higher paid workers.[14] Schoolchildren were able to obtain free health care and the poor had access to the district Poor Law doctor. Very often people would have to queue for hours at the casualty department of the voluntary charitable hospitals.

Some GPs had different waiting rooms for health insurance patients and private fee-paying patients, or would only see private patients in their own homes. As more money was available from people living in the richer areas, doctors became concentrated in the more affluent neighbourhoods and the poor areas were deprived of care. There were twice as many doctors per head in London as in South Wales and four times as many doctors per head in Bournemouth as in the industrial Midlands. In the latter example, the age structure of Bournemouth would, of course, be one factor leading to extra doctors being needed.[15]

After the First World War an influenza epidemic revealed the fact that the general population was unfit. That led to the formation of the Ministry of Health in 1919.[16] Its role was co-ordinative and advisory rather than executive; however, its existence implied a strong government interest in the issue of health. In the following year the Dawson Report advocated a single integrated health service based on health centres. In 1926 the Royal Commission on national health insurance argued that the health services should be financed directly from public funds.

The 1929 Local Government Act gave authorities permission to provide a whole range of hospital facilities. State institutional support was thereby linked through local government control with the expanding community services already under the Medical Officers of Health. In 1930 the British Medical Association published a plan for general medical services and called for national health insurance provision. In the period before the Second World War the state sector

14 Abel-Smith, 1978, p. 1.
15 Abel-Smith, 1978, p. 2.
16 Eckstein, 1970, p. 85.

expanded and in the mid-1930s it provided about 80 per cent of the nation's total bed capacity.[17] During this time the inefficiency of having a huge variety of private health care systems became apparent. In 1938 a revised version of the British Medical Association's plan envisaged public hospital services being provided by groups of local authorities, each covering about 100,000 people.

The outbreak of the Second World War led to the formation of the Emergency Medical Scheme in 1939. It was formed in the expectation that there would be enormous casualties from enemy bombing.[18] In 1942 the Beveridge Report called for the setting up of a National Health Service, as indeed did the British Medical Association in a report published in the same year.

In 1944 the wartime administration produced a White Paper which announced the government's intention to introduce a National Health Service. At the end of the war 24 million people – about half the British population – were covered by compulsory health insurance.[19] However, the service was, according to at least one observer, in a 'deplorable state'. He summarised the problems that existed before the NHS under five main headings.

- There was a shortage of trained workers and facilities. The Nuffield Foundation calculated that the number of beds needed to be increased by one-third. Although this figure may seem high, there was very high bed occupancy.[20]
- Facilities and trained personnel were maldistributed. For example, Kensington had seven times as many doctors per unit of population as did South Shields.[21]
- Poor organisation aggravated the lack of personnel and facilities. Administrative boundaries often crossed urban areas and barred patients from some hospitals which were efficient and within easy distance. Sometimes services were duplicated and so resources were wasted.[22]
- Lack of funds meant that large-scale organisational changes were needed to extend the services. Some fashionable hospitals had an excess of charitable donations while others were grossly under-funded.[23]

17 Taylor, 1984, p. 5.
18 Titmuss, 1950.
19 Eckstein, 1970, p. 19.
20 Eckstein, 1970, p. 20.
21 Eckstein, 1970, p. 61.
22 Eckstein, 1970, p. 68.
23 Eckstein, 1970, p. 71.

- There were faults in the clinical approach to medicine, some of which were due to the four preceding points but others of which were due to other causes. The fact that only 20 per cent of doctors were in partnership meant that in cases of their own illness and during their holidays care was disrupted. Furthermore, the insurance scheme did not cover the cost of hospital care, only that of GPs.

When the changes were proposed the medical profession as a whole did not welcome them. Their comments led Aneurin Bevan to redraw the plans substantially. However, by 1958 two-thirds of doctors told Gallup that they supported the NHS and if they could be given the chance to go back ten years they would have been in favour of its creation.

THE BRITISH NATIONAL HEALTH SERVICE 1948–90

The setting up of the NHS entailed the creation of a massive administration – fourteen regional hospital boards, thirty-six boards of governors for teaching hospitals (which were given special status in the legislation), 380 hospital management committees and 138 executive councils. It had certain important characteristics.

A All encompassing
Britain was the first European country to have an integrated system. Important here was an argument developed by the Socialist Health Association that the NHS should be directed to everyone. The association argued that a service directed primarily to the poor would inevitably become a poor service.[24] However, it was not simply the Left who saw the value of an integrated service; Winston Churchill stated: 'Disease must be attacked in the poorest or in the richest in the same way as the fire brigade will give full assistance to the humble cottage as readily as to the most important mansion.'[25]

B The General Practitioner
As we have seen, as long ago as 1911 the setting up of national health insurance created a central role for the GP. The Act meant that members of the working population below a certain income level were insured. The administration was conducted by the insurance

24 Eckstein, 1970, p. 107.
25 Yates, 1995, p. 4.

committees that were set up – one for each county or county borough. Since that time in many respects the family doctor has been the lynch pin of the British health system. The National Health Service Act of 1946 maintained their position and incorporated general practice as the basis for the health care system.[26]

When the NHS was created, a total of 138 executive councils was set up. The members were appointed by the Minister, the local authority and local professional committees. GPs had a list of people to look after. They were paid a capitation fee and were free to take on what other work they chose.

We mentioned earlier the maldistribution of doctors over the country. With the foundation of the NHS the Medical Practices Committee was set up to try to engineer a better distribution of GPs. The committee published lists of areas which were short of doctors and restricted permission for doctors to enter areas which were over-subscribed.[27] A single doctor was originally allowed to be paid for 4,000 patients on his or her list. This was reduced to 3,500 in 1952.

Observers tend to agree that a mistake was made when a committee was set up in 1955 to consider long-term demand. It recommended that Britain was training too many doctors and proposed a 'reduction of student intake by about one tenth, from as early a date as is practicable'.[28] This led to a reduction in the number of doctors in the early 1960s and Britain became heavily dependent on doctors who were trained abroad.

One problem with the GP service which came to prominence in the early 1960s was that district nurses, midwives and health visitors looked after clearly defined local areas. Doctors cared for patients from a much wider area, which meant communication was more difficult. From the mid-1950s some Medical Officers of Health began to employ health visitors and (later) district nurses in areas where GPs only provided services to patients on their practice lists. This system grew quickly so that by 1974 over three-quarters of GPs worked with district nurses and health visitors.[29]

To introduce more equity and promote some improvements in services, a major change in the payment for GPs was made in 1966. The role of the capitation system was reduced. A flat-rate allowance was

26 Taylor, 1984, p. 6.
27 Abel-Smith, 1978, p. 10.
28 Abel-Smith, 1978, p. 15.
29 Abel-Smith, 1978, p. 23.

introduced for the first thousand patients and extra payment was made for continuing responsibility for patients outside normal hours, including a fee for night calls. For those working in under-served areas, extra money was also made available for any patient over the age of 65 and to those doctors who attended specified postgraduate courses. The changes became known as 'The Doctors' Charter'; the result was that under half of their salary came from capitation payments.[30] Under the charter doctors began to be reimbursed for their rent and rates, which helped those in high rent areas. They were also paid 70 per cent of the costs of employing staff. The charter led to loans being provided to doctors for new buildings; one result was an increase in the number of health centres. These grew from 30 in 1965 to 523 in 1973. By 1974 one doctor in seven worked in a health centre designed to house a basic primary care team which meant that maternity and child health facilities were offered on the same premises as the treatment services of the GPs.

C The role and organisation of the hospital
British consultants are arranged in teams formerly known as firms. These are hierarchical groups which usually include doctors at various stages of training and experience – known as senior registrars, registrars and senior house officers. A consultant oversees the work and attempts to maintain the standards of service. The consultants receive a good salary and in addition can (officially) derive up to 10 per cent of their income from private practice. The 1948 legislation permitted private practice in hospital pay beds, and also introduced a new system of merit awards whereby those consultants deemed by their peers to be serving with distinction began to be paid extra financial rewards over and above their salaries.[31]

The NHS was an efficient service and the percentage of funds spent on management was relatively low, as we shall see (p. 53).

D Unnecessary surgery
The evidence from other countries shows that unnecessary operations are often carried out for financial gain. This is seen to be a particular problem in some countries. In a major article, Bunker pointed out that citizens of the United States underwent twice as many operations per head as did those in Britain.[32]

30 Abel-Smith, 1978, p. 24.
31 Klein, 1984, p. 21.
32 Bunker, 1970.

E The patients' voice

The introduction of community health councils and such organisations as the Patients' Association have led to the voice of the people being heard.

PROBLEMS OF THE NHS BEFORE THE CHANGES

On 7 December 1987 the presidents of three Royal Colleges issued a joint statement about the problems they were then facing:

> Each day we learn of new problems in the NHS, beds are shut, operating rooms are not available, emergency wards are closed, essential services are shut down in order to make financial savings. In spite of the efforts of doctors, nurses, and other hospital staff patient care is deteriorating. Acute hospital services have almost reached breaking point. Morale is depressingly low.
>
> It is not only patient care that is suffering. Financial stringencies have hit academic aspects of medicine in particular, because of the additional burden of reduced University Grants Committee funding. Yet the future of medicine depends on the quality of our clinical teachers and research workers.
>
> Face saving initiatives such as the allocation of £30 million for waiting lists are not the answer. An immediate overall review of acute hospital services is mandatory. Additional and alternative funding must be found. We call upon the Government now to do something to save our health service, once the envy of the world.

This was signed by the presidents of the Royal College of Physicians, the Royal College of Surgeons and the Royal College of Obstetricians and Gynaecologists. The fact that the heads of these normally conservative bodies came out so publicly and forthrightly is indicative of the frustration which the medical profession was feeling at the time. The service faced a number of problems.

A Lack of finance

The *British Medical Journal* published a 'New Year Message' in January 1988.[33] This pointed out that government expenditure on the NHS since 1980 had not kept pace with the targets agreed by its own

33 Smith, T., 1988c.

health ministers and presented in evidence to the House of Commons Social Services Committee. These were for expenditure to rise by 2 per cent each year, a figure arrived at because of the need for an increase of 1 per cent to account for the steady increase in old people, 0.5 per cent for medical advances and 0.5 per cent for policy objectives such as better community care. The *British Medical Journal* drew attention to the government's own admission that funding had been well below 2 per cent and that cumulative underfunding of hospital and community services for the period 1980–6 was over a billion pounds.[34] Furthermore, the article pointed out that the government had agreed to a series of pay awards for doctors, nurses and other health workers in excess of the allowance made to the NHS for inflation. Medical and nursing staff were painfully aware that their pay rises had to be funded by health care economies. This was not because pay was excessive; in 1988 the salaries of about two in five of the country's nurses were below the limit set by the Low Pay Unit.

There was evidence that other countries were giving their health service a higher priority. In this respect the *British Medical Journal* quoted figures produced by *The Financial Times* concerning the expenditure on health in selected countries.[35] As a proportion of gross national product, Britain spent 6 per cent, France 8.5 per cent, Germany 9.5 per cent, Switzerland 7.4 per cent and the Netherlands 8.5 per cent. These figures are influenced by the levels of income in the different societies, and it is therefore instructive to express the health figure as the number of dollars spent on health per person each year. The expenditure for Britain was $493, France $853, the Netherlands $828, Germany $1,000, and Switzerland $1,111. *The Financial Times* commented:[36]

> This gap is too large to be explained easily away. Assuming British preferences are similar to those elsewhere the figures suggest that an extra £10,000 million or so a year could be spent on health care in the United Kingdom without distorting the overall allocation of economic resources.

The *British Medical Journal* commented that those who said Britain could not afford to spend more because of poverty should look at the expenditure on defence. Here Britain was at the summit of the European league.[37]

34 Social Services Committee, 1986.
35 Smith, T., 1988c.
36 Anonymous, 1987.
37 Smith, T., 1988c.

In 1988 Tony Smith began to publish a series of articles in the *British Medical Journal* entitled 'Listening to Consultants'. Specialists were asked a series of questions and invited to comment on their working conditions and job satisfaction. The series showed how the overall restrictions on funds affected the personal work of doctors.

Dr K the cardiologist

The doctor said that compared to five years earlier he was disappointed. The technological advances in cardiology made it possible for him and his colleagues to do a great deal more for their patients. He stated:[38]

> We have sorted out so many things, like who should have operations and who shouldn't. So we know precisely what to do for our patients and.we can't do it. The technology has gone far ahead of the budget. I've been a consultant 10 years and it was great at first, but recently I have felt that practising medicine is like constantly walking up hill; and there is always something in your way.

He went on to say that this lack of funds was felt most acutely in the 'high tech' specialities where many of the big advances had been made. However, these were also the costliest. He then gave as an example the fact that if a surgeon puts in an internal mammary artery graft during a coronary bypass, the prognosis is much better than that for a vein graft. However, the operation is more difficult technically; two consultants are needed to carry it out, and so there are limits to what they can do. 'We are constantly faced with a waiting list for surgery of a year – and that means people will die on the waiting list...that's a state of affairs that is just not heard of in the United States.'

The limitations on resources sometimes left him with difficult choices. In an emergency the shortage of laboratory facilities might mean that the only way he could treat the patient would be by cancelling all the other operations for the day. Some patients might have been waiting for up to two years, some might have had their pre-meds, and yet they had to face further delay. This situation could be avoided by having two laboratories – one investigational and the other interventional – and sharing the load between the two.[39]

The shortage of administrative help meant that this cardiologist had

38 Smith, T., 1988a.
39 Smith, T., 1988a, p. 46.

to pay £250 a month out of his own salary to get NHS typing done. He ended by saying that the service should be funded properly so that he and his colleagues could give the first-rate service they were capable of providing.

Mr Q the urology surgeon

From a personal point of view, Mr Q was pleased that he had moved from adult urology to paediatrics and his morale was high. He worked with two other consultants who dealt with the adults. He drew attention to the fact that the adult service had faced major cutbacks which went back at least ten years. Despite being gainers in the Resource Allocation Working Party process, which set out to distribute NHS funds more fairly, they had faced the closure of a hospital and the number of beds available had fallen from 36 to 29. He commented:[40]

> We had an enormous throughput of prostates and other urological procedures and to be told that we were to lose seven beds when we were already working very close to the bone really was a major disaster. It's brought us, I believe, right to the very edge of safety limits. It is not only a potentially dangerous level but is also an incredibly inconvenient level.

Every patient due to be treated had to ring up on the morning of the proposed operation to see if there was likely to be a bed available. If there was they then went to a waiting room until the bed became free. Some people had to wait from 10 o'clock in the morning until 6 o'clock in the evening to find out if another patient had stopped bleeding sufficiently in order to go home. He added that the beds were never cold. If bleeding patients did not recover in time the waiting patient had to return home untreated. He took the view this was an unacceptable way to run a unit.

It is clear that lack of financial support was one of the crucial problems in the NHS in the late 1980s.

Growth in the number of elderly

During the period 1980–8 the population of England and Wales rose by 2.3 per cent. However, the percentage rise in those over the age of 75 years was over a fifth (22.8 per cent).[41] Other data revealed that the

40 Smith, T., 1988b, p. 124.
41 Beck et al., 1993.

elderly were more expensive in terms of health care than the rest of the population. In 1986, for example, health and personal social services expenditure per head of population for England and Wales was an average of £360. However, for those aged 65–74 it was £520, 44 per cent above the national average; and for the age group 75 and over it was £1,570, over four times the national average.

Between 1980 and 1988 the population of England and Wales rose from 49.2 million to 50.4 million. If this increase had been uniform across the age groups it would have implied an increase in expenditure of £388 million in 1988. However, because of the relatively great increase in the number of elderly, the rise in requirement was £864 million – two and a half times the sum calculated simply from overall data.

These data show the importance of considering structural shifts in the population. However, a further breakdown of figures shows that the highest rate of increase was for those over the age of 85 where the increase was more than two in five. This group will continue to rise, with important resource implications.

B Class divisions
Reducing class differentials could improve the overall health statistics of the country considerably. As reported in the introduction, there were two major studies of the class divisions in health before the government changes were introduced – the Black Report of 1980[42] and *The Health Divide* in 1992.[43] More recent data are available from other sources.

Definition of social class
Most researchers use the revised Registrar General's classification, which divides the population into six groupings as follows:

1   Professional (for example, lawyer, architect, doctor).
2   Intermediate (manager, nurse, schoolteacher).
3N   Skilled non-manual (secretary).
3M   Skilled manual (motor mechanic, butcher, carpenter).
4   Partly skilled (bus conductor, postman, agricultural worker).
5   Unskilled (cleaner, dock worker, labourer).

This classification does have some limitations because it is not a measure of income. Indeed, the Black Report said, 'Every effort should

---

42 Black *et al.*, 1992.
43 Whitehead, 1992.

be made to make the classification in the rankings of occupations as objective as possible, by taking into account current and lifetime earnings, fringe benefits, security, working conditions and amenities.'[44]

There is clear evidence of occupational class differences in mortality in the 1980s and early 1990s which applied at every stage of life. The earliest measure is the perinatal mortality rates which apply from twenty-four weeks' gestation to the first seven days of life. The data show that families in the lower working class had 50 per cent higher mortality than those in the highest two classes. These class differences which begin in the womb remain throughout life. In the first month of life the risk of death amongst unskilled workers was double that of professional families. Children of skilled manual workers (social class 3M) have a 1.5 times greater risk.[45] For the next eleven months the ratio widens. One estimate was that if all infants and children up to the age of 15 enjoyed the same survival chances as the children from social classes 1 and 2, then over three thousand deaths a year would be prevented. Furthermore, bringing all adults aged 16–64 up to the mortality experience of social class 1 would mean 39,000 fewer deaths per year.[46]

Data from the 1970s showed that men and women from social class 5 had a two and a half times greater chance of dying before retirement age than those in social class 1.[47]

Detailed data for the period 1979–83 found that in sixty-five of seventy-eight disease categories for men the death rates were higher in classes 4 and 5. In fact there was only one disease – malignant melanoma, a form of skin cancer associated with over exposure to the sun – for which the reverse trend was evident.[48]

For women, sixty-two of the eighty-two categories of disease showed higher death rates for classes 4 and 5. Only four showed the reverse trend. These were malignant melanoma, breast and brain cancer and chronic lymphoid leukaemia.[49]

The work indicated that the major and minor killer diseases affected the poorest occupational groups more than the rich. The Standard Mortality Ratios (SMRs) for deaths from all causes for men in Great Britain 1979–83 are set out in Table 2.1.

....
44 Townsend and Davidson, 1992, p. 41.
45 Townsend and Davidson, 1992, p. 44.
46 Whitehead, 1992, p. 229.
47 Townsend and Davidson, 1992, p. 43.
48 Townsend et al., 1988.
49 Whitehead, 1992, p. 231.

Table 2.1   *Standard Mortality Ratios from all causes for men 1979–83*

Age	Non-manual	Manual	Ratio
20–54	76	115	0.66
55–64	82	117	0.70
20–64	80	116	0.69

Note The Standard Mortality Ratio would be 100 for each group if there were no excess deaths.
Source Marmot and McDowall, 1986.

Table 2.1 shows that in the age group 20–54 the middle classes had only 66 per cent of the death rate of the working classes. In the age group 55–64 it had 70 per cent of the death rate.

More striking than these overall figures are the studies of single occupations. A well known study of Whitehall civil servants examined over seventeen thousand office based workers from 1967 to 1969 and then followed their health for over a decade. This study found that the lower grades had a higher mortality for every cause of death except genito-urinary diseases. There was a greater than threefold difference between the highest and lowest grades, which is a much greater disparity than was revealed in the national data.[50]

The social class gradient is also more pronounced when years of potential life lost is used as a measure rather than the SMR. This measure for the period showed a threefold difference between social classes 1 and 5 for men of working age compared to a 2.5-fold difference using SMR. For women the measure showed a 2.2-fold difference between the top and bottom of the social scale, compared with a 1.9-fold difference in the SMR.[51] This contrast is, in part, due to the fact that accidents and violence are much more prevalent in the working classes, often occurring in early life with a greater loss in potential years. In fact accidents are the most important cause of death amongst children aged from 1 to 14 years.[52]

Widening class divide
Comparison of the years 1976–81 with the subsequent years 1981–3 confirmed that there was a widening class divide in mortality between

50 Whitehead, 1992, p. 232.
51 Blane *et al.,* 1990.
52 Townsend and Davidson, 1992, p. 118.

non-manual and manual workers of working age.[53] A separate study found that there had been a general improvement in mortality for men of working age between 1971 and 1981. However, for men of social class 5, mortality expressed as the number of years lost actually increased. In further examination of the three major causes of death, the length of years lost either remained stationary or increased for all three manual classes, not just class 5. Improvements were confined to social classes 1, 2 and 3N.[54]

It is not just the death rates that reveal such differences. The evidence of chronic illness painted a similar picture. Trends in chronic sickness were analysed for the years 1972–88. They showed that manual groups had higher rates of long-standing illness than non-manual groups in every year. Furthermore, the gap widened over the sixteen-year period. This effect was particularly evident over the period 1974–84; from then until 1988 there was no further increase.[55]

A different approach to considering health differentials was taken in an international study by Valkonen, who compared mortality by level of education. For the 1970s and 1980s he studied the age range 35–44 in five country groups: Denmark, England and Wales, Finland, Hungary and Norway. Overall the highest mortality for men was in Hungary and Finland. For women it was in Hungary and Denmark. However, in each of the countries there were decreased death rates with increased levels of education. In England and Wales there was increased inequality during the 1970s. For men the lowest educational group had no decline in mortality whereas other groups' positions improved by between 10 and 20 per cent. For women there was a large increase in the health gap due to a decline of more than 40 per cent in the death rates of the highest educational category.[56] The research found that France had the greatest inequality of mortality. England and Wales, Hungary and Finland were in an intermediate position; and differences in Denmark, Norway and Sweden were the smallest. Over the two decades occupational differences in mortality had increased in England and Wales, Hungary and France, and remained constant in Norway, Denmark and Finland.

This research confirms the findings of British researchers of a widening class divide. Indeed in some respects the health of the lower occupational groups has actually deteriorated against an improvement

53 Goldblatt, 1990.
54 Blane et al., 1990.
55 Whitehead, 1992, p. 273.
56 Valkonen, 1989.

in the population as a whole, for – while death rates have been declining – rates of chronic illness have risen and the gap in illness rates has been rising, especially in the over-65 age group.

The exception to this general trend was in the deaths of babies around the time of birth and in the first year of life. These declined rapidly for social class 5 in the 1970s and, although the continued improvement was not sustained during the 1980s, the evidence does show that class differences are not inevitable and can be reduced.[57]

Class differences in health: personal choice or social structure

This is a very important issue. If class differences in health are due largely to personal factors such as excess smoking, then a need to change personal behaviour is indicated. However, if the differences are mainly due to social conditions, there is a need for government action.

One possible explanation for the class gradient in health is natural selection: those with poor health are downwardly mobile. If this were to be a primary explanation, the health differences would be inevitable. The evidence does, in fact, suggest that there is some tendency for unhealthy people to be downwardly mobile, however, estimates indicate that this effect would make only a small difference in the overall figures.[58] Furthermore, some of the differences in health may themselves be due to differences in social conditions. Whitehead reported that in Sweden young adults who claimed to have suffered economic hardship in childhood stood a larger chance of downward mobility.[59] The longitudinal evidence from the National Child Development Study found that a number of factors were closely associated with social class differences at the age of 23. These were low social class, living in rented accommodation, overcrowding, large family size and receipt of free school meals. However, taking account of all ages, there was little evidence that the selection effect accounts for only a small proportion of the overall differences between the social classes.[60]

Individual factors

One of the crucial differences between the social classes is in cigarette smoking. The percentage of all smokers declined from 52 per cent in 1972 to 30 per cent in 1988. As far as social class 1 is concerned, the

57 Whitehead, 1992, p. 276.
58 Whitehead, 1992, p. 313.
59 Lundberg, 1991; Whitehead, 1992, p. 314.
60 Whitehead, 1992, p. 314.

percentage of men who smoked declined from 33 per cent in 1972 to 16 per cent in 1988, a reduction of over half during the sixteen years. For social class 5, the unskilled manual workers, the percentage of smokers declined from 64 per cent to 43 per cent. This substantial reduction of 21 per cent nevertheless still leaves men in the lowest social grouping more than twice as likely to smoke as those in social class 1. The decline for women was less marked. The percentage of women smoking fell from 42 per cent in 1972 to 30 per cent in 1988.[61]

It may well be that the diet of the working classes is still inadequate. A 1985 study found that men and women from social classes 1 and 2 were 1.8 cm and 2.8 cm taller respectively than those in classes 4 and 5. The Whitehall study mentioned earlier similarly showed that those in the highest grade of the civil service were on average 4.7 cm taller than those in the lowest grade.[62] A study of families in poor areas of London found that a low amount of money spent on food in a household was strongly correlated with poor growth in children.[63]

In addition to smoking and diet, there is evidence that the middle classes are more likely to engage in sporting activities such as jogging, swimming, tennis, football and cricket. These are likely to have health benefits.[64] There are also class differences in terms of consumption of alcohol.

Structural factors and health

There is a great deal of evidence that the availability of good social conditions can influence health. These are the areas where there may be some need for government action.

Table 2.2   *Housing and health 1971–81*

Housing tenure	Standard Mortality Ratio	
	Men	Women
Owner occupied	84	83
Privately rented	109	106
Local authority	115	117

Source Whitehead, 1992, p. 241.

61 Whitehead, 1992, p. 318.
62 Whitehead, 1993, p. 236.
63 Whitehead, 1993, p. 331.
64 Townsend and Davidson, 1992, p. 112.

Table 2.2 shows that people in owner occupied houses had only 83 per cent of the deaths that might have been expected and those in local authority housing had 16 per cent extra. Evidence from a longitudinal study on cancer survival was that council tenants had poorer survival for cancers overall and that this difference was irrespective of age, cause of death or prognosis of cancer. Analysis of the reason for this showed that council tenants presented later for treatment; this delay was judged to be one of the main factors in the survival differences.[65]

The cost of heating may be one factor leading to the differences in death rates. Each year about forty thousand more people, mainly very elderly, die in Britain in the winter than in the summer. A few of these deaths are due to hypothermia, but the majority are due to cardiovascular diseases. Lowry found that at a room temperature of 12 degrees Celsius, changes occur in the heart and blood vessels which increase the likelihood of heart attack and stroke.[66]

Income and health

There have been a number of studies in this area. In a study of occupational mortality in twenty-two occupations over the twenty years from 1951 to 1971, the occupations which had increased their share of income in comparison to average earnings tended to decrease their mortality rates. Those where the income had fallen had an increased mortality relative to the average. The study also showed that the death rates of old people varied according to the real value of state pensions.[67]

In a sensitive discussion of the problems of poor families Whitehead stated that many mothers often have a difficult juggling act to perform in order to look after their children within a low budget. Pregnant women going to hospital out-patients departments had twice as far to travel as those going to their local GP. They also had great problems when travelling with young children. She suggested that research indicated that unhealthy palliatives may be given to the children in an attempt to prevent tension; for example, sweets may be provided in order to keep children quiet on trips. Breastfeeding may be abandoned to allow more time for other members of the family.[68]

---

65 Whitehead, 1992, p. 241.
66 Lowry, 1989, p. 1326.
67 Wilkinson, 1986.
68 Whitehead, 1992, p. 333.

International data on income have provided some interesting findings. Whitehead reports a comparison between the average life expectancy and income for the twenty-three countries in the Organisation for Economic Co-operation and Development. Over a sixteen-year period this revealed almost no correlation between increase in income and longevity. However, an important discovery was that *countries with more equality of income between the rich and the poor had the highest life expectancy*. Countries which gave an increased proportion of disposable income to the least well-off were associated with faster increases in life expectancy.[69] This theme will be considered further in the last chapter.

Reducing class differentials
If class differences in health could be removed and health for all increased so that it approached that of social classes 1 and 2 then there would be a great overall reduction in mortality rates. Writing in the *British Medical Journal* in 1992, Wilkinson asserts that the international data show that if Britain were to adopt policies leading to more equal income distribution – similar to those of other European countries – then about two years would be added to British life expectancy. Any policies which lead to greater inequality will lead to wider class differences in health and an overall decrease in the potential for improvements for health.

The importance of social class as a health indicator led Davey Smith and Eggar to speculate in the *British Medical Journal* about why the reduction of social class differences was not included as a target in *The Health of the Nation*. They suggest that the reasoning seems to be that inequalities are present in all industrialised countries and 'have always been with us' and so it is not realistic to make their reduction a goal of health policy.[70] There is evidence of growing inequality in the years during which Mrs Thatcher was in office as Prime Minister. One piece of research showed that while the richest 10 per cent of the population gained £87 a week from tax cuts and shifts to direct taxation, the poorest 10 per cent lost £1 a week.[71] An official report from the Department of Social Security showed that when housing costs were taken into account the poorest 10 per cent of the population suffered a 14 per cent loss in real income between 1979 and 1990–1. In contrast

69 Whitehead, 1992, p. 330.
70 Davey Smith and Eggar, 1993, p. 1085.
71 Oppenheim, 1993.

the richest fifth of the population had over a 20 per cent rise.[72] A striking figure that shows the increase in inequality is that in 1979 only 9 per cent of people had incomes less than half the national average. This figure rose to 25 per cent by 1990–3.[72]

From the evidence we have presented it would seem likely that the growth in inequality would lead to greater class differences in health. Much of the evidence of class differences comes from the decennial census, and the results for 1991 will not be available until around 1996–7.[73] However, some evidence is emerging that increased mortality differentials resulted from the social polarisation. A study in the Northern Regional Health Authority showed that between 1981 and 1991 there were large increases in mortality differences between the most deprived and the most affluent electoral wards.[74] Similarly, in Glasgow mortality differentials between the affluent and deprived areas grew between 1981 and 1989, and also Glasgow – which contains 80 per cent of the most deprived postcode sectors in Scotland – has shown a worsening of mortality compared to the rest of Scotland.[75] So it seems clear that when the more detailed analysis is completed, it will reveal greater social class differences in health than in the past and an increase in deaths.

Relative inequality and life expectancy

In an earlier work on economic growth we have argued that once countries have developed past a certain point a crucial factor is not further economic growth but rather the way in which money is spent within the society. So countries like the United States had worse health statistics than countries such as the Netherlands because of a greater amount of inequality and an underclass unable to share in the benefits of the society.[76]

Other evidence suggests that the class differential in death rates has increased or declined in line with the increase or decrease in relative poverty.[77] It would therefore be expected that the rapid growth in inequality during the late 1980s would lead to a widening of class differentials in health and to a worse overall performance in terms of health indicators. Richard Wilkinson has produced an excellent report

72 Department of Social Security, 1993.
73 Davey Smith and Eggar, 1993.
74 Phillimore et al., 1994, p. 1125.
75 Forwell, 1993.
76 Francome and Wharton, 1973; Francome, 1990.
77 Wilkinson, 1989, p. 307.

which documents some of the changes in health indicators in the period leading up to the NHS changes. He showed that during the period 1985–91 there was a dramatic widening of the income differentials between the top 20 per cent in society and the bottom 20 per cent. This was accompanied by a marked slowing down of the decline in death rates for infants, children and adults below middle age. During this period there was an overall increase in crime of 80 per cent, with violent crime increasing by 90 per cent.[78]

There is an alternative explanation for the worsening position of Britain as regards international comparisons of health. This is in terms of the breakdown of the family, resulting in poverty for single parents who in some cases have not been able to provide adequate role models for their children. However, Wilkinson rightly points out that the proportion of married and co-habiting couples fell from 92 per cent in 1971 to 81 per cent in 1991, a relatively small drop, and so this was unlikely to be the total explanation. Furthermore, international comparisons show that Japan and Sweden, first and second in the international league tables of health, have low crime rates. While Japan comes close to the traditional model of a nuclear family with low births outside marriage and low divorce rates, Sweden is only surpassed by Iceland in the degree of its departure from the nuclear model. He argues that one of the reasons why single parents in Sweden are able to maintain good health figures is that only 2 per cent of Swedish children in lone-parent families were in relative poverty, contrasted to an average of 21 per cent for a group of eight countries in the OECD.[79]

C Ethnic differences

The varieties of health patterns in the different ethnic groups constitute another important source of information. It might be expected that people who had settled in this country would be faced with more housing problems and more difficulties in understanding their way around the health system than others. Another major health risk factor could be racism. There is some evidence of special difficulties; Francome found that women who had settled in this country from the New Commonwealth and Pakistan made up over half the deaths from illegal abortion in the first few years after the Abortion Act came into operation.[80] However, this effect was small and overall the evidence is

78 Wilkinson, 1994, p. 1.
79 Wilkinson, 1994, p. 11.
80 Francome, 1980.

that settlers in this country suffered fewer deaths than the average population. The most likely explanation for this is that those who choose to emigrate are not a representative sample of the population because of self-selection. The healthier members of society are more likely to be the ones to travel to other countries.

More information is now available because in 1969 data on place of birth began to be collected at the time of death. The early information, for 1970–2, showed some important ethnic differences. Overall Caribbean men had an SMR of 95 compared to 99 for men from the Indian sub-continent. Women in each of these two groups did worse both than the men and the average population.[81] When considering different illnesses, the most striking are those in the area of circulatory disease. There was a strong sex difference. Caribbean men had an SMR of 90, while women had one of 166. For heart disease Caribbean men had an SMR of only 45. This means the group suffered less than half the number of deaths than might have been expected. However, they had twice as many strokes compared to the average population, and the SMR was 207. For Caribbean women the SMR for strokes and heart attacks was higher than for the men. At an SMR of 227, there were over twice as many as would be expected. They had an SMR of 88 for heart attacks.[81]

Both men and women from the Caribbean and the Indian sub-continent had lower rates of cancer than the average for society in the age group 20–69. In fact men from the Indian sub-continent had less than two thirds (64 per cent) of the cancer rates that might be expected and women had 84 per cent of the expected level. Men from the Caribbean had only 77 per cent of the cancer deaths expected, while the women had 88 per cent.

In contrast to the findings for these two ethnic groups, men from the African Commonwealth had 33 per cent more deaths than expected overall. The women had 44 per cent excess deaths. The African men had a very similar death rate for strokes to that of the Caribbean men. However, their death rate for heart attacks was twice the Caribbean level.[81]

These differences are very important and open up possibilities for research. They are clearly not all due to biological factors, although these may be an important component in some of the findings. For explanations of the variety in the figures we must consider factors such as diet, level of exercise, amount of smoking and drinking, accessibility

81 Radical Statistics Health Group, 1987, p. 25.

of care, presentation for early treatment and general lifestyle. Research on the reasons for the differences is ongoing and could lead to changes in the quality of care amongst different groups and so lead to overall improvements in health. Some spectacular improvements have been made in other countries. In the United States, for example, the mortality for white men and women from cardiovascular disease fell by 33 per cent between 1972 and 1993. This was largely due to a reduction in smoking and improved lifestyle.

DELAYS IN TREATMENT

A lack of funds often led to delays in operations especially those not regarded as urgent. In 1940–50 the proportion of GNP spent on the NHS was 3.8 per cent. This actually fell, so that by 1953–4 it was 3.4 per cent.[82] Although it rose to 5.9 per cent in 1988, it was still well behind that of comparable countries.[83]

WITHHOLDING OF TREATMENT

In 1983 restrictions on public expenditure meant that limitations were made on the treatment of kidney patients. The then Prime Minister, Margaret Thatcher, rejected an appeal by the British Kidney Patient Association that either regional health authorities should be told to spend more or the government should provide more funds from its central budget. In 1981 it was estimated that four thousand people, mainly elderly, died of renal failure because of the shortage of hospital facilities.[84] This figure was expected to rise sharply after the health service freeze and staffing cuts.

In protest against this, Professor Stewart Cameron – a kidney specialist at Guy's Hospital – supported a campaign to encourage hospital doctors to refuse to sign the death certificates of kidney patients who died because of the health cuts. He acted after three patients died after being refused treatment at Guy's. He said that he hoped such steps would 'make coroners feel as perturbed as we are that someone has died as surely of neglect as if he had been left to freeze to death in the streets in the winter'.

82 Eckstein, 1970, p. 217.
83 Ham, 1994a, p. 38.
84 Pallister, 1981, p. 6.

CONCLUSION

This brief review of the state of British health care before the 1990 changes shows that it had some excellent features. Administrative costs were below those of many other countries and there was less unnecessary surgery. There was great strength in the health care professions. The doctors, nurses and other staff were very often dedicated and strongly committed to improving the health of their patients. We have seen, however, that the NHS did have a number of problems. Underfunding meant that some of the most appropriate kinds of treatment were not available to the British public. There were also delays in treatment. As Coulson points out, 'free at the point of need' often meant 'free for those prepared to wait'.[85] Secondly, there were problems with evaluation and a lack of statistics, and care was not always properly monitored in order to ensure the most effective treatment was carried out. Thirdly, there were class and ethnic differences which needed to be reduced. If the health of the poor had been improved to equal that of the wealthy, and if the health of all ethnic groups could match that of the best, then the overall health of the nation would have been greatly enhanced. Fourthly, there were clear signs that health and health care were very important to the British people and that there existed a great opportunity to improve what was basically a sound structure.

However, as we shall see, the opportunity was not grasped. Instead the health care system of the British people came under the influence of American academics. The British chose not to learn from the best, but rather from those whose system was the most fragmented, inefficient and under-achieving of all the countries in the developed world.

85 Coulson, 1995, p. 12.

CHAPTER THREE

THE IDEAS BEHIND THE GOVERNMENT'S CHANGES

We can by no means lay prostrate before the
power of the market.

The health changes can be seen in the light of other social changes introduced by successive governments since the Conservatives came into power in 1979. One observer has argued that it was in the 1970s that the debate about the balance about state, market and society was convincingly won by the right.[1] The victory of the Conservatives allowed these ideas to be put into place. Some have argued that since the early 1980s Britain has been undergoing a great experiment in which the country has been following a set of ideas espoused by a group of US economists after the publication of Hayek's book *The Road to Serfdom*. However, the ideas given the most prominence in this country were those of Milton and Rose Friedman, who in 1980 had their own BBC television series based on their book *Free to Choose*. In this they called for the reduction of government intervention and a return to individual and family control over people's own lives. They welcomed the 1979 election as a sign that the tide was turning in this direction. Their ideas were influential in subsequent government changes. Their view of capitalism was relatively simple and has an appeal to some lay people, although it is less accepted by professional economists.[2] The argument underlying the views of the New Right as set out for popular consumption by the Friedmans can be summed up as a number of propositions.

1 Modern economics can be traced back to the ideas of Adam Smith in *The Wealth of Nations*, which analysed the way in which a market system could combine the freedom of individuals to pursue their own objectives with extensive co-operation to produce goods to meet the nation's needs.[3]

2 They advance the view that the greatest good for society is

1 Wallace, 1994, p. 22.
2 Wallace, 1994.
3 Friedman, 1980, p. 20.

achieved by individuals working for the benefit of themselves and their family. Each person working for his or her own interests serves the interests of the society.[4]

3   They assert that if an exchange between two people is voluntary, it will not occur unless both believe they will benefit. A free market presents an 'invisible hand' in such a way as to make everybody better off.[5]

4   They are concerned that governments have a tendency to grow and interfere with the freedom of individuals, and argue that this should be resisted. One problem is that when people are spending the money of others they are not as careful as when they are spending money on behalf of themselves.[6]

5   They maintain having resources owned by the government is negative because 'when everybody owns something, nobody owns it, and nobody has a direct interest in maintaining or improving its condition'.[7]

6   They believe the role of government should be limited but it should have four responsibilities – the first three of which come directly from Adam Smith. They are to protect society from violence and invasion, to protect members of society from injustice or oppression, and to maintain certain public works. The Friedmans felt that it was necessary to add a fourth, to protect individuals who cannot be regarded as 'responsible'.[8] They believed that, although some government activity is necessary, it is open to abuse and so a 'watchful eye' should be kept on it.

7   One of the reasons for their advocacy of a limited role for government is that they believe private enterprise is more efficient.[9]

8   Unions and such organisations as the British and American medical associations all restrict entry. In order to obtain higher incomes they aim to deny the opportunities of others. The Friedmans believe that a free market, in contrast, will create benefits for all.

9   Any movement towards reducing inequality will lead to a stifling of initiative, an increase in bureaucracy and a reduction of economic growth. They argue that a country which puts equality ahead of freedom will end up neither equal nor free.[10]

4 Friedman, 1980, p. 32.
5 Friedman, 1980, pp. 20, 31.
6 Friedman, 1980, p. 146.
7 Friedman, 1980, p. 43.
8 Friedman, 1980, pp. 52–4.
9 Friedman, 1980, p. 144.
10 Friedman, 1980, p. 177.

10 Where health care systems are led by the government, they result in the condemnation of thousands of people to wait for years for life-saving operations – as is the case in the British NHS. This is in contrast to the situation in the United States where people get their operations immediately.[11]

THE INFLUENCE OF NEW RIGHT IDEAS

There is no doubt that the ideas of the self-styled 'New Right' underlie much of the policy of the British government during the period 1979–95. The back cover of the paperback edition of the Friedmans' book quotes the *Observer*: 'With unabashed monetarists in Downing Street...Milton Friedman now has a chance to see if a Government acknowledging his influence can put principle into practice.' Since then we have seen the wholesale privatisation of industry. The New Right philosophy also explains some rather unusual statements such as Mrs Thatcher's claim: 'There is no such thing as society. There are individual men and women and there are families. And no government can do anything except through people and people must look after themselves first.' In this comment she was following the general theme of the argument advanced by the New Right in proposition 2 above.[12]

New Right theory and health

We have mentioned the Friedmans' view that entrance into the medical profession should not be restricted, and that private enterprise will work more efficiently than state systems in health care.

There are several problems with this theory. The first is that it leads to winners and losers. Robert Wharton, a business consultant with one of the major City firms, has commented: 'The New Right theorists believe that everyone will be a winner. However, history shows that to be a mistaken belief.'[13]

Evidence shows that policies advocated by the New Right lead to greater inequality. Indeed, over the past decade the poorest 10 per cent have suffered a real drop in income, and if housing costs are taken into account there has been an absolute fall for the bottom 20 per cent.[14] As we have seen the evidence shows that inequality leads to poorer health in society overall, while economic growth does not appear to lead to

11 Friedman, 1980, p. 15.
12 Thatcher, 1995, p. 626.
13 Personal communication, June 1995.
14 Wilkinson, 1994, p. v.

better health once societies have developed past a certain level.[15] In fact, Wilkinson estimates that the widening of income differentials in the period up to 1986 slowed the increase in length of life to such a degree as to deprive the average British citizen of a year in life expectancy.

A second criticism of New Right theory in relation to health is that it places too much faith in the 'invisible hand' of the market. This is clearly seen in the attitude of the Friedmans to the drug thalidomide. It was first marketed for morning sickness in 1957 and was by 1962 known to be responsible for deformities in children.[16] According to one estimate, about twelve thousand babies were deformed by the drug until a worldwide ban was imposed in 1962.[17] Fortunately for US women, the Food and Drug Administration refused to give the drug a licence and consequently deformities in the USA were prevented. In gratitude President Kennedy gave a gold medal for distinguished government service to Dr Frances Kelsey, who prevented the drug's distribution. The Friedmans attacked this decision and the process of control of drugs, arguing that it is better to let market forces regulate the flow. In this respect they noted that the companies had to pay tens of millions of dollars in damages which they believed would be an incentive against similar episodes in the future.[18] They further argued that government restrictions would lead to drugs of potential benefit being denied to people.

So Milton and Rose Friedman would support the removal of the safeguards which prevented thousands of women from having deformed children. In their view, economic theory should take precedence over the problems of families that have to face such disabilities. Subsequent information about the sale of the drug casts doubt on the ability of the market and the legal system to provide redress. On 20 January 1995 the front page of the *Guardian* reported that the trust fund set up twenty years before to support the victims of the thalidomide tragedy was becoming rapidly depleted. Freddie Ashbury, the 35-year-old chairman of the Thalidomide Action Group, commented: 'Many of the victims are desperately short of money. I am severely disabled and it makes life very expensive. We have been conned for twenty years...our only hope is to wage war on Guinness and if we have to go to court so be it.'[19]

....
15 Francome and Wharton, 1973; Wilkinson, 1994, p. 47.
16 Francome, 1984, p. 81.
17 Brown, A., 1994.
18 Friedman, 1980, p. 247.
19 Dyer, 1995.

Even in Western countries, then, there are doubts about legal redress. Furthermore, thalidomide is still causing deformity. In 1965 Brazil was given permission to use the drug to fight painful attacks of leprosy. Virtually all Brazil's 240,000 leprosy sufferers are illiterate and live in slums. Often they were not aware of the dangers of thalidomide. Arthur Custodio, president of the Movement for the Reintegration of Leprosy Patients, estimates that there are more than a thousand children in the new thalidomide generation. For example, Lucienne das Dores was offered the drug to relieve her stomach cramps. In May 1994 she gave birth to a baby son who had no arms or legs. Horrified, she fled from the hospital, returning two weeks later for her son. His tiny, deformed lungs gave out on 26 July.[20] No money can compensate for such an experience even if it were available to poor women in the Third World.

There is also British evidence that two of the men accepted as being damaged by thalidomide have fathered babies with similar defects. This led to questions in 1994 about whether the drug was a mutagen. The idea was criticised by Smithells, who pointed out that the two cases were a small minority of the 350 children born to parents affected by thalidomide. But the examples show that great problems may be caused for future generations and we cannot simply lay prostrate before the power of the market and permit the misery that can follow drug-induced illnesses to continue if they can be prevented.[21]

This discussion of the New Right and health is important to understand the background to the NHS changes. It was not politically possible for the government to introduce a wholesale market-place in health, as occurs in parts of the USA. The Prime Minister during the 1980s, Margaret Thatcher, had said on many occasions that the NHS was 'safe' in her hands. Therefore an alternative set of arrangements was introduced which led to a degree of privatisation.

ENTHOVEN AND GOVERNMENT CHANGES

One of the important developments in the government's changes was the creation of the internal market with a purchaser/provider split. This was proposed by the Stanford economist Alain Enthoven, who visited this country to study the NHS in 1985.[22] In 1994 an editorial in *Social*

20 Brown, A., 1994, p. 20.
21 Smithells, 1994, p. 477.
22 Enthoven, 1985.

Science and Medicine called him 'one of the intellectual godfathers of the health care reforms in the Netherlands ("Dekker Report") and the UK ("White Paper")'.[23] Enthoven has had some good ideas. He pointed out, for example, that economies of scale are possible for open-heart surgery. In California in 1991 open-heart surgery was performed in 119 hospitals, about half of which did fewer than two hundred cases. Enthoven called for regional centres which would specialise in heart surgery. He also acknowledged that there were problems with the US system; in the US the incentives were wrong because the system 'systematically pays providers more for doing more, whether or not there is any evidence more is beneficial for the patient'.[24] He did not believe that the power of the market would have an 'invisible hand' to produce the best care. In fact, he commented that 'because of human ingenuity, new market imperfections will constantly appear'.[25] In some ways, therefore, Enthoven can be seen as more realistic than economists such as Milton and Rose Friedman.

In his earlier work Enthoven pointed out that the British system was more efficient than that in the United States. However, he drew attention to areas where he believed there could be improvements and the system could be made more 'patient friendly':[26]

> I am told most consultants say to their patients 'You need the operation; it will take place some time in the next year or so, and we'll call you a week in advance to tell you when to come into hospital.' The alternative would be to say 'Here is my operating schedule for the next year; pick a vacant space that suits you.' That would restore the patient's sense of control over his own life.

He went on to say that the economic interests of the consultant were opposed to the reduction in waiting lists because this would reduce the number of private patients. He also argued, if less persuasively, that GPs risk antagonising consultants if they send patients to other districts.

Enthoven made two suggestions which he believed might help improve efficiency. The first was the development of an internal market in a few experimental districts in the NHS. He believed this could provide incentives to seek the best care and improve efficiency by

23 Wynand *et al.*, 1994, p. 1408.
24 Enthoven, 1994, p. 1414.
25 Enthoven, 1994, p. 1416.
26 Enthoven, 1995, p. 19.

obtaining cheaper services. The second alternative was to reduce waiting lists by introducing some smaller market mechanisms between districts or by buying cheap private sector operations. He argued that one problem was that the NHS did not know its own costs and so could not recognise a good bargain when it saw one.

Enthoven drew from experience in the United States to suggest that it would be a good idea to have a few doctors – about three or four hundred – trained in management, who could look for efficiencies. He also said that if competitive tendering cut catering costs by 20 per cent it would save enough money for thirty thousand hip replacement operations.

Enthoven's suggestions sometimes seem logical, but he often over-stresses the role of finance within health care. A clear example occurred in 1994 when he set out an ideal which approximates to the perfect market:[27]

> The search for a perfect incentive scheme might suggest the following scenario. At the time of the annual enrolment, each prospective enrollee appears in an examination room with completed medical record, before doctors from each health plan. The doctors can then examine the patient and ask questions. Then each health plan submits a sealed bid for that person's capitation payment for the coming year.

He continued that such a perfect market would have prohibitive transaction costs and so the only hope was an approximation to this system. In fact there is a fundamental problem with this approach. Doctors would be diverted away from seeing patients for the purpose of their health and towards examining them to satisfy economic needs. This factor was kept to a low level in the British system in operation before 1991. One of the weaknesses of Enthoven's approach, therefore, is that he did not explore adequately the possibility of improving the system whereby financial and market factors, instead of being developed to the maximum, were kept to a minimum. He did stress the need to pilot changes, and if the government had followed his suggestion the problems caused by the NHS reforms could have been confined to certain areas of the country.

As mentioned in the previous chapter, the British system in operation until 1991 was underfunded in comparison with the systems in some other countries. However, it did have many attractive features.

27 Enthoven, 1994, p. 1418.

Enthoven noted that it was much cheaper than the US model. In addition the local GPs' role was important in the diagnosis of illness and the provision of primary care. The hospitals were generally held in affection by local communities – as became evident when, as a result of the changes, there were plans to close many. Instead of proposing changes which, as we will see, had very unfortunate effects on British health care, it might have been better for economists from the United States to have concentrated on the setting up of an efficient system like the British one in the USA.

THE WHITE PAPER

Enthoven's suggestions were dismissed by the NHS Management Executive as unworkable and not piloted. A management simulation in which forty managers took part broke down in the third year. However, the government still pressed on. The then Prime Minister was attracted to Enthoven's ideas and the 1989 White Paper *Working for Patients* led to the reforms being imposed on England and Wales in April 1991.[28]

These changes in the health service did not attempt to deal with the problems directly. Rather, following the 1989 White Paper, the aim was to introduce market mechanisms which proponents believed by their very nature would lead to improvements in care. In the foreword, the Prime Minister said that the NHS would continue to be available to all and largely financed out of general taxation:[29]

> But major tasks now face us: to bring all parts of the NHS up to the very high standard of the best, while maintaining the principles on which it was founded; and to prepare for the needs of the future. We aim to extend patient choice, to delegate responsibility to where the services are provided and to secure the best value for money. All the proposals in this White Paper put the needs of patients first.

So the government policy document called for competition, decentralisation, incentives for efficiency and consumer choice. One part of the argument was that there was wastage in the health service and that this could be removed by the application of commercial principles. There was not to be a real market in health but rather an internal market, and the government attempted to assure the public

28 Jones, 1994e.
29 Department of Health, 1989.

that it was not an attempt to undermine the NHS. However, there were those who believed that many of the changes would in due course lead to privatisation as this was the general policy of the government. There have been those who have talked of a 'hidden agenda'(see pp. 65–7). Furthermore, messages were often confused and parts of the White Paper did stress the promotion of the private sector. It stated, for example: 'As health authorities become more businesslike in their approach to the provision of services, and to the use of the resources at their disposal, they are increasingly looking at the scope for involving the private sector.'[30] One of the benefits predicted from the changes was that they would create an environment where successful hospitals could flourish, and the introduction of self-government would encourage a stronger sense of local ownership and pride.[31]

The White Paper said that hospitals and their consultants needed a stronger incentive to look to GPs as people whose confidence they should gain in order to have patients referred to them. It stated that at the time there were problems with doctors referring out of their area. In order to give patients more choice of hospital, the White Paper announced that larger GP practices with over eleven thousand patients would be the first to be free to apply for their own NHS budgets for a range of hospital services.[32] They could obtain the services in private or NHS hospitals. There would be three categories of hospital services in the scheme:

1 Out-patient services.
2 A defined group of in-patient and day-case treatment including hip replacements and cataract removals.
3 Diagnostic tests such as X-ray examinations and pathology tests, which are undertaken at the direct request of GPs.

Comments on the White Paper

Although the White Paper spoke of giving people greater choice, for many people the workings of the market have led the local hospital to close or services to be cut back. It is in the area of accident and emergency units that evidence of the effect of the reforms has clearly disproved the statements about what would happen in the White Paper. This talked of there being five certain core services to which patients need guaranteed local access. The first of these was accident and

30 Department of Health, 1989, p. 19.
31 Department of Health, 1989, p. 22.
32 Department of Health, 1989, p. 49.

emergency units. This was followed by a commitment to providing immediate admission to hospital from an accident and emergency unit. There would also be immediate admission for most general medicine and many hospital geriatric and psychiatric services'.[33] We shall see (Chapter 9) that the number of accident and emergency units has fallen so far that many people do not now have a local service and either have to travel great distances or go to see their local GP. In June 1995 the *British Medical Journal* reported that over the previous three years the number of out-of-hours calls – between 10 p.m. and 8 a.m. on weekdays and on Saturdays and Sundays – had doubled.[34] This is likely to be in large part due to the reduction in service from accident and emergency units.

Furthermore, health authorities or fundholding GPs have a contract with (usually) one hospital. The patient then has no choice or at any rate less than previously. We can also see areas of confusion and error within the White Paper. For example, it said:[35]

> The NHS employs over 48,000 hospital doctors, of whom nearly 17,000 are consultants. The reforms proposed by the Government in this White Paper will make it easier for consultants and their colleagues to get on with the job of treating patients.

Despite the optimistic forecast that the reforms would help patient care, we shall be providing evidence from nearly five hundred consultants that they introduced serious problems. Even in the White Paper itself the government announced an intention to change the merit award so that it would not be awarded to consultants who had simply demonstrated clinical skills. For an award there would normally need to be in addition a commitment to management and service development.[36] Although the merit award system certainly needs evaluating, this approach – by introducing management criteria – would be distracting consultants from their primary activity of caring for patients.

One of the assumptions behind introducing more financial awareness was that it would lead to more efficiency. In this respect Dr Tim Evans of the Independent Health Care Association commented:[37]

33 Department of Health, 1989, p. 34.
34 Beecham, 1995, p. 1553.
35 Department of Health, 1989, p. 39.
36 Department of Health, 1989, p. 44.
37 Evans, T., 1994.

> The Government's introduction of more sophisticated financial procedures would encourage a level of competition and service between state and private sector providers that could only be beneficial. By enabling purchasers and providers to make better decisions, taxpayers and patients would be able to benefit from an empowering environment which facilitates informed choice and encourages the raising of professional standards across a range of ideas.

The underlying assumption is that introducing financial controls into medicine cuts waste and raises standards. There are clearly advantages to planners in having a knowledge of the costs of various activities. However, there are good reasons for believing that the major problems of the NHS are caused by underfinancing, and that this was the problem that should have been addressed. There are also disadvantages in introducing financial concerns into medicine, as we shall now show.

THE CASE FOR LIMITING THE ROLE OF FINANCE IN HEALTH CARE

There are important reasons why paying great attention to financial considerations can cause major problems. These may be considered under a number of different headings.

Setting up a market is expensive

We showed in Chapter 2 that in the 1980s the NHS was noticeably short of money. However, when extra funds were injected after the changes, they were used for other purposes than the care of patients. Costs for the setting up of fundholding were officially estimated at £42 million, but further analysis showed that this figure accounted for under a half of the true costs.[38] Furthermore, official figures show that the setting up of NHS Trusts as self-governing units has cost over £120 million.[39] An investigation by the *Observer* newspaper said that there had not been a fully comprehensive evaluation but still the shake-up had cost in excess of £3 billion.[40]

Even so, it seems that the setting up of the internal market has been underfunded. Professor J. D. Ward of the Royal Hallamshire Hospital said:[41]

38 Brindle, 1995f.
39 Brindle, 1995b.
40 Jones, 1994e, p. 4.
41 Ward, 1995.

[We] swim in the bureaucracy of this ridiculous purchasing/ providing farce. Purchasing and providing is not possible without an enormous investment of money and the professionals believe that if half of this money were spent on improving patient care this would go a long way to solving the problems of the NHS.

So there is an argument that, if the previous structure had been kept intact but been given extra resources, then the major problems of the health service would have been removed.

The market has great defects

There are some economists who believe that the market in itself will introduce efficiency. However, there are also potentially great weaknesses. It fell to Richard Smith, the editor of the *British Medical Journal*, to point out that the perfect market beautifully analysed by Adam Smith over two hundred years ago causes many people to be fervent about markets. However, a precondition of this market is that individual buyers are too small to move the price by themselves and that sellers have perfect information about goods. He said these conditions are seldom, if ever, met in practice. In fact Adam Smith wrote in *The Wealth of Nations*: 'People of the same trade seldom meet together for merriment and diversion, but the conversation ends in a conspiracy against the public'.[42]

In the light of such a comment it might be surprising that those believing in the power of the market should belong to the Adam Smith Institute. Adam Smith would not share their faith in the virtue of market power, nor would he believe that markets are the impartial arbiters of wealth and production. We should also recognise that over and above other areas, attempts to bring the market-place into health care have special problems. First of all, it is not like other market areas because those who need care are rarely those with money. The evidence shows that the most vulnerable groups are the elderly, pregnant women and those with serious illnesses. These are not usually the people who are the main earners, so if finance is the criterion they will not command the resources. Instead these may flow from rich people with minor ailments.

Secondly, inequality in society leads to resources being misdirected. There may be considerable money available, for example, for cosmetic surgery because people have the money to pay for it. However, it may

---

42 Smith, R., 1993a, p. 216.

be more important for the surgeons involved in this area to be working in other areas where there is not much money but a great need. Furthermore, we know that people with private health insurance have almost twice as many operations as those on the NHS.[43] Some of these may be unnecessary, for – as we have seen in particular in the United States – much unnecessary surgery is carried out and insurance companies have been concerned that doctors may encourage people to have surgery in order to generate increased profits.[44] We have shown in a previous work the high numbers of unnecessary caesareans carried out in the United States.[45] Furthermore Cook has pointed out that the incidence of hysterectomy in the US is four times that in Britain. This seems to be due in part to the generally higher rates of intervention in the US and in part to the fact that doctors earn more money the more operations they carry out.[46]

Another of the reasons why the perfect market outlined by Adam Smith does not work for health is that the patients' knowledge is so much less than the doctors'. This is clearly a big problem in the US. The introduction of more market-led decisions will almost certainly lead to this problem being accentuated.

One reason why any market for health is very imperfect is that outside large cities, hospitals have local monopolies. People have very little choice and they have insufficient information on which to base that choice. The best solution is to have good quality care available everywhere.

In addition to these problems of finance, there are very often conflicts between business interests and good health practice. For example, Chris Ham draws attention to the fact that as long ago as 1848 the Public Health Act gave powers to enable the construction of water supply and sewerage systems as a means of controlling infectious diseases. It was a great step forward but it was opposed by commercial interests who were able to make money out of insanitary conditions.[47]

Currently we can identify a variety of ways in which there are potential or actual conflicts between good health care and commercial interests. One of the main ways in which advertisers of private health care attract new members is through delays in waiting lists and the

43 Yates, 1995.
44 Bunker, 1970.
45 Francome et al., 1993.
46 Cook, 1988, p. 8.
47 Ham, 1994, p. 6.

opportunity for queue jumping. If the NHS improves and offers prompt care to all, such demand is likely to fall and profits also will fall. Furthermore, companies often have unresolved conflicts between the safety of their workers and profits.[48]

One of the great conflicts in the health service is that of junior hospital doctors who work over-long hours to keep a creaking service going, very often at the expense of their own health – as we shall see in the next chapter. This is not something that is new. The problem should have been dealt with many years ago. Its continued existence indicates that in some ways the reforms have changed things that were working well and neglected to improve practices which were clearly in need of reform.

There are general problems with a market in health and any market economy may throw up specific unpredicted difficulties. For example, in December 1993 the Minister of Health had to intervene to prevent Camden and Islington Health Authority from switching £20 million from University College Hospital.[49]

A report from the Central Consultants and Specialists Committee said that consultants are frustrated because of the disadvantages of the internal market. They identified fast-tracking of the patients of fundholders and the misuse of waiting-list funds to treat those who have been waiting a long time at the expense of more clinically urgent cases.[50] The only sensible solution is for there to be consistently high standards for all groups of people.[51]

An important point about bureaucratic systems is that they may create benefits for some by creating shortages. This issue had some wide publicity when a window cleaner earning £120 a week had a daughter with a heart defect. The family were told that an NHS operation was months away and managed to raise £8,500 for the operation. It transpired that the operation was scheduled for early treatment and so the family paid out the money and incurred debts unnecessarily.[52] It is unacceptable that people should have this kind of stress and worry. In the next chapter we shall be giving some examples of hospitals and consultants making money by having waiting lists and encouraging people to pay privately for immediate treatment.

48 Doyal, 1985, p. 67.
49 Brindle, 1993.
50 Beecham, 1994, p. 1587.
51 Smith, 1993a, p. 216.
52 Hunt, 1993.

The role of medicine should be health, not profit

Health is a primary need of individuals. People may have the latest car or the most fashionable clothes, but if they are feeling ill they are not able to enjoy them. It is important for society that health care should be given the highest priority.

As we have suggested one of the major problems in terms of finance is that the people who need the most care are often those with the least money. We have seen (pp. 24–5) that the elderly, especially those over the age of 75, are the group which has the greatest need. A practical example of the way competition may operate to the detriment of the British population occurred in 1995 when the private firm BUPA signed an agreement to treat Libyans in any one of Britain's twenty-eight BUPA hospitals. This agreement means that rich Libyans will be treated while poor British people remain on waiting lists.[53]

Competition may introduce more bureaucracy

The NHS, as it existed before the reforms, collected its money in a very efficient way and furthermore had relatively few administrators. When the government introduced the NHS changes they produced a new group of managers who were not directly involved with care, diverting resources from patients. Alan Milburn MP obtained data from parliamentary questions which can be tabulated as shown in Table 3.1.

Table 3.1   *NHS salary costs in England in million pounds*

	1989–90	1993–4
Managers	158.8	609.6
Administration/Clerical staff	1038.9	1546.2

Source Brindle, 1995c.

The results show that the management costs have risen by almost four times and administrative and clerical costs by 46 per cent. Adding increases since April 1994, costs were estimated to have increased by over a billion pounds per annum by February 1995. Milburn was quoted as saying: 'The red-tape bill in the NHS is spiralling out of control. Precious resources are being diverted from the sharp end of patient care where they are most needed.'[54]

53 Mihill, 1995a.
54 Brindle, 1995c.

This kind of increase did not come as a very great surprise to us. One of us had noted in an earlier work that Britain's traditional system did not entail much expenditure on management:[55]

> The Director of Britain's Institute of Health Service Management said in 1987 that the cost of managing the British Health Service was only 4.5 per cent of the budget compared to 12 per cent in France and 21 per cent in the United States.

With a movement to US-style practices we would expect administration costs to rise. The increase did, however, seem to come as something of a surprise to at least some members of the government responsible for the changes. In 1993 the then Welsh Secretary, John Redwood, said that he was 'astonished' that, since the NHS reorganisation in 1990, Wales had seen a growth of 1,500 managers and only twenty more doctors.[56] He attacked an 'over enthusiasm for administration and management', and argued that the quality of service, patients' choice and efficiency should be the yardsticks. A report in September 1995 disclosed that the number of managers in September 1989 was 4,630. They increased to 23,350 by 30 September 1994, a fivefold increase. Over the same period the number of nurses fell by 7.7 per cent. Over the latest period, in the year to September 1994, the number of managers had grown by 15 per cent. The number of midwifery and nursing staff fell by 3.1 per cent, but this was in part due to a decision to stop counting student nurses in the total. David Brindle, the social services correspondent of the *Guardian*, states that these figures are the last in which direct comparison with previous years is possible. From October 1994 thousands of managers who need to have professional qualifications for their job would be reclassified as nurses or other health workers. This will automatically cut the number of managers and increase the published total of qualified nurses.[57]

The information on a movement of funds from nurses to managers was supported by our survey of orthopaedic surgeons (Chapter 10). It showed that one of the main complaints these surgeons have is the amount of money now being spent on administrators. Our surveys of Directors of Public Health also revealed critical comments on the rise of 'managerialism' (Chapter 4).

55 Francome, 1990, p. 89.
56 White, 1993, p. 4.
57 Brindle, 1995c, p. 4.

If we go outside health we see that one of the problems recently highlighted in British industry has been that leaders of industry have been giving themselves large pay rises. At the beginning of 1995 figures were released which showed that the salaries of the directors of self-governing trusts set up by the government reforms would cover the salaries of eleven thousand nurses. A study of 237 trust boards showed that they cost an average of £293,000 a year to run, totalling approximately £70 million a year. Each trust contains up to five salaried executives and five non-executive directors.[58] The *British Medical Journal* reported that during the period 1993–4 the chief executives of NHS trusts had pay rises of 6.6 per cent, although the government had imposed a limit of 1.5 per cent on the pay bill of the public sector. The difference led a spokesperson from Unison to comment: 'Our members are feeling the pain and chief executives are making the gain.'[59] So there is an argument that resources spent in this way could be more profitably used in patient care.

There may be problems in identifying any future increases in the number of NHS managers, for, as mentioned above, it was reported in October 1994 that thousands of NHS managers were to be reclassified as nursing, scientific and professional staff. The change occurred after official figures showed the number of managers rising by 13 per cent a year and nursing staff falling by 1 per cent. The number of managers recorded in England increased from 4,540 in 1989 to 20,010 in 1993, although there are different opinions about the interpretation of these figures. The government has argued that some senior nurses were reclassified as managers and that this could account for 45 per cent of the rise. If that figure is accurate it would mean that the number of managers has only tripled instead of increased five times. However, the evidence from those on the wards is that there has been a substantial rise. Christine Hancock, General Secretary of the Royal College of Nursing, was quoted as saying: 'Numbers of managers continue to rise sharply as the numbers of qualified nurses drop. Nurses are rushed off their feet.' She described the government changes in classification as manipulation. 'At a stroke it will be possible to claim improved nursing numbers and a reduction in management posts.'[60]

58 Brindle, 1995d, p. 3.
59 Warden, 1995a, p. 77.
60 Brindle, 1994e.

The medical profession should not be diverted

In our surveys of GPs we shall see that over 97 per cent of them said that the NHS changes had led to their having more administrative work to do. Many GPs pointed out that they had much more paperwork and that this has restricted the time they can spend with patients. This led to Dr Christopher Kimberley, writing in the *General Practitioner*, to say:[61]

> I am not surprised by the rise of complementary therapies. What they have in common is mystique and time to assess their patient's complaints. We no longer have this. We have to fit in our health promotion, administration, computerisation and acquisition of business skills. I am a doctor and I would like to go on doing the work of one. What I am really short of is time. If we could stop having all this change we would have more time for our real work.

The medical literature is full of comments from doctors bewailing the change in role away from traditional doctoring. Dr Blackwell-Smyth from Cornwall wrote to *General Practitioner* that these days computing degrees seem to be more appropriate for general practice than medical ones:[62]

> For GPs particularly bogged down as we are by administrative tasks and financial considerations, not to mention care packages, case conferences, counselling, and so called health promotion, it is all too easy to forget that we are doctors and that our basic qualifications are in medicine, surgery and obstetrics.

The overwhelming evidence is that the government changes are diverting doctors from their primary functions. Their time is being deflected from looking after patients, developing new ideas for improving care and reading about the latest medical developments. As far as possible doctors should be above concern with financial matters, which should be left to those with skills in that area.

Voluntary help for hospitals

There is a great deal of goodwill in society towards the health service and this is important in many respects. The campaign for saving Great

61 Kimberley, 1994.
62 Blackwell-Smyth, 1994.

Ormond Street Children's Hospital has raised a great amount of money and certain individuals have been able to improve services by their fund-raising efforts. Sir Jimmy Saville, for example, has raised £30 million for the Stoke Mandeville Hospital. Other people raise funds for such things as cancer and kidney research. The amounts of money collected by voluntary efforts are small compared with the total NHS budget. However, they do help – not only financially but in developing ties between communities and their local hospitals. They also help people to develop their feelings of altruism. The same goes for blood donations which are not simply lifesaving gifts but are also ways in which people can help the community without seeking material reward for themselves.[63]

The introduction of financial considerations is likely to damage these voluntary contributions, especially if people hear of extraordinary amounts of money being paid to administrators of hospitals. Furthermore, the introduction of business practices may lead to the loss of a sense of community. In April 1994 five senior doctors at Raigmore NHS Trust in Inverness wrote to the chairman to tell him of their feelings about the change in the year since trust status was taken:[64]

> The new regime has transformed a previously close knit, public spirited hospital community into one that is horribly dispirited. Staff who loved the hospital and gave freely of their time and energy to improve it are now treated with disregard bordering on callousness. The Trust is entirely driven by financial imperatives rather than a will to deliver better health care, a situation that would have been unthinkable two years ago. The management rules by diktat and operates with an excess of zeal, officiousness and discourtesy, imposing cash limits with little regard for effectiveness and commonsense.

It is a sad reflection on the reforms that these doctors have had to face such a deterioration in their working conditions and to see the negative effects of the changes on patient care.

Competition can conflict with openness
The pursuit of profit may lead to the creation of certain secrets and lead to information not being freely available for the benefit of all. The

63 Titmuss, 1968.
64 MD, 1994.

most famous example of this in medical history is the case of forceps delivery. This was kept secret by the Chamberlain family for over a hundred years and many women who might have benefited from an assisted delivery were denied it during that time.

In medicine it is essential that defects in standards of care are analysed and remedied, but the recent changes in the NHS make this less likely. Many hospitals have introduced confidentiality clauses, which mean that people are not allowed to bring problems into the open and may lead to scandals being kept secret and perpetuated.[64]

In an article on 'whistleblowing', Dave Lewis, Reader in Law at Middlesex University, drew attention to the extent to which NHS trusts have attempted to impose 'gagging' clauses in their contracts. One of his examples was from the Mount Vernon Trust. This states:[65]

> During the course of your employment you may see, hear or have access to information on matters of a confidential nature relating to the work of the hospital or the health and personal affairs of patients and staff. Under no circumstances should such information be divulged or passed onto any unauthorised person(s) or organisations. Disciplinary action will be taken against any employee who contravenes this regulation.

One of the debates that came to the fore in November 1994 was to whom the doctor has first responsibility. Roy Lilley, a leading figure in the NHS Trust Federation, said doctors needed to sort out their attitudes to their work. He argued that their first responsibility was to the trust for which they worked and not to their patients. This led to a debate in which the Department of Health reinforced the view that patients come first.[66] However, the fact that this kind of debate is occurring shows how much we have moved away from the fundamental principles on which the NHS was founded.

In April 1994 the newspapers reported a scandal in which a consultant at the Luton and Dunstable Hospital found that after he had opposed the policies of one of the newly appointed managers she tapped his phone. Katz reported:[67]

64 MD, 1994.
65 Lewis, 1994, p. 8.
66 Brindle, 1994g.
67 Katz, 1994, p. 2.

Police had been called to the hospital after a bugging device was found attached to the phone of a senior doctor. To make matters worse the bug had been found by the consultant himself. And, to make them really bad, it appeared the eavesdropping equipment had been installed on the orders of the hospital's own chief executive...The chief executive has been forced to resign in the face of mounting criticism. A new administration is battling to win back the confidence of a medical staff pushed near to mutiny by what many saw as the grossest breach of trust between an employer and employee.

P. J. H. Venn from the Queen Victoria Hospital, East Grinstead, wrote in a letter to the *British Medical Journal* early in 1994, 'I have recently been made aware of an unpleasant side of the new business environment.' He went on to relate how three representatives from his hospital attended an informal meeting on improving patient care at an NHS trust. The consultant who chaired the meeting had skills from which the representatives sought to learn for the benefit of everyone. They were told that a visit would cost £300. Venn attacked this change in practice:[68]

I wonder if this new business approach will also apply to clinical information in the future, with trusts attempting to levy charges on journals for clinical research published from their units? This dangerous precedent serves to underline the commercial attitudes engendered in many trusts' executive boards, which eventually must compromise patient care.

There is a case for arguing that within medicine there should be openness not secrecy. Instead of competition there should be co-operation, with everyone working together to produce a healthy environment and the best possible care.

A business environment can damage research

On examining research work on improving health care conducted within NHS trusts, one also encounters examples of good practice which are not disseminated, purely so that a particular trust will be able to retain a 'commercial advantage'.

In July 1994 there was an exodus of some of Britain's major medical

---

68 Venn, 1994, p. 63.

researchers. These included Professor Michael Chapman, pioneer of fetal heart surgery, who went to Sydney; and Professor Lucio Luzzatto, head of haematology at Hammersmith and a leading expert on sickle cell anaemia, who went to New York. In all, seven major researchers left London in a short time – some took posts elsewhere in Britain. Professor Bob Williamson, famous for his part in the discovery of the gene for cystic fibrosis, went to Melbourne. He said that he had always resisted head-hunting offers in the past but that now he felt that things had gone too far and were preventing him from carrying out his research adequately:[69]

> Research needs co-operation between the centres involved, but now what we have is hospitals competing for patients and money. Ten or fifteen years ago people would put up with the expense and inconvenience of London because of its clinical and academic excellence. Now there is far less co-operation between different hospitals because they are run by competing trusts. Obviously there is a major disruption in training and research.

Although these scientists did not discuss their resignation plans beforehand, they decided to present a common front to the press.

Competition interferes with the public service ethos
There are many people within the health service who have 'gone the extra mile' for their patients. They have worked harder than they needed because they believed in providing a good service. This kind of altruism occurs when the health of the nation is not seen as a way for a few people to make a profit but rather as a joint enterprise in which the people work together to try and improve the health of society. We shall see from our own research that various orthopaedic surgeons drew attention to the fact that this ethos was being damaged. A similar point was made by Malcolm Benson, a consultant at the John Radcliffe Hospital in Oxford. He commented:[70]

> Another victim of the reforms is a loss of such concepts as care and compassion. Quality is defined only in things that can easily be measured and recorded, such as waiting lists, throughput and outcomes. Nowhere does the Patient's Charter feature the skill and empathy needed in helping a

69 Dyar, 1994, p. 291.
70 Benson, 1994, p. 24.

dying patient. Such attributes have been eroded in the increasing drive for cost efficiency. Performance-related pay is likely to push this process even further.

Some people argue that the privatisation of services leads to dissipation of feelings of unity and working together for a common goal. John Sheldon commented:[71]

> My union has always maintained that privatisation and contracting out cuts corners, not costs. If ministers bring in private sector methods, managers and companies to do public sector work, they can hardly complain if the first thing to be ditched is public sector accountability, integrity and probity.

Financial scandals could undermine health care

As the financial year for 1994 ended there were four different stories related to financial scandals reported in four separate newspapers.

Story 1

A man had died after a leading hospital had told him that he would have to wait until the new financial year for his operation. The *Guardian* led with a story headed 'Patients Die through NHS Market Delays'. The report published 4 March included the following:[72]

> Patients are dying because their treatment is being delayed by the working of the National Health Service market, a leading specialist claims today. Dr Duncan Dymond, of St Bartholomew's Hospital in London, said that those at risk are patients whose condition is judged insufficiently serious for them to be treated as emergencies by hospitals which say they have run out of funds for other operations. In a letter to the *Guardian*, Dr Dymond says: 'Clearly a patient who is admitted to Hospital in an unstable state can be easily recognised as an emergency, but below the obvious lies a tier of patients who clinicians would wish to treat urgently with no or minimal delay, but who are not (yet) emergencies. These patients are the real victims of the internal market and some of them will come to grief.'
> Dr Dymond is responding to Mary Lambert, of

71 Sheldon, J., 1994.
72 Brindle, 1994f, p. 1.

Buckhurst Hill, Essex, who described in a letter to the *Guardian* on Monday how her husband, Bert, died after being told Barts could not treat him for his urgent heart condition until the new financial year in April.

The report continued by saying that the Health Minister had admitted that treatment of some urgent cases had been delayed by hospital providers which claim to have fulfilled their contracts with their purchasers. More serious was the fact that this was not an isolated incident. Surveys by the British Medical Association and the Royal Colleges have indicated that one in two hospitals had slowed or stopped treatment because of the contract position. The British Medical Association also reported that one cancer surgeon had been told to reduce the number of operations he performed each week from 7 to 4. There will be few who do not see the situation whereby people are not given the best possible treatment as anything but a national disgrace.[72]

Story 2

The front-page headline of the British newspaper *The Mail on Sunday* on 6 March 1994 read: 'NHS Deal in Donor Blood'. The story stated that the new NHS was to give the blood of British volunteers to a private hospital for foreigners and expected to make £450,000 profit out of the trade. The report continued that surgeons and MPs had warned that national blood supplies would be stretched because, despite a successful advertising campaign, the supplies were still 15 per cent below what was desirable.[73]

There is a danger that people voluntarily giving their blood will be discouraged by others profiting from their donations. It will be especially galling if blood is sold outside the health service and as a result operations are cancelled because of a blood shortage. A consultant at the Glasgow Victoria Hospital, Ian Anderson, stated, 'My major concern is that I don't want anything to detract from the superb system we have and the generous voluntary donation of blood.'

Story 3

The headline in the London *Evening Standard* on 21 March 1994 was: 'Patient offered Gag as Anaesthetic Runs out'. The story reported that St Thomas's Hospital, London, had run out of local anaesthetic

---

72 Brindle, 1994f, p. 1.
73 Brough, 1994.

because it had gone over its budget. The patient was a local nurse. Her husband, a musician, was reported as saying:[74]

> She went in on Thursday to have two benign cysts removed. She had the first one done and then was told there was no more local anaesthetic left as they had run over budget. They offered her a gag to bite on to deal with the pain. It's absurd. She could have come back, but she decided to grit her teeth and bear it. They make incisions to cut the cyst out and it's a very painful 15 minute operation. I don't know how they can get away with it, running out of something so basic as local anaesthetic in a major Hospital. We don't blame the doctor involved. This is just indicative of the way things are in the NHS.

Story 4

While the report above was about insufficient money for proper care, in the same week there were reports that the new breed of managers were treating themselves to expensive perks and thus diverting money from patient care. *Today* newspaper reported on 16 March 1994:[75]

> Damning evidence of Virginia Bottomley's NHS gravy train emerged yesterday with the revelation that trust hospital bosses have increased spending on cars by 350 per cent in a year. And the lavish spending managers have shelled out millions on plush new offices while patients have to sleep on the floor in casualty or Hospital corridors...In Leeds Department of Health bureaucrats have also treated themselves to a new £55 million office block with a swimming pool and an exercise suite. Yet at nearby St James Hospital – famous as TV's Jimmys – hundreds of operations have been cancelled because of a long running bed crisis. Seriously ill patients have endured painful overnight stays on narrow trolleys in the casualty departments. Other sufferers from painful illnesses have been made to wait for a Hospital bed.

The Prime Minister defended the expenditure and said that the cars were mostly being used by hospital staff to make home visits to patients. However, it is clear that a great deal of money has been

74 Stean, 1994, p. 21.
75 Pope and Campbell, 1994, pp. 1, 5.

diverted from patient care. We shall see that similar evidence is offered by those who have been working in the hospitals since the introduction of the reforms.

There may be a change in attitude towards litigation

In the United States there are pages of advertising by lawyers advising people of the fact that they may have a claim against doctors. A typical one in *Newsday*, the Long Island NY newspaper on 22 November 1994, read: '*INJURIES, No recovery, no fee, however, costs and disbursements payable by client at conclusion. Car accidents, Falls, Medical malpractice. Free consultation. We come to you. Call us First.*'

The problem with malpractice in the United States is not new, however in recent years the problem has become much worse. In one group of three thousand doctors in New York State, 30 per cent had a claim notified against them in one year. In 1987 insurance premiums were over £50,000 for obstetricians and £10,000 for family doctors, in contrast to £576 in Britain for GPs. The average doctor in the United States was paying about sixteen times more for malpractice insurance than a comparable British doctor. These costs are passed on to patients who themselves then have higher insurance payments. This climate in the United States has led to many doctors carrying out 'defensive medicine' – that is, they call for patients to have a great number of tests which are probably unnecessary but which cover the doctor in the case of litigation.

As we reported in our book *Caesarean Birth in Britain* the rate of births by caesarean section in the United States rose to 24.7 per cent in 1987. In a series of publications we have shown that the rate in England and Wales has now risen to over 15 per cent and that the rate of increase in caesareans has been rising. We have found that fear of litigation was a major reason for the rise in the rates.[76]

Other evidence comes from a report in the medical journal *Update*, which said that in the thirty years after the Second World War complaints against British doctors showed a gradual but slow increase. However, from 1975 onwards the numbers of complaints and the costs incurred increased dramatically. In 1975 one in a thousand doctors had claims paid on their behalf; by 1988 this had risen to thirteen in a thousand.[77]

In February 1994 it was revealed in the *Observer* that payments

76 Francome, 1994b.
77 Hoyte, 1994.

made to victims of medical negligence had reached record levels. The cost of compensation claims had more than doubled in four years. It had risen from £53 million in 1990 to an estimated £125 million in 1994. The report stated that the government was worried that the increase in the bills could bankrupt some of the new trust hospitals and that costs could continue to rise by 25 per cent a year.[78]

It is still the case that the vast majority of people do not complain when they face problems with their treatment. For example, a survey by Nottinghamshire Local Medical Committee found that eleven million contracts gave rise to only 293 objections. This means that 99.997 per cent did not complain. However, fear amongst doctors of having an allegation of malpractice is often high. Hoyte suggests that excess litigation may well lead to defensive medicine and unnecessary investigations. This may inconvenience the patient and could lead to maldistribution of the scarce NHS resources.[79] There appears to be a danger of Britain moving towards the situation in the United States. There people undergo unnecessary tests and have extra expense because of the general attitude of distrust that exists between many doctors and patients.

The changing role of the General Practitioner
All GPs experienced a major change in role following the NHS reforms. Irvine wrote in the *British Medical Journal* that the role of the GP was painfully changing from that of gatekeeper of hospital care to the provider of comprehensive health care in the community. Writing in 1993, he said:[80]

> Tomorrow's General Practitioners will need greater clinical and interpersonal skills, epidemiological skills for assessing the health of their practice population, the ability to play a part in practice management and skill in operating practice based quality assurance systems.

The next chapter will show how the intervention of the new market-style policies has reduced the amount of time a doctor can spend with each patient and produced a situation where over four out of five doctors do not believe that they have enough time to keep abreast of medical developments.

78 Jones, 1994c, p. 3.
79 Hoyte, 1994.
80 Irvine, 1993, p. 696.

Some hospital consultants are concerned that the new system will undermine the relationship between doctors and patients. Malcolm Benson, consultant at the John Radcliffe Hospital in Oxford, has drawn attention to the fact that the GP is increasingly becoming a rationer of care. This places the doctor in a position of conflict because of his or her role of advocate for the patient. Benson argued that it would inevitably undermine the trust at the heart of the patient–doctor relationship.[81] One of our major new research findings is the erosion of doctor–patient trust perceived by a majority of the Directors of Public Health (Chapter 4).

THE HIDDEN AGENDA?

We have seen in this chapter that there are problems in introducing the market into medicine. Dr Marion Newman, a North London GP, told us:

> '...I believe that the Government had a hidden agenda of undermining the National Health Service. They were moving to a private and insurance based solution. Furthermore they removed the entitlement to free eye tests and are managing to drive dentists from the NHS. They wanted the middle classes to take out private medical insurance and run a cheap system for the poor. However, with the growth in unemployment the middle classes are concerned. With the possibility of redundancy for everyone, private insurance became potentially unaffordable and so they realised they need a good health service...'

We heard a number of similar comments during our surveys. One of the consultant orthopaedic surgeons said that the government was: 'dishonest to the public and professionals. The welfare state is being broken up and they should say so.' A debate on whether there was a hidden agenda occurred in the British Medical Journal in 1994. Chris Ham[82] had suggested that the government was not led by a

> hidden agenda which, through a series of incremental steps, will result in more private involvement in the financing and delivery of health services...Politicians are not that clever

81 Benson, 1994.
82 Ham, 1994b.

[and] for any government to undermine the NHS would be electoral suicide. In practice, health policy is more a result of cock-up than conspiracy.

Ham's apparently complacent view was challenged by two critics of the government. Peter Draper, a respected academic, argued that if there was a master plan to dismantle the service then it did not need cleverness but rather 'duplicity laced with ideological zeal...We are likely to learn whether there was a successful conspiracy at Cabinet level only when a minister's memoirs are written'.[83]

However, a retired GP, Julian Tudor Hart, said that of course there was a conspiracy. He argued that when the Conservatives first took office in 1979 they had a simple agenda to devolve decisions from the elected government as far as possible so that they became by-products of the pursuit of profit in deregulated markets. He suggested that the government knew that people wanted the health service and realised it could not make its aims clear: 'Our government therefore proclaims its reverence for the principles of the NHS while it injects the energy, corruption and ultimate disintegration of the business world throughout the service.'[84]

He drew attention to Iliffe's report of a 1987 conference between Conservative politicians, senior figures in the NHS and members of New Right think tanks.[85] This produced a seven-point plan to transform the health service:

- Establish the NHS as an independent statutory body with decentralised financial accountability.
- Bring the NHS and private medical care together in an integrated and interrelated market.
- Extend direct charging in a costed market.
- Devolve all responsibility for patient care to directly funded district health authorities, dismantling the regional health authorities and their planning functions, with individual hospitals encouraged to opt out and compete for patients.
- End national wage bargaining for NHS staff.

These five aims, he suggested, had already been achieved. Two were left. These were:

- Retitle the NHS to reflect the new business era.

----

83 Draper, 1994.
84 Tudor Hart, 1994.
85 Iliffe, 1994, pp. 3–15.

- Create a national insurance scheme jointly with the private insurance companies.

He continued that these two things would not be achieved this side of a general election. Tudor Hart's evident distaste for the government changes is possibly stronger than that of the average doctor. However, in the two surveys that we have carried out with random samples totalling over five hundred GPs, we have seen that the vast majority of both fundholders and non-fundholders have supported the basic principles of the NHS but regard the government's changes as undermining these. Information about this will be provided in the next chapter.

CONCLUSION

The evidence produced so far has suggested that the introduction of the NHS changes occurred without adequate testing and/or due consideration of their likely side-effects, many of which could have been easily predicted. In the next chapter we consider what GPs and Directors of Public Health feel about the changes.

CHAPTER FOUR

GENERAL EFFECTS OF THE GOVERNMENT'S CHANGES

*'The NHS should be able to work as in the past
without* money *being the first consideration.'*
A General Practitioner

In this chapter we look at the overall impact of the reforms as perceived by GPs and Directors of Public Health and begin a discussion of hospitals. However, the effects on accident and emergency units will be discussed in Chapter 9 and the attitudes of orthopaedic surgeons and nephrologists (kidney specialists) will be considered in Chapter 10.

THE CHANGING ROLE OF GENERAL PRACTITIONERS

The White Paper *Working for Patients* claimed that the health reforms would change and improve the role of GPs and enable them to deliver better care. It stated that general practice would 'become a still more satisfying job'.[1] Furthermore, it said that the government health reforms would lead to shorter waiting times, greater choice of hospital and greater incentives to put patients first. There are some who believe the government health changes are a great success. For example, Rhidian Morris, the chairman of the National Association of Fundholding Practices, wrote in *The Times*: 'fundholding has emerged as a dynamic force for improving healthcare both in hospitals and in the community'.[2] He maintained that the reforms had been beneficial to patients.

The research of the two linked projects reported here seeks to identify what the reality has been for two random samples of doctors drawn in conjunction with medical mailing companies. The first was carried out in 1992 and the second in 1994.

1 Department of Health, 1989, p. 48.
2 Morris, 1994.

Methodology

For the 1992 survey of GPs a random sample of 400 GPs was chosen. Of these 315 (79 per cent) replied, although 35 of those who replied gave reasons why they could not fill in a questionnaire: that they were part-time, had retired from practice or that they were only recently appointed.[3] In the 1994 survey a random sample of 396 GPs was drawn. The first mailing was sent out on 27 February and reminders were sent on 19 March and 3 August 1994. Several questions were identical to those asked in the 1992 survey and 306 doctors (77 per cent) replied. There were two refusals. The respondents fell into three main groupings. These were fundholders (53), non-fundholders (198) and those who could not complete a questionnaire (55). The response rate overall was 74 per cent. Further details are included in the appendix.

RESULTS

The increase in day care and the closure of hospital beds has led to the possibility that patients are being sent out of hospital too early. The GPs were asked: *'Have any of your patients had to be returned to hospital because of too early discharge in the past year?'* The results can be tabulated as shown in Table 4.1:

Table 4.1   *Number of patients returning to hospital after too early discharge*

	None		1 or 2		Over 2		Total
Fundholders	8	16%	14	29%	27	55%	49
Non-fundholders	28	15%	67	36%	92	49%	187
All (1994)	36	15%	81	34%	119	51%	236
95% Confidence	10.7–19.8%		28.3–40.4%		44.0–56.8%		
All (1992)	84	30%	144	51%	52	19%	280
95% Confidence	24.6–35.4%		45.6–57.3%		14.0–23.1%		

Note In the tables 95 per cent confidence means that 95 per cent of the actual figures are within the sample estimates stated.

The results show that there had been a marked increase in the number of patients that doctors had to return to hospital after 'too early discharge'. The proportion of doctors with more than two patients who had to be

---

3 Francome, 1992a, 1992b.

returned to hospital increased from one in five (19 per cent) in 1992 to over half (51 per cent) in 1994. This difference, based on 516 doctors over a two-year period, is statistically significant (Chi Square 74.8 P>0.001). The 95 per cent confidence intervals for the difference are from 24.0 per cent–39.7 per cent. The proportion of doctors with no such problem fell by a half from 30 per cent to 15 per cent over the same period.

It is probable that these figures underestimate the number of patients who return to hospital. One fundholder said that 'none of his patients had returned that he was aware about'. This draws attention to the possibility that in some cases the doctor may not be informed. This could happen if, for instance, patients presented at accident and emergency units rather than seeking help from their GPs.

These results show that the policy of closing hospital beds and letting patients out early is leading to doctors having the extra work of seeing these patients and having some of them readmitted.

EFFECTS ON GENERAL PRACTITIONERS OF HOSPITAL POLICY

Another trend has been towards day care. To test the effect of this the 1994 survey asked doctors: *'Is day surgery increasing or decreasing pressure on you as a GP?'* The results are tabulated in Table 4.2:

Table 4.2   *Effects of day care in increasing or decreasing pressure on GPs*

	Increasing		The same		Reducing		Other/No reply	All
Fundholders	32	64%	18	36%	0	0%	3	53
Non-fundholders	136	72%	50	27%	2	1%	10	198
Total	168	70%	68	29%	2	1%	13	251
95% Confidence	64.8–76.4%		22.8–34.3%		0.1–3.0%			

The results show that seven doctors out of ten in 1994 said that day care was increasing pressure upon them. Only one in a hundred said that there was decreasing pressure. This question was not asked in the 1992 study as day care was less of an issue at that time.

This finding brings into question some of the government data showing that extra patients are being treated under the NHS reforms. If patients are sent home from hospital too early and then have to return, when they are readmitted they will be counted as another case.

TIME WITH PATIENTS

In 1994 we asked: 'During the past three years has the amount of time you can spend with each patient increased or decreased?' Table 4.3 shows the response to this:

Table 4.3   *Amount of time spent with each patient*

Time	Fundholders		Non-fundholders		All levels		95% confidence
Risen	2	4%	17	9%	19	8%	5.0–12.5%
Remained same	8	16%	65	36%	73	32%	25.6–37.6%
Fallen	39	80%	100	55%	139	60%	53.9–66.5%
Not know/No reply	4		16		20		
All	53		198		251		

The results show that three in five doctors felt there had been a decrease in the amount of time they could spend with each patient. Amongst fundholders it was four out of five. Only one in twenty-five of the fundholders and one in ten of the non-fundholders said they could spend more time.

The figures in Table 4.3 may be analysed on a regional basis, as shown in Table 4.4.

Table 4.4   *Amount of time spent with each patient by region*

Region	More		Same		Less		Total
East Anglia and Oxford	1	4%	12	52%	10	44%	23
North Thames			6	29%	15	71%	21
South Thames	2	8%	8	32%	15	60%	25
South West	1	4%	7	31%	15	65%	23
West Midlands	3	16%	5	26%	11	58%	19
North West	1	5%	5	26%	13	69%	19
North East and Yorkshire	3	14%	8	38%	10	48%	21
Trent	3	15%	7	35%	10	50%	20
Wales	2	20%	2	20%	6	60%	10
Scotland			9	31%	20	69%	29

Note Some doctors removed the identifying number from their questionnaire and so their region could not be identified.

The results shown in Table 4.4 reveal that in each area of Great Britain more doctors said they had less time to spend with patients than said they had more time. In the two London regions thirty (63 per cent) of the forty-eight doctors said they had less time to spend with patients. In Scotland seven out of ten of the twenty-nine doctors responding said they had less time for patients.

AMOUNT OF ADMINISTRATION

Another question we asked the doctors in both 1992 and 1994 was the amount of clerical work they performed per patient. The wording was the same in the two surveys except to take account of the fact that the reforms had only been in place for a year when the first survey was carried out, contrasted with three years the second time. The wording in the 1994 survey was as follows: *'During the past three years has the amount of clerical work per patient increased or decreased?'* The results are tabulated in Table 4.5:

Table 4.5   *Change in amount of clerical work due to the reforms in 1992 and 1994*

	Fundholders		Non-fundholders		All 1994 95% confidence		All 1992	
Increased	51	(100%)	181	(98%)	232 95.7–99.5%	98%	272	97%
Stayed same			3	(1.5%)	3 2.6–3.7%	2%	6	2%
Fallen			1	(0.5%)	1 0.1–3.0%	0%	2	1%
Total	51		185		236	100%	280	100%

Note Two fundholders and 13 non-fundholders did not respond in 1994.

The results show that in 1992, 97 per cent said that the amount of paperwork per patient had increased. This percentage had risen to 98 per cent in 1994. Every fundholder answering the question in 1994 said there had been an increase in clerical work and many specified that there had been a large increase.

ENOUGH TIME TO STUDY

A further question asked was: *'Do you feel that you are getting enough time to keep abreast of medical developments?'* The response is shown in Table 4.6.

Table 4.6   *Enough time for study (1994)*

	Fundholders		Non-fundholders		Total	
Enough time	5	9%	40	20%	45	18%
					13.2–22.7%	
Not enough time	47	89%	147	75%	194	77%
					72.1–82.5%	
Not know/No reply	1	2%	11	5%	12	5%
					2.5–8.2%	
Total	53		198		251	100%

The replies show that overall only one in five (18 per cent) of the sample said that they had enough time to keep up with developments. Fewer than one in ten of the fundholders said they had sufficient time to study. Some doctors made the comment that they kept up to date at the expense of their family life. Only three of forty-nine doctors (6 per cent) in the two London regions said that they had enough time. More than nine out of ten doctors in Scotland and Wales said that they did not have enough time. It would be interesting to know how doctors felt about this issue in the past.

PRIORITY GIVEN TO FUNDHOLDERS

In 1994 doctors were asked a question on priority that was not included in 1992. It was: *'Are there differences in priority given to fundholders in your area?'* The results in Table 4.7 show that overall seven out of ten of the doctors said that fundholders were given priority. Just over two in ten said they were not given priority and nearly one in ten did not know.

Table 4.7   *Inequality of referral of doctors in 1994*

Priority	Fundholders		Non-fundholders		All	
Differences exist	40	75%	134	68%	174	69%
						63.6–75.0%
No differences	13	25%	43	22%	56	22%
						17.2–27.5%
Not sure/No reply			21	10%	21	9%
						5.3–12.5%
Total	53		198		251	

In fact the majority in all areas of the country felt that fundholders were given priority. Some doctors said that they had no evidence about this, mainly because fundholding did not exist in their locality. Because of this it might be argued that the priority given to fundholders was not a country-wide phenomenon. It is instructive to look at the information for Scotland and Wales and the eight English regions. See Table 4.8.

Table 4.8   *Inequality of referral by region*

Region	Priority given			No priority		Total
East Anglia and Oxford	21	88%	68–97%	3	12%	24
North Thames	17	100%	81–100%	0	0%	17
South Thames	25	93%	76–99%	2	7%	27
South West	18	72%	51–88%	7	28%	25
West Midlands	15	75%	51–91%	5	25%	20
North West	15	79%	54–94%	4	21%	19
North East and Yorkshire	17	77%	55–92%	5	23%	22
Trent	14	74%	49–91%	5	26%	19
Wales	5	50%	19–81%	5	50%	10
Scotland	15	56%	35–75%	12	44%	27

The results show that at least seven doctors out of ten in all the eight regional health authorities in England reported that priority was given to fundholders. In the two London regions this was noted by over nine out of ten doctors. Those responding from Wales and Scotland were less likely to report that fundholders were given priority.

A second question on fundholding asked: '*Do you feel the system would be fairer if all doctors were either fundholders or non-fundholders?*' The response is shown in Table 4.9.

Table 4.9   *Attitude towards a single system of funding for GPs*

Attitudes	Fundholders		Non-fundholders		Total		95% confidence
Agree	44	84%	153	91%	184	90%	85.6–93.9%
Disagree	8	16%	15	9%	21	10%	6.1–14.4%
All	52		168		205		

The results show that nine out of ten of non-fundholding doctors and over eight out of ten of the fundholders thought the system would be fairer if all doctors were one thing or the other.

FREEDOM OF CHOICE

A question about freedom of choice asked: '*Over the past three years has the freedom of referral of your practice improved, remained the same or deteriorated?*' In 1992 the question asked about the past year.

The response to the question in 1994 from 13 per cent of GPs was that their freedom of referral had improved, while nearly a half said that it had deteriorated. Perhaps the most surprising thing is that only a minority of fundholders reported an improved freedom of referral. However, there was a difference in the figures; over two in five of the fundholders said their freedom of referral had improved, contrasted to fewer than one in twelve of the non-fundholders.

PRINCIPLES OF THE NHS

The White Paper '*Working for Patients*' stated: 'The government will keep all that is best in the NHS. The principles which have guided it for the last 40 years will continue to guide it into the twenty-first century.'[4]

The views of GPs on this issue are important, so the following question was asked: '*The NHS was designed as a high quality service available to all irrespective of their ability to pay and free at the point*

---

4 Department of Health, 1989, p. 3.

of need. Do you agree these basic principles are an ideal we should still work towards?' The results are shown in Table 4.10.

Table 4.10   *Views on the principles of the NHS*

Principles of NHS	Fundholders		Non-fundholders		All 1994 95% confidence		All 1992	
Agree	34	64%	153	78%	187	76% 70.0–80.8%	228	82%
Neither	7	13%	19	10%	26	10% 6.7–14.3%	26	9%
Disagree	12	23%	23	12%	35	14% 9.8–18.4%	24	9%
All	53		195		248	100%	278	100%

The table shows that overall three-quarters of the sample agreed with the basic principles of the NHS (95 per cent confidence intervals: 70.0–80.8%) and only 14 per cent disagreed with them. There was a difference between fundholders and non-fundholders which was statistically significant (95 per cent limits: 0.2%–28%). Four out of five of the non-fundholders were in support of the statement, compared with just under two-thirds of the fundholders. Almost one in four fundholders was opposed to the basic principles of the NHS, more than twice the percentage of non-fundholders opposed to those principles. The percentage of GPs who disagree with the principles of the NHS rose from 9 per cent in 1992 to 14 per cent in 1994, which is not statistically significant.

A further question regarding the philosophy of the NHS was asked: *'Do you think that the recent reforms have enhanced these principles?'* Table 4.11 shows the results.

Table 4.11   *Have the reforms enhanced the principles of the NHS?*

	Fundholders		Non-fundholders		All 1994 95% confidence		All 1992	
Enhanced	9	17%	8	4%	17	7% 4.0–10.6%	35	12%
Not enhanced	42	79%	175	88%	217	86% 82.2–90.7%	229	82%
Not know/ No reply	2	4%	15	8%	17	7% 4.0–10.6%	16	6%
Total	53		198		251	100%	280	100%

The results show that over eight out of ten doctors felt that the changes had not enhanced NHS principles (95 per cent confidence limits: 82.2–90.7%). The comparison between 1992 and 1994 shows a decline from 12 per cent to 7 per cent in the percentage believing that the reforms had developed its principles.

DOCTORS DO NOT BELIEVE IN FUNDHOLDING

In 1994 we asked *'Do you believe in the principles of fundholding?'* The response is shown in Table 4.12.

Table 4.12   *Belief in the principles of fundholding in 1994*

Belief	Fundholders		Non-fundholders		Total		95% confidence
Believe	34	64%	25	13%	59	24%	18.6–29.2%
Not believe	19	36%	169	87%	188	76%	70.8–81.4%
All	53		194		247		

The results show that overall fewer than one in four GPs agreed with the principles of fundholding (95 per cent confidence intervals: 18.6–29.2%). However, there was a clear difference between the two groups. Over three in five (64 per cent) of fundholders agree with the principle, compared with only one in eight (13 per cent) of non-fundholders. These figures show slightly more support amongst non-fundholders compared with those of Appleby, who found only 10 per cent support and 83 per cent opposed in 1993.[5]

5 Appleby, 1994.

Fundholders' views

Despite the fact that fundholders were largely in support of the principles of fundholding, wholly positive comments from them were rare. However, they included the following: '*I feel fundholding encourages practitioners to consider clinical priorities at a local level.*' Another positive comment was: '*I feel that the overall quality of hospital care has improved.*' A third respondent said: '*The GPs are in the best position to decide need.*'

More often fundholders supporting the practice expressed a certain ambivalence. One commented simply '*needs must*'; while another supporter said: '*It would have been better if the principles had been clearly thought out beforehand and not rushed through for political reasons.*' A third comment came from a doctor from the East Anglian and Oxford Region who said he was in support, '*but with many reservations, particularly where expensive treatments and potentially expensive patients are involved*'. Another said he was in support, '*but only if there is equal opportunity. Larger practices have clearly received financial incentives and benefits of unfair prioritisation.*'

In contrast, other fundholders said they did not agree with fundholding in principle. One commented simply: '*We have no choice.*' A second said: '*I believe it detracts from patient care and imposes a further strain on the doctors.*' A third, who opposed fundholding in principle, commented: '*Some aspects of it are helpful, some unfair to other patients and many are wasteful of money and managerial time.*' Another – about to be a fourth wave fundholder – said: '*It has been forced upon us. It shifts responsibility for care to us and this will be our downfall.*'

A Welsh doctor said: '*They have succeeded in dividing and ruling. Each fundholder is now to blame when things do not work.*'

Non-fundholders

Amongst this group a doctor from South London said: '*The NHS should be able to work as it did in the past without* money *being the first consideration.*' One from the West Midlands said: '*Doctors were not trained to be commercial managers.*' Several made a similar point to that of a GP from the North West Region: '*Doctors are there to treat their patients and not purchase and count the cost of treatment.*' Another doctor from the North West Region said: '*It is extremely inefficient and wasteful with excessive management costs. The GP's time is not really budgeted for and furthermore the two tier system goes against the principles of the NHS.*' Others also criticised the two-tier system. A doctor from the North West Region said: '*I believe in a service responsive to a whole population's needs and not just those of a few GPs.*'

An opponent of fundholding from North London said: '*It is ethically dangerous, there is a massive time commitment and is invariably wasteful.*' A doctor from the West Midlands said: '*It is likely to alter the doctor/patient relationship. We can no longer be the patient's advocate.*' One from the South Western Region called fundholding '*a bureaucratic sledgehammer to crack a small nut*'.

Several people felt the government was using fundholding to shift responsibility. A doctor from the West Midlands said: '*We should not be expected to decide when to deny treatment to a patient.*' Another from this region said: '*It is the Government trying to create a system where patients will blame GPs for underfunding.*'

Several made practical objections. One from the South Western Region said, '*It is the most socially divisive scheme ever conceived.*' Another, from North London, said, '*making several small contracts reduces the choice for patients in each individual practice. Large Health Authority budgets could organise more contracts and more choice but they don't.*'

Several doctors pointed to increased administration. One from the South Western Region said: '*An extra layer of bureaucracy does not make things more efficient.*' A South London doctor said: '*[Fundholding] seems to be introducing a new tier of management costs and a two tier system. I predict that when more practices are fundholding the cost cutting will start in earnest.*'

Some doctors saw more sinister motives in fundholding. One from the West Midlands commented: '*It is a Government con trick to divide the profession.*' Another, from North London, commented that fundholding was '*part of the mechanism to dismantle the NHS. GPs will find they are totally at sea once the "con" is revealed even more obviously.*'

There were a wide variety of comments, but overall the balance was strongly against fundholding. A doctor from the North East and Yorkshire Region said simply, '*I preferred the old system.*'

REFERRAL AND WAITING TIMES

We asked: '*Over the past three years has the freedom of referral of your practice improved, remained the same or deteriorated?*' In 1992 the question was asked about the past year. The results are as shown in Table 4.13.

Table 4.13   *Freedom of referral*

Freedom	Fundholders		Non-fundholders		All 1994		All 1992	
Improved	20	43%	8	5%	28	13%	12	4%
Remained same	19	42%	72	41%	91	41%	179	64%
Deteriorated	7	15%	97	54%	104	46%	88	32%
Not know/No reply	7		21		28		1	
Total	53		198		251		280	

The results show that in 1994 overall 13 per cent of GPs said that their freedom of referral had improved while nearly a half said that it had deteriorated. Perhaps the most surprising thing is that only a minority of fundholders replied that they had an improved freedom of referral (95 per cent confidence: 24.8–52.1%).

Table 4.13 indicates a clear difference in experience between the fundholders and non-fundholders. Over two in five of the fundholders said their freedom of referral has improved, contrasted with fewer than one in twelve of the non-fundholders.

The question asked about waiting times was as follows: '*Over the past three years have your waiting lists risen or stayed the same?*'

The results can be tabulated as shown in Table 4.14.

Table 4.14   *Changes in waiting lists*

Waiting time	Fundholders		Non-fundholders		All	
Risen	10	23%	83	46%	93	41.5%
Remained same	14	32%	79	44%	93	41.5%
Fallen	20	45%	18	10%	38	17.0%
No response	9		18		27	
All	53		198		251	

Source Yates, 1995.

Table 4.14 shows that overall more than twice as many had an increase in waiting lists as had a reduction. There was a clear difference between fundholders and non-fundholders. Twice as many fundholders had a reduction in waiting lists as had an increase. In fact, nearly half the fundholders experienced a reduction in waiting lists. This was the case for only one in ten of the non-fundholders. One doctor reported that he had had an increase in waiting time until he became a fundholder, when it fell.

SUMMARY OF SURVEY OF GENERAL PRACTITIONERS

Overall these results reveal a disquieting situation. First, despite the rhetoric of the supporters of the changes, the results show clearly that the government's health changes have interfered with the traditional role of doctors. GPs are in a different position from specialists in that they need to have knowledge about a wide variety of areas. It is therefore important that they have plenty of time to see their patients, to read the medical literature and to be aware of the latest developments.

Secondly, not only have the government changes interfered with the doctors' role, what is more important is that fundholders have found their position is worse than that of the non-fundholders in terms of the amount of primary care they can give. Any further increase in fundholding is likely to make matters worse. When we read the early proposals for change in the health service, we see that the proponents such as Enthoven suggested that the innovations should be piloted.[6] This did not happen. Doctors and epidemiologists are rightly expected to conduct random controlled experiments to determine the effects of their treatments before adopting them on a wide scale, but this is not the case for governments. The political parties should agree that future administrations would not introduce changes without proper testing of the likely effects. Furthermore, they should not interfere with the traditional role of the doctor.

Overall, these results suggest that the government should be working out ways for doctors to have extraneous tasks moved from their remit. The medical profession is well paid – and rightly so. Doctors should not have to be concerned with money but rather be able to concentrate on the needs of their patients. With this in mind, the whole approach of the reforms needs to be put into reverse. A start could be made by winding down fundholding and at the same time working out other ways of allowing doctors to get back to the basic role of caring for people.

This study comes in addition to others which have shown unhappiness among the medical profession. A survey of nearly six

6 Enthoven, 1985.

hundred consultants published in October 1994 showed that almost two-thirds of them believed that 'once the move towards local autonomy for trusts is complete, the NHS as we know it will disintegrate'.[7] Furthermore, newspaper reports have told of the fact that the government's Chief Medical Officer is known to be concerned about 'rock bottom morale among doctors'.[8] He organised a meeting of the main members of the British medical establishment to decide what the role of doctors should be.

Morale is not going to be improved by moves to increase the number of fundholders against the wishes of the majority of GPs. From this research it seems evident that what is needed is not more of the same treatment, but rather a fundamental review of the changes to identify what can be done to free doctors from the excessive amounts of paperwork and extra managerial tasks which are interfering with their primary work. Changes are needed to allow them time to go back to their role of being medical men and women rather than economists or managers.

Fundholders and possible reduction of costs

Overall the results of the survey we have given in this chapter have shown many disadvantages to fundholding. There is, however, some evidence that fundholders could reduce the cost of prescriptions.

In 1991 the cost of NHS prescriptions was £55 a person in the United Kingdom. When the government health reforms were introduced, one of the priorities was to control these growing costs. There were two schemes. The one which proved most successful in terms of saving money was that devised for fundholders. Their drug budgets were calculated on the basis of the size and characteristics of their practice population. The budgets were cash limited and any savings made could be transferred into a different budget, such as hospital care, or spent on other ways within the practice.[9]

Non-fundholders were also presented with indicative prescribing amounts which were based on the estimated size and changing needs of their population. However, the savings were to be treated differently. The authority was allowed to keep half of these for schemes to improve the primary health care of patients.

A study of the effect of these two alternative schemes in the Oxford Regional Health Authority over two six-month periods in 1991 and

7 Hann and Ward, 1994.
8 Jones, 1995.
9 Bradlow and Coulter, 1993, p. 1186.

1992 found that the cost of ingredients amongst dispensing fundholders grew by 10 per cent while that of non-dispensing fundholders grew by 13 per cent and that of non-fundholders grew by 19 per cent. Dispensing fundholders increased the percentage of generic drugs dispensed from 27 per cent to 34 per cent. The percentage for non-dispensing fundholders rose from 44 per cent to 49 per cent while that of non-fundholders remained the same, at 47 per cent. The authors concluded that fundholding has helped to curb increases in prescribing costs.[9]

DIRECTORS OF PUBLIC HEALTH

These have a central role in the new health care market-place of the 1990s. Directors are responsible for assessing the health needs of the population and for ensuring needs are met by delivery of appropriate services. As principal advisors to purchasers, the directors actively implement health policy through contracts specifying quality, throughput and price. Furthermore, they are in a position to observe, influence and appraise the impact of the NHS reforms at a local level. They might be expected to be more supportive of the reforms than other doctors because of their close links with the purchasers. To some extent they have had to be apologists for change, although the extent is not always clear. One piece of evidence came to us by accident when a director whom we were about to interview apologised for being late. He explained he was being given tuition as to how best to behave to sell the closure of the local hospital to the local population at a public meeting. He said, *'She told me to stand with my arms open wide as if welcoming suggestions – not closed up as if I was defensive.'* Subsequent events showed that this particular hospital closure met with universal hostility. The incident, although anecdotal, suggests that those directors closely involved in such policies as hospital closure will not be totally objective in their analysis of the changes. However despite our awareness of this we were interested to seek the views of Directors of Public Health, particularly in relation to the impact of the reforms on the underlying principles of the NHS, the resources available to implement them, and their general effect on the health of the population.

In an earlier study we asked Directors of Public Health to give their opinions about the likely impact of the reforms six months after their

9 Bradlow and Coulter, 1993, p. 1186.

introduction.[10] The study used a postal survey of 186 public health directors identified in England at that time. They were sent two mailings. The high response rate of 84 per cent and the nature of the comments received suggested that the directors welcomed an opportunity to give their opinions about the reforms. The 1991 survey suggested that they believed that the reforms would weaken some of the important principles of the NHS. One in three stated that the basic principle of public funding of the NHS would be weakened. Only 4 per cent felt that public funding would be strengthened. A similar body of opinion believed that the principle of trust between doctors and patients would be weakened. The only principle which a majority (67 per cent) felt would be strengthened was meeting the needs of the population.

The majority of directors in 1991 felt that the reforms would provide inadequate resources to assess health needs, formulate and monitor contracts, and safeguard the quality of care. The majority also believed that the effectiveness of services would deteriorate as a result of the 1 per cent efficiency savings per annum, individual patient billing and GP fundholding. On the other hand, greater effectiveness was predicted as a result of the purchaser/provider split and the establishment of clinical directorships.

Regarding the quality of care, the majority of directors foresaw no change – although a significant minority predicted a deterioration in choice of specialist, and improvements in community care, hospital nursing care, medical care, waiting times for in-patient treatment of urgent cases and hospital surroundings. With regard to the potential impact on specialists' clinical freedom, the majority predicted no change.

Whether the early predictions from 1991, ranging from guarded optimism to anticipated deterioration, were borne out by three years of post-reform experience can be judged from the survey conducted in 1994. The objective of this study was to evaluate the impact of the reforms on the NHS principles, effectiveness and quality of health care in the light of three years' experience. The survey provides an authoritative evaluation on the impact of the reforms by a group of well-informed participant-observers.

Methodology
The second survey, using a similar questionnaire to that used in 1991 but modified slightly to allow for the longer time period, was conducted in April 1994.

----

10 Francome, 1991.

The questionnaire was sent to directors in all 143 districts in the UK which could be identified at that time. Non-respondents were sent reminders in June and July 1994. Eight districts had merged with a neighbouring district, reducing the total to 135. Five directors declined to participate and a further 9 did not reply leaving a final sample size of 121, a response rate of 90 per cent. The results of this survey therefore represent the views of almost the entire population of public health directors working in the UK.

Results

The first area of interest is whether the reforms were perceived as having strengthened or weakened the underlying principles of the NHS. The distribution of answers to this question is given in Table 4.15.

Table 4.15   *Have the reforms strengthened or weakened the following basic NHS principles?*

	Strengthened	Weakened	No change
		(1992 figures in brackets)	
Funding from taxation rather than private sources (101)	4% (5%)	33% (40%)	63% (55%)
The trust between doctors and patients (103)	2% (4%)	50% (41%)	48% (55%)
Equal access of care for all patients (117)	18% (27%)	56% (44%)	26% (29%)
Providing a comprehensive local service (115)	25% (27%)	25% (44%)	30% (33%)
Meeting the needs of the population (115)	60% (73%)	10% (12%)	30% (15%)

Note For ease of comparison those who answered 'don't know' are excluded from the table. The numbers reflect this fact.

The results show that three out of ten felt there had been no change in relation to the matter of funding from taxation rather than from private sources. However, one in three thought this basis had been reduced. With regard to the second principle, 50 per cent of directors felt that the trust between doctors and patients had deteriorated as a result of the reforms, and only 2 per cent thought that it had improved. This figure had worsened since the first six months of the reforms. On the third question a majority felt that the principle of equality of access to care for all patients had been weakened by the reforms. The only area where the majority of directors felt that the reforms had been an improvement was that of meeting the needs of the population; 60 per cent supported this view. However, against this was the opinion stated by 51 per cent – that there were insufficient resources for health needs assessments to be conducted properly.

Resources and related problems
We asked, *'Have you had any problems (e.g. lack of resources) in assessing the health needs of people in your area? Please specify.'* The response showed that 51 per cent of directors had resource problems in connection with their duty to conduct health needs assessment. Associated problems which were reported included data problems (23 per cent), a neglect of health needs in the contracting process (17 per cent) and a lack of the necessary methodological and statistical expertise within their departments (12 per cent). Problems mentioned less often were an inadequate research base (4 per cent), the unwarranted assumption by others that health needs assessment was 'easy' (2.5 per cent), problems with the definition of health (2.5 per cent), problems resulting from mergers (3.3 per cent) and a few problems of diverse kinds (16 per cent).

Effectiveness
A third area of interest is how the directors perceived the effectiveness of services to have been altered by the reforms. Their responses to this question are given in Table 4.16.

Table 4.16   *The reforms and effectiveness of services*

	Improved		Deteriorated		No change	
			(1991 figures in brackets)			
1% efficiency savings per annum (98)	15%	(8%)	30%	(59%)	55%	(33%)
GP fundholding (107)	45%	(23%)	25%	(49%)	30%	(28%)
Competition between hospitals (116)	24%	(35%)	19%	(25%)	57%	(40%)
Purchaser/provider split (115)	57%	(69%)	9%	(17%)	34%	(14%)
Clinical directorships (105)	57%	(79%)	1%	(2%)	42%	(19%)

Note For ease of comparison those who answered 'don't know' are excluded from the table. The numbers reflect this fact.

The results show that in two areas the majority of directors said there had been an improvement. These were for the purchaser/provider split (57 per cent) and clinical directorships (also 57 per cent). However, the comparison with 1991 shows that the percentages taking this view had fallen from 69 per cent and 79 per cent respectively in 1991. Just under a half thought that GP fundholding had led to improvements; however, this figure showed an increase from 23 per cent in 1991. Fewer than three in ten thought the merger of district health authorities had improved the effectiveness of services.

THE EFFECT ON HOSPITAL SERVICES

There has been a continued decline in acute hospital beds. These fell by a third between 1981 and 1992/3, from 145,000 to 114,000. Predictions by House of Commons researchers suggested the numbers would fall by around a further third by the year 2001 to a figure of between 95,000 and 100,000.[11] This is, of course, not necessarily an adverse consequence of the changes. There may be good reasons why people might be spending less time in hospital:

- We are treating more people in the community. This subject will be discussed in Chapters 7 and 11.
- There has been a move to more day-care treatment.
- Some illnesses may well be better treated outside hospital altogether.

11 Brindle, 1994d.

With regard to this, in 1993 the *British Medical Journal* carried an important article.[12] It considered the care of 236 children who were newly diagnosed with diabetes. Of these 138 were not admitted to hospital, but received supervised management based at home. The findings showed that newly diagnosed diabetics can be safely managed outside hospital. Fewer children who received management at home were later admitted to hospital for reasons related to diabetes than were readmitted from the group treated in the hospital. The decline in the number of hospital beds was not due to decline in need due to changes in care, however. There is much evidence on shortages. Wendy Savage, a consultant obstetrician at the Royal London Hospital, set out some of the difficulties.[13]

> When I qualified in 1960, the UK spent £19 per head on health care, almost 80% of the OECD average of £25, and was joint eighth in the league table, below the US (£51) and Sweden (£32) and about the same as France (£20) and Germany (£22). Following successive reorganisations we now have a situation where people are being denied lifesaving treatment and are spending hours on trolleys while doctors or bed managers vainly search for a bed in which to admit them. One sees wards being run by one or two exhausted nurses, dealing with extremely ill patients. The extra money the Government claims it has spent on the NHS has disappeared into the salaries, executive suites and company cars of the managers, or been wasted on an even greater scale on grandiose computer building schemes. In 1990 we spend £582 per capita on health and the OECD average is £966. France and Germany spend £1,046 and £1063. We are now sixteenth in the league, well below the European average of £779 and overtaken by Italy, Belgium and Denmark.

There is also evidence of a decline in the number of hospitals. In April 1995 figures collected by the House of Commons Library revealed that 245 hospitals had closed in England since 1990 – one in eight of the total. Only twenty-one have opened, so there have been over ten times as many closures as new hospitals. In December 1994 the government provided figures for closures in the rest of the United Kingdom since

12 Swift *et al.*, 1993.
13 Savage, 1993.

April 1991, the start of the market system. These were seventeen in Wales, thirty-four in Scotland and eight in Northern Ireland.[14] These reductions were bound to bring problems. For example, in the eight months from April to November 1993, 44 per cent of surgical divisions were instructed to cut down on clinical activity.[15] Furthermore, data published in May 1994 showed NHS waiting lists reaching an all-time high, having increased by 7.1 per cent during the year. They rose from 992,324 in March 1993 to 1,065,349 in March 1994.[16] Of the people involved, 64,661 had been waiting for more than a year, in breach of the Patients' Charter. When people are referred from their GP to a hospital there are very often delays. Data on this are not kept routinely by the NHS; however, it is possible to compare a 1984 survey of 163 districts by the *British Medical Association* with a 1994 one by the College of Health Helpline. Table 4.17 gives details.

Table 4.17   *Average waiting time in weeks for a routine NHS out-patient*

Speciality	1984 (weeks)	1994 (weeks)
Orthopaedics	16	25
Ophthalmology	15	19
General surgery	8	13
Ear, nose and throat	14	14

Source Yates, 1995, p. 3.

The results show that in three of the four specialities listed there has been an increase in waiting times and in the other one the situation has remained constant. In the case of orthopaedics, there has been an increase of over two months. If things were really improving, these times would be decreasing.

We have seen that when it was set up the NHS aimed to provide a service that was based on need. However, it is now becoming clear that those with money are able to get much quicker treatment than those without. Yates pointed out that while the NHS keeps its orthopaedic patients waiting an average of twenty-five weeks for an appointment,

14 Brindle, 1995c.
15 Yates, 1995, p. 6.
16 Brindle, 1994d.

those who can pay to see the same surgeons only wait two weeks. He commented:[17]

> The waiting times in public and private sectors are starkly different. In effect, one sector measures time in months, while the other measures it in days. It is difficult even to put the two sets of figures on the same scale. Of private patients 96% see a consultant in under a month, but in the NHS, only 9% have such an option.

In human terms there are personal dilemmas. Daniel McGannon developed a back injury in January 1995. He gave us permission to tell his story. He was in tremendous pain, could not work and lived on his own. For part of the time, he looks after his children – aged 10 and 11. Through his work insurance, which covered only an assessment visit, he was able to see a consultant immediately. After a body scan he was told he needed an operation which would solve the problem in a short time. For £8,000 or more he could have the operation within a week. However, if he wanted to have the operation on the NHS he would have to wait six months or more. Being in such pain and unable to continue his working and sporting lifestyle, Daniel considered the possibility of 'going private' and finding the money himself rather than waiting for an unspecified time on the NHS. His GP pointed out that Daniel should consider the possible further costs, such as the expense of post-operative complications should things not go as planned. This could lead him into debt. His final decision was that unknown factors prevented him from taking the 'get well as soon as possible' choice. He felt that as long as the eventual NHS treatment exhibited the same quality as private sector treatment then, hopefully, the end result would be the same. 'What a choice!' Daniel said, still off work four months later, trying to fulfil a 50 per cent single-parent role to his two very lively boys and still wondering when the NHS call would come. He finally had his operation after four months wait.

This illness, though painful, was not life threatening. As the magazine *Doctor* reported in 1994, some patients die while waiting for an operation.[18] Cases such as Daniel McGannon's raise several issues. The first is that of those who cannot pay. The NHS was not set up to force poor people to live in pain while the rich get immediate treatment. Secondly, it appears that it is in the interests of the private

---

17 Yates, 1995.
18 Anonymous, 1994a.

hospitals, and possibly in the financial interests of the consultant to keep waiting lists long to maximise revenue. There are more than sixty specialities listed by the Department of Health as having waiting lists. The eight with the longest lists all appear in the highest nine earning specialities reported to the Monopolies and Mergers Commission.[19]

Shortage of consultants

Every investigation of medical staff conducted since the early 1970s has called for an increase in the number of consultants, according to an editorial in the *British Medical Journal*. There have been repeated calls for a growth in staff of 4 per cent a year, but the actual rate has remained at around 2 per cent and in 1992/3 it was 1.9 per cent. At this level it has fallen behind an increase in demand. Brearley comments:[20]

> The number of patients treated in NHS hospitals continues to increase. The patient's charter, numerous local additions to it, and the increasing technical complexity of new medical treatment all require that an ever greater proportion of care should be provided by consultants in person. Educational initiatives and recently the Calman Report [into hospital doctors' training], require consultants to devote more of their time to training junior staff, and the demands made by audit and administration have also increased considerably. A survey in 1989 showed that consultants worked on average 50 hours a week for the NHS, excluding on call commitments.

The article continued that, although the Calman Report had called for a reduction in the training time for consultants from twelve years to seven years, it did not offer a solution to the problem of how to increase numbers. The government has refused to earmark extra funds to implement it. The editorial concludes by saying that an increase in consultants is vital to ensure high standards of care.

Junior doctors' hours

Despite the attempts to reduce the hours of junior doctors, evidence published in March 1994 indicated that 1,200 of the around 28,000 junior doctors were working over eighty-three hours a week. This was

19 Yates, 1995, p. 6.
20 Brearley, 1994, p. 1246.

despite the fact that all posts over eighty-three hours were supposed to be eliminated by the end of 1993.[21] In the following month the newspapers headlined the fact that a 27-year-old junior hospital doctor, Alan Massie, had dropped dead after completing an exhausting 86-hour week. His father was quoted as saying: 'We believe it was the system that killed him. When he was working his body was running on adrenalin – when he had the first chance to relax properly, there was nothing to keep him going. The day before he died he looked absolutely clapped out.[22] The Health Minister said that no doctor would be on call for more than seventy-two hours or actually 'on their feet' for more than fifty-six hours by the end of 1994. However, the Department of Health's own figures showed that one in seven of the 28,000 junior doctors in Britain was on duty for over seventy-two hours a week.[23] Other observers pointed out that over half were working these hours for a salary as low as £12,500 a year.[24] In January 1995 a second father wrote about his child working as a junior hospital doctor. He did not allow his name to be published to protect her:[25]

> I wish to explode the myth that junior doctors' hours have been cut. My daughter has just worked 133 hours out of a possible weekly total of 168 hours in one of London's teaching hospitals...she had to work from Tuesday 9am all day and night, all Wednesday day and night, and all Thursday until 7pm (a total of nine hours' sleep). She was then allowed a normal night's sleep and was back from Friday 9am to 7pm and was allowed another night before starting a weekend duty on Saturday at 9am. The weekend was very busy; she only managed 3 hours sleep on Saturday night and Sunday was a nightmare. She was by now extremely tired and on Sunday morning had to deal with a desperately ill young woman...my daughter was emotionally and physically exhausted but still had to finish Sunday and be on call for another busy night and work all Monday before she could have a proper night's rest. On Monday her team took pity on her and sent her home early

21 Mihill, 1994c.
22 Jones, 1994d.
23 Rogers and Thomas, 1995.
24 Pilkington, 1995.
25 Letters, 1995.

(at 5.30pm) which is when she should have finished anyway. She was then back to work at 9am next morning and had to work every day and Thursday night before her weekend off. How much longer can our young doctors go on being exploited?

Shortly after this, in January 1995, *The Sunday Times* reported that the Health's Minister's own daughter was working over eighty hours a week as a junior doctor. The report said that junior doctors were angry that the government had agreed to cut hours without increasing staff sufficiently. In the light of this kind of evidence it is instructive to note that an article in the *British Medical Journal* about hours of work and health drew attention to a European Council directive. The directive proposed a minimum daily rest period of eleven consecutive hours in each 24-hour period, at least one rest day a week and four weeks' annual leave. According to the report, the British government was challenging the legal basis of the directive before the European Court of Justice.[26]

POSITIVE EFFECTS OF THE REFORMS

Although we have been very critical of the overall effects of the reforms, there have been some areas in which even left-wing analysts have noted benefits from the changes. A consultant from a major London teaching hospital has stated that one area was the issue of consultant power and its abuse:[27]

> This especially manifests in the big London teaching hospitals, and has been a concern for many years. Attempts to curtail it and to introduce more accountability into the way consultants conduct themselves should be welcomed. The extension into excessive levels of (often ineffective) management is, of course, to be condemned but the principle of applying the same accountability to consultants – measuring their performance – in the same way as other workers needs more acknowledgement.

A second factor is the number of abortions on the NHS. Wendy Savage, Consultant at the Royal London Hospital Trust, commented to us: 'I am generally opposed to the reforms but I am pleased that they have

26 Harrington, 1994, p. 1581.
27 Personal communication, 7 October 1995.

led to an increase in the number of free abortions available to women.'
This was almost certainly an unintended consequence of the reforms.

CONCLUSIONS AND RECOMMENDATIONS

Overall the general effect of the reforms can be seen to be negative.
Instead of co-operation there is competition; in place of the idea of
service there is pursuit of profit; in place of the needs for the patients
there is the demand of the market. Where there was dedication there is
now cynicism and frustration. The reforms have introduced
fragmentation when there was a coherent system and there is the
wastage of an artificial internal market. In the following chapters we
shall be considering the evidence available both on the target areas
chosen by the government in *The Health of the Nation* and on other
matters outside the government targets.

It is interesting to reflect on why the government has not been more
critical of its own changes. There has been very little beyond that of
John Redwood (p. 53) and fragmentary evidence that MPs have fought
to save their own local hospitals. One of the reasons may be that the
government, believing its own publicity and surrounding itself with
those sympathetic to the changes, has not been sufficiently critical. In
this respect it is instructive to consider the views of Professor J. D.
Ward, a diabetes consultant, on the image and the reality.[28]

Image   *An improved modern NHS treating more patients more
efficiently.*
Reality *Stress and dangerous practice relating to the pressures.*
Image   *Five star hospitals seeing patients within ten minutes.*
Reality *Quick assessment but allocation to a wait of hours before
being seen by a doctor.*
Image   *The image is of money pouring into the NHS.*
Reality *The reality is that it is to pay an endless line of accountants,
corporate managers and budget holders.*
Image   *The image is of warm community care.*
Reality *The reality in Sheffield is that community care does not exist at
the weekends.*

He concluded there is a need to close the gap between image and
reality.

....
28 Ward, 1995.

Overall some conclusions of this chapter are as follows:

1   We need to improve the position of GPs who are the backbone of the health system. The time they spend on administration needs to be reduced. The time gained should be spent in seeing patients and keeping up to date with developments.
2   The present inequalities in treatment need to be eliminated in order that people are treated according to clinical need.
3   Resources are needed to reduce waiting times so that treatment is delayed for clinical reasons only and not because of scarcity of resources.
4   Improvements in the primary care system are needed to remove the two-tier system and to restore trust between doctors and patients in cases where it has been weakened. This could be achieved by equalising the purchasing rights of fundholding and non-fundholding GPs.

CHAPTER FIVE

CORONARY HEART DISEASE AND STROKES

*More than seven out of ten men and eight out of ten
women fell below the level of physical activity
necessary to achieve a health benefit.*

The government decided to include coronary heart disease and strokes in *The Health of the Nation* partly because there was scope for the prevention of diseases of the cardiovascular system, and partly because addressing the risk factors associated with them – unbalanced diet, smoking, raised blood pressure, alcohol misuse and lack of physical activity – would also help in the prevention of many other diseases. Coronary heart disease accounts for an estimated five million deaths a year worldwide. It is the leading cause of death in Western industrialised societies and is growing in importance in the developing countries. Heart disease kills more people in the UK than does any other disease – almost five hundred a day.

Scotland and Northern Ireland have amongst the highest rates of heart disease in the world.[1] Reports in 1994 stated that women in Glasgow had a heart disease rate of 256 per 100,000, which made them nine times more likely to suffer from the condition than women in Barcelona – where the rate is 30 per 100,000. Men in Glasgow had a rate of 823 per 100,000, which was higher than for the women but still behind parts of Finland – where the rates were 915.[2] The differences were not due to age or sex, which were corrected for the study. However, the results may have been influenced by the fact that there was no correction for social status. In the United States approximately 1,250,000 million people suffer a heart attack each year and 500,000 of these die. About one half of the deaths occur within one hour of the onset of symptoms.[3]

Death rates from heart disease have fallen in the UK; they dropped by 22 per cent between 1979 and 1989. However, other countries have

1 Jones, 1994b.
2 McKie, 1984, p. 10.
3 Dracup *et al.*, 1995.

experienced greater reductions. For example, Japan dropped by 32 per cent over the same period. *The Health of the Nation* targets were as follows. These are to be achieved by the year 2000 with a 1990 baseline.

- To reduce the death rates for both coronary heart disease and strokes in people under 65 by at least 40 per cent.
- To reduce the death rate from coronary heart disease in people aged 65–74 by at least 30 per cent.
- To reduce the death rate for stroke for people under 65 by at least 40 per cent by the year 2000.
- To reduce the death rate for stroke in people aged 65–74 by at least 40 per cent.

There are also some subsidiary targets which will be discussed in the text.

RESULTS FROM THE FIRST YEAR

The data available on progress after the first year suggest that improvements need to be made. The report for the first year found that seven out of ten men and eight out of ten women fell below the activity level necessary for health benefit.[4]

International efforts to combat heart disease began in the late 1970s, when many countries began to realise that more information was needed over and above that collected in routine death certificates. In the early 1980s the MONICA project, which has become the largest study of heart disease ever undertaken, was set up. Over seven million people aged 35–64 were investigated by thirty-eight research teams in twenty-one countries over ten years.[5] The project aimed to **MONI**tor trends in and causes of **CA**rdiovascular disease. It was originated by the cardiovascular diseases unit of the World Health Organization in conjunction with numerous national research bodies. Countries involved in the study were Australia, Belgium, Canada, China, the Czech Republic, Denmark, Finland, France, Germany, Hungary, Iceland, Italy, Lithuania, New Zealand, Poland, Russia, Sweden, Switzerland, the UK, the USA and the former Yugoslavia.[6] The organiser of the study, Prof Hugh Tunstall-Pedoe from Dundee

4 Department of Health, 1993d, p. 55.
5 Bonita, 1994, p. 685.
6 Mihill, 1994b, p. 5; Tunstall-Pedoe *et al.*, 1994, p. 586.

University, said: 'We have found huge population differences in coronary heart disease rates.'[7]

Some countries have achieved dramatic improvements in their death rates, which suggests that the United Kingdom has great potential for reducing deaths. Age and sex data show heart disease is twice as high for men as for women under the age of 65. Over the age of 65 cardiovascular disease is equally common amongst the sexes. However, one in nine women aged 45–65 is affected by the disease and a quarter of women who die of heart disease under the age of 65 are in fact under 45 years.[8]

Furthermore, some evidence suggests that the survival of women after a heart attack may be worse than that of men. A study of 216 women and 607 men with acute myocardial infarction found that event-free survival was 76 per cent for men and 63 per cent for women. Women tended to be treated with thrombolysis less often than men, although the differences were small. Substantially fewer women than men were discharged from hospital with beta blockers.[9] The authors conclude that sex should not be regarded as an independent predictor until the differences in treatment are eliminated.

One instructive finding is that there are wide differences in death rates between ethnic groups in Britain. In 1984 the first comprehensive study of mortality of settlers in England and Wales was published. This evidence shows that there have been very great differences in mortality through circulatory diseases. The data relate to the years 1970–2. What they showed was that deaths from all causes were slightly below average for those from the Indian sub-continent and the Caribbean. They were, however, 33 per cent above average for those from the African Commonwealth.[10] As already discussed (p. 35), this masks the finding that Caribbean men had only 45 per cent of the number of heart attacks that might be expected, yet they had more than twice as many strokes. Caribbean women had 88 per cent of the expected number of heart attacks and two and a quarter times the number of strokes suffered by the overall population. It does not seem that physical factors can be the sole reason for these differences. African men had twice the death rate from heart attacks of Caribbean men. In contrast African women had fewer heart attacks than Caribbean women. Men and women from the Indian sub-continent

7 Tunstall-Pedoe et al., 1994, p. 604.
8 Jackson, 1994, p. 555.
9 Wilkinson et al., 1994, p. 566.
10 Radical Statistics Health Group, 1984, p. 25.

had an excess of one-fifth in their rates of both strokes and heart attacks.

These ethnic differences are likely to be due to a mixture of biological and social factors and to be at least partly related to stress, housing conditions, physical habits, drug use (including drink and tobacco) and diet. They indicate a promising area for research, for once the causal factors are identified they could indicate lifestyle changes that might improve the health of other groups. The Chief Medical Officer's report for 1991[11] focused attention upon the health needs of black and minority ethnic groups. Publication of *The Health of the Nation* in 1992 was followed by the publication of *Ethnicity and Health*,[12] which highlighted the greater risk for most of *The Health of the Nation* targets among minority ethnic groups. The Health Education Authority[13] published a report on a national survey of the health and lifestyles of black and minority ethnic groups in England. The survey, conducted by MORI's Health Research Unit, revealed a wide range of significant differences between the UK population at large and black and ethnic minorities. While the proportion of the UK population who described their health as poor was 8 per cent, the proportions for African-Caribbeans, Indians, Pakistanis and Bangladeshis were 17 per cent, 16 per cent, 20 per cent and 29 per cent respectively. The prevalence of reported illness or disability was generally higher among ethnic minorities, as was the prevalence of illnesses and diseases – particularly among Pakistanis and Bangladeshis.

The disability and illness reports were associated with a number of striking differences in reported risk factors. Generally speaking, the ethnic minority groups do not perceive lifestyle factors to have as bad an effect on their health as do the UK population in general. Stress and worries at home were seen as more important, however, as were such factors as being unemployed, the amount of violent crime locally, the quality of housing and the amount of racism experienced. Major differences also occurred in the frequencies of health-enhancing activity, with much lower frequencies occurring in minority groups for sports, general physical activity and attention to diet. Minority groups also reported significantly higher usage of GP care in spite of longer waiting times. Further data from this survey will be presented later in the chapter.

11 Department of Health, 1992.
12 Balarajan and Raleigh, 1994.
13 Health Education Authority, 1990.

Death rate per 100,000 from coronary heart disease England 1970–92

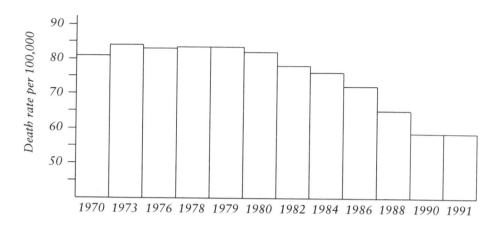

The histogram above shows that the death rates were falling steadily through the 1980s. This might be expected to continue, especially as Britain was still lagging behind much of the rest of the world over the period shown.[14]

The death rates from stroke were also falling:[15]

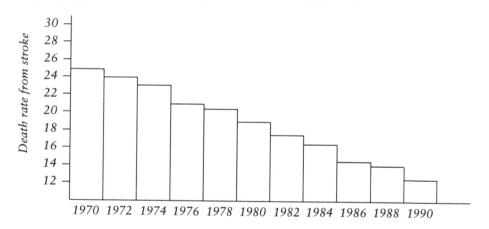

There are several factors which are associated with reducing heart attacks. These will be considered before we move on to discuss treatment.

14 Department of Health, 1993d, p. 47.
15 Department of Health, 1993d, p. 48.

Cholesterol

Our medical adviser, Dr Marion Newman, reports that ischaemic heart disease is due to a hardening of the arteries to the heart. Doctors call the plaque that is deposited *atheroma* – which comes from the Greek for porridge. The cause of atheroma is controversial but dietary fat is implicated, as is cholesterol.

A primary cause of heart disease is believed to be high blood cholesterol, which is determined to a great extent by eating patterns. Some cholesterol is needed for good health. However, at high levels, it contributes to blocking of the arteries which, in due course, may lead to heart attacks. The liver makes cholesterol from a wide variety of foods, especially saturated fats, cream, pastry, butter, cakes and biscuits. Foods associated with healthy, clear arteries are whole foods, fruit, vegetables, and fibrous and starchy foods such as bran.[16]

A health survey published by the Office of Population Censuses and Surveys (OPCS) in 1993[17] identified 32 per cent of women and 27 per cent of men as having blood cholesterol levels above 6.5 mmol/l, a level considered too high.[18] Evidence of benefits from a reduction comes from an article in the *British Medical Journal* based on a sample of 21,515 men over a seven-year period. It found that a 10 per cent reduction in serum cholesterol led to a 30 per cent reduction in ischaemic heart disease.[19]

Another important paper reviewed the combined evidence of the ten largest cohort studies, three international studies and twenty-eight randomised controlled trials. It stated that the evidence was conclusive that lowering a person's serum cholesterol concentration helps to protect against ischaemic heart disease. These benefits are related to age. A 10 per cent reduction in serum cholesterol concentration produces a reduction in ischaemic heart disease of 50 per cent at the age of 40 years, 30 per cent at age 60 and 20 per cent at 70. The greater part of the improvement occurs after two years and the full benefit comes after five years.

The article continued that the lowering of serum cholesterol is critical in reducing mortality from ischaemic heart disease. It made two suggestions. The first was the proper labelling of food to ensure that people are fully informed about the content of their diet. The second is

---

16 Jones, 1994b.
17 OPCS, 1993.
18 Jones, 1994b.
19 Law, Wald, Wu *et al.*, 1994, p. 366.

that there is a need for a policy on food subsidies linked to health priorities.[20]

Exercise

People who take exercise are at much less risk of coronary heart disease than those who do not. The vigorously active have about half the risk of the inactive, and exercise is of particular value to the elderly.[21] Most people in Britain are not taking enough exercise to obtain these benefits.

If GPs could persuade their practice populations to increase their activity levels, then benefits could follow in the form of lower rates of cardiovascular disease, reduced numbers of hip fractures, less depression and improved functional ability. However, there is a question mark over the effectiveness of exercise programmes in changing the behaviour of non-athletes, and an editorial in the *British Medical Journal* has called for more randomly controlled trials.[22] One problem is that those who normally do no exercise can damage themselves by starting it. Two studies in the *New England Journal of Medicine* reported interviews with over a thousand subjects. These led the authors to report that all heavy exertion – including shovelling snow, jogging and sexual intercourse increased the risk of a heart attack. The researchers concluded that those who are already fit could take comfort from the fact that the increased risk was confined to those who did not take regular exercise.[23]

Obesity

There is a subsidiary *Health of the Nation* target of reducing the proportion of men and women aged 16–64 who are obese from 8 per cent to 6 per cent of men and from 12 per cent to 8 per cent of women. This is a reduction of 25 per cent for men and 33 per cent for women. However, by 1991 the proportion of men who were obese had in fact risen to 13 per cent and the proportion of women had risen to 15 per cent so the situation had deteriorated. The 1993 figures showed the proportion of obese men remained at 13 per cent but that of obese women rose slightly, to 16 per cent.[24] The risk of death for the obese at

20 Law, Wald and Thompson, 1994.
21 Iliffe *et al.*, 1994, p. 495.
22 Iliffe *et al.*, 1994.
23 Minerva, 1993b.
24 Mihill, 1995.

the age of 45 is three times that of a person of target weight. The risk is twelvefold for the severely obese aged 25–35.[25]

The definition of obesity was in terms of Body Mass Index. This is calculated by the following formula:

$$Body\ Mass\ Index = \frac{Weight\ (Kg)}{Height\ (m)\ squared}$$

A score of 20 to 25 is regarded as acceptable. A score below 20 is regarded as underweight and 25 to 30 as overweight. The definition of obesity is a score of over 30; those with a score over 40 are severely obese. A man of 1.83 metres (6 foot) who weighs 80 kilos (12 stone 9 lb) would have a Body Mass Index of 23.9 (80 divided by 1.83 squared).

Although a higher percentage of women are obese, women are less likely than men to be overweight. Overall (including the obese) 57 per cent of men and just under half (48 per cent) of women were overweight in 1991.[26] Just under one in ten women (9 per cent) were underweight and only 6 per cent of the men.

US data published in 1994 showed that 33 per cent of the population were overweight, which was an increase from 24 to 25 per cent between 1960–80. Overweight meant in this context around 20 per cent excess over standard body weight tables. The Center for Health Statistics reported also that the percentage of young people aged 12–19 years old who were overweight had increased from 15 per cent in the late 1970s to 21 per cent. The *New York Times* commented that the experts had ruled out methodological errors:[27]

> Their best guess is that the weight gains are due to some combination of excess calories and reduced physical activity. Fatty foods, too much television, a sedentary lifestyle that favors computer games over active sports, a host of labor saving devices all take their toll. No doubt a decline in smoking desirable on health grounds, exacerbates the problem. The danger is obvious. Obesity increases the incidence of cardiovascular disease, diabetes, hypertension, stroke and some forms of cancer. The cure is

25 West, 1994.
26 Mihill, 1995c.
27 Editorial, 1994.

equally obvious for many, if not most Americans. Eat less. Exercise more. Everyone knows that. All too few do it.

As part of the aim to achieve an overall reduction of weight among a proportion of the population in Britain, there are plans to improve the quality of food. One of the subsidiary *Health of the Nation* targets was to reduce the average percentage of food energy derived from saturated fatty acids by at least 35 per cent by the year 2005. This would be a reduction from 17 per cent to 11 per cent. However, little progress has been made in this direction; the National Food Survey for 1992 indicated that the proportion had only fallen to 16.3 per cent.[28] Another subsidiary food target was to reduce the average percentage of food energy derived from fat from 40 per cent in 1990 to no more than 35 per cent by the year 2005.[29] This is a very modest reduction, of 12 per cent. By 1988 the American Heart Association had proposed a level of 30 per cent, which is 5 per cent below the British target and they were talking about further possible reductions.[30] Their actual level was 37 per cent. The target for England may be modest, but the actual situation shows a slight deterioration. In 1992 the proportion of food energy derived from fat was 41.7 per cent.[31]

One of the problems is the conflict between the interests of the food industries and the health of society. There are many fewer advertisements for fruit and vegetables than there are for less healthy items. In fact one study of children's TV showed that 96 per cent of food advertising on Saturday and Sunday children's TV programmes was for sweets.[32] In 1994 the National Forum for Coronary Disease Prevention produced a report, which stated that propaganda from the food industry, together with the erosion of the school meals service, was resulting in a change in diet that would lead to a generation of children who may face an increased risk of heart disease and strokes.

The report generated little publicity and even less action. It was, however, very important. Amongst its findings were the following.

28 Department of Health, 1993a, p. 51.
29 Department of Health, 1993a, p. 46.
30 Francome, 1990, p. 59.
31 Department of Health, 1993a, p. 51.
32 Francome, 1990, p. 58.

> ### *Facts about British children's exercise and diet*
> - *In a week the typical 11-year-old consumes seven bars of chocolate or sweets, seven biscuits, seven cakes or puddings and three bags of chips, four packets of crisps and six cans of soft drink. In contrast the intake of fruit and vegetables is equivalent to four small carrots and three small apples.*
> - *Only 4 per cent of boys and 1 per cent of girls aged 11–16 reach levels of physical activity necessary to maintain cardiovascular health.*
> - *Three-quarters exceed nationally agreed guidelines for intake of fat and sugar.*
> - *Consumption of dietary fibre which may help prevent cancer and other diseases of the bowel in later life is low.*
> - *Ten per cent of children are overweight and iron deficiency is widespread amongst adolescent girls.*
> - *A study of 11-year-olds found that chips and crisps comprised their largest source of energy.*

Imogen Sharp, director of the National Forum, stated that industry was targeting unhealthy food products at schools. The 1980 Education Act abandoned minimum nutritional standards for school meals and the duty of councils to provide them. In 1979 64 per cent of children had school meals. By 1994 this had fallen to 42 per cent. Often children are eating unhealthy snack food instead. Imogen Sharp proposes that like some other countries, we should limit advertising directed towards children until after 8.00 pm.[33]

Smoking

Evidence indicates that nearly ten times as many people lose their legs because of smoking than through accidents. This is because smoking may lead to arterial disease, which restricts the blood flow and leads in a number of cases to gangrene and the need to amputate.[34]

In the period up to 1994, smoking has been increasing amongst women. Jackson suggested that this may be due to social and work stresses in conjunction with clever advertising. In some cases a factor may be a desire to lose weight. Pre-menopausal smokers have three

33 Nicholson-Lord, 1994.
34 Francome 1990, p. 72.

times the rate of infarction of non-smokers, and women who smoke over forty cigarettes a day increase their risk twentyfold.[35]

The Health Education Authority's *Health and Lifestyle Survey*[36] showed that while women from ethnic minorities smoke less than the UK population as a whole, men from ethnic minorities (except Indians) tend to smoke more. The smoking levels of Bangladeshis are particularly high. Cessation rates are also lower for ethnic minorities than for the UK population as a whole.

Passive smoking

Passive smoking has been confirmed as a cause of lung cancer, as we shall see in the next chapter. Furthermore, passive smoking at home has been identified as a cause of heart disease. There has been some debate over whether passive smoking at work is a factor in heart disease. Some earlier studies have shown no relationship. However, an article based on Chinese women published in February 1994 showed that there were significant increases in the risks of coronary heart disease due to passive smoking at work, even when the results were adjusted for passive smoking at home and other risk factors. It therefore called for urgent health measures to reduce smoking at work in China. The results also clearly support the attempts to reduce smoking in the workplace in Britain.[37]

Alcohol

As we shall discuss in the next chapter, the recommended maximum daily levels of alcohol specified by the Royal College of Medicine are currently twenty-one units for men and fourteen for women. In 1989 it was estimated that one in four men and one in twelve women exceeded these recommended maximum levels. In 1994 the government decided to review the changes in view of reports that light drinkers have fewer heart attacks than teetotallers or heavy drinkers.[38] It was suggested that alcohol consumption, particularly of red wine, is one of the reasons behind a French paradox. People in the south of France have a low rate of heart disease although their fat consumption is not much different from that of people in Britain. There is a possibility that alcohol gives some protection against heart disease by affecting the fats

35 Jackson, 1994, p. 556.
36 Health Education Authority, 1990.
37 He *et al.*, 1994, p. 384.
38 Kemm, 1993, p. 1373.

in the blood and by changing the clotting mechanisms so that the blood becomes less sticky.[39]

A Danish study investigated thirteen thousand people in Copenhagen aged 30–79 over a twelve-year period. It found the lowest death rate amongst those who had between one and six alcoholic drinks a week. There was a U-shaped curve; those not drinking at all had a relative risk of 1.37 whereas those taking more than seventy alcoholic drinks a week had a relative risk of 2.29. However, amongst the drinkers the risk was only increased significantly for those who drank over forty-two units a week.[40]

The reasons for these findings are being debated. American researchers have identified a chemical in red wine – revastoral – as being beneficial against heart attacks. Other scientists have drawn attention to the fact that red wine is rich in salic acid. This is the basic ingredient of aspirin, which is known to thin the blood and is often recommended for people who have survived a heart attack.

However, there are opponents to the view that non-drinkers are more prone to heart disease than drinkers. One is Professor Gerry Shearer, head of the British Regional Heart Study, which is studying the health of seven thousand middle-aged men. He takes the view that most non-drinkers are either reformed alcoholics who have been damaged by their previous alcohol intake or are non-drinkers because of some illness.[41] A similar view was expressed by Marks[42] in criticising the methodology of a prospective study of British doctors.[43] A group of Oxford epidemiologists claimed there is a U-shaped relationship for three categories of mortality, which include alcohol-augmented diseases. However, of nineteen deaths recorded among self-reported non-drinkers, ten had resulted from conditions which occur infrequently among non-drinkers (liver cancer, cirrhosis of the liver and cancers of the upper aerodigestive tract). This reveals that at least ten of the nineteen (53 per cent) doctors who had claimed never to have been drinkers were very likely to have been ex-drinkers whose consumption of alchohol had been extremely high. Marks calculated that when the necessary corrections are made to the U-shaped curves, there is a linear relationship between alcohol consumption and mortality. In the light of this debate it would be instructive to conduct a

39 Mihill, 1994b, p. 3.
40 Groenbaek et al., 1994.
41 Mihill, 1994b, p. 3.
42 Marks, 1995a.
43 Doll et al., 1994.

randomised controlled trial of moderate alcohol drinkers over a five-year period. They would have to volunteer to become abstainers for this period if need be, but that does not seem an insurmountable problem, provided participants could be shown not to differ from non-participants on other risk factors.

As part of the government reforms there are a number of minor initiatives to deal with the problem of excessive and inappropriate consumption of alcohol. These include a review of the Health Education Authority's alcohol programme, encouragement of employers to introduce policies limiting cunsumption of alcohol, finance of a consultancy service in conjunction with Alcohol Concern and work to develop and disseminate further information on units of alcohol. These developments are all well intentioned but 'small beer' compared to the promotional activities of the breweries.

Overall the evidence from the *Health Survey for England for 1991* shows that there is a great need for change. Only 12 per cent of men and 11 per cent of women were free from all the four major risk factors for coronary heart disease and stroke. These are smoking, raised blood pressure, raised cholesterol and lack of physical activity.

In July 1993 new arrangements for health promotion were set up under the GP contract to prevent heart disease and strokes. More than 90 per cent of GPs are offering a full range of services, including a programme for diet, physical activity and control of alcohol intake. All GP practices were provided with health promotion documents commissioned by a working group under the direction of the Chief Medical Officer.

Poverty

In 1993 the *British Medical Journal* published a major study into premature mortality in each of the fourteen regions of England.[44] It showed wide variations, with poor areas having particularly high rates of coronary heart disease. The areas that had the worst results in terms of social deprivation had much higher rates of death from heart disease and the differences in standardised mortality rates were particularly high for women. Women in the Northern Region had 44 per cent excess deaths, in the North Western Region they had 36 per cent extra and in Merseyside 31 per cent. These regions were amongst the most deprived in terms of overcrowding, percentage unemployed and housing tenure. In contrast, women in East Anglia had 36 per cent

----

44 Eames *et al.*, 1993.

fewer deaths than expected, South West Thames had 35 per cent fewer and Wessex had 26 per cent fewer deaths. These areas all fared well in terms of measures of deprivation.[44]

For men the North Western Region had 26 per cent excess deaths, the Northern Region 21 per cent and Merseyside 18 per cent. By contrast East Anglia had 23 per cent fewer deaths, South West Thames 20 per cent fewer and Oxford 19 per cent fewer. Commenting on their results, Eames, Ben-Shlomo and Marmot suggest that progress towards national targets could be achieved if the mortality rates of the least favoured areas could be reduced to the same level as those of the richer ones. They also report that there is some evidence that social cohesion, community solidarity and family stability help to reduce the risk factors to health.[45]

TREATMENT OF HEART DISEASE

In 1989 the British Heart Foundation published the proposals of a working group for the early treatment of myocardial infarction. These proposals were felt to need implementation because of the number of lives that were being lost unnecessarily due to the lack of prompt provision of resuscitation skills and equipment and, in some cases, early thrombolytic treatment.[46] In 1994 the guidelines were updated in a special issue of the *British Medical Journal*. They stated that the goal was to reduce morbidity and mortality from heart attack. In order to achieve this it was necessary to reduce the time between the onset of the attack and the beginning of treatment, which should comprise the provision of resuscitation skills, adequate analgesia, adequate assessment and diagnosis, and, where appropriate, early thrombolytic treatment. The British Heart Foundation working group commented:[46]

> Improvements are required in several areas, including the response of the patient or bystander to symptoms, the response of the general practitioner or ambulance to a call for assistance, treatment before arrival at hospital, earlier thrombolytic treatment, and the hospital's response to the admission of a patient with suspected myocardial infarction.

44 Eames *et al.*, 1993.
45 Eames *et al.*, 1993, p. 1101.
46 Weston *et al.*, 1994, p. 767.

Up to 30 per cent of patients with myocardial infarction have a history of coronary heart disease. These patients may have taken some contingency measures of their own. Educating the rest of the population about the disease would clearly be beneficial. The working party called for the general public to be educated in training in cardiopulmonary resuscitation according to European Resuscitation Council guidelines. These emphasise the importance of contacting the emergency services immediately.[46]

One target is that each patient should receive thrombolytic treatment within ninety minutes of the emergency services being alerted.

Large-scale placebo-controlled trials show that the earlier people are treated, the more lives are saved. Results are reported in Table 5.1.

Table 5.1   *Early appropriate thrombolytic treatment*

Time elapsed	No. of lives saved per 1,000 cases
Below one hour	65
One to three hours	27
Three to six hours	25

Source Dracup *et al.*, 1995.

A study conducted in the Grampian region found that there was a clear and significant reduction in both mortality and in left ventricular damage if thrombolysis was started by the GP.[47] US evidence has also indicated the importance of early administration of the drug. The shorter the interval since a heart attack, the better the outcome. When administered within three hours of the onset of symptoms, mortality is reduced by 23 per cent and when administered within the hour mortality is reduced by about 50 per cent. Furthermore, the quicker the treatment, the better the subsequent cardiac function.[48] The options to speed up treatment depend on local circumstances. In general, a prompt integrated response by GPs and by ambulance and hospital staff is required. The guidelines proposed that those with coronary disease and their relatives should be provided with details of what to do in an emergency.

46 Weston *et al.*, 1994, p. 767.
47 GREAT Group. 1992, p. 548.
48 Dracup *et al.*, 1995.

One problem identified by the working group is that an earlier study showed that fewer than half of all patients presenting with heart pain receive adequate analgesia. It proposed that GPs should administer either diamorphine or morphine sulphate.[49]

The guidelines made proposals for four different groups of people. The principal ones were as follows.[50]

A General Practitioners

The report stressed that GPs have a valuable role to play because their knowledge of the patient may facilitate accurate diagnosis. Furthermore, in most cases patients contact their GP first rather than the emergency services.[51] Research has shown that a rapid response from GPs is possible, with a median response of ten minutes in a random controlled trial of thrombolysis before arrival at hospital.

GPs were advised to develop practice policies to respond quickly to people with chest pain and to inform their ancillary staff. In addition, high-risk patients and their families should be told of practice policy. Where possible the GPs should arrange to go to the patients' home and meet up there with the emergency ambulance. They should also be ready to provide an analgesic, oxygen, aspirin and nitrates.

On the question of aspirin, an international study showed a 25 per cent reduction in mortality when 160 mg of aspirin was given within the first four hours of the onset of chest pain.[52] The mechanism by which this occurs is not clear. The report criticised British practice; in a survey of 137 patients admitted to hospital suffering from acute chest pain, only one-fifth of them were found to have been given aspirin before admission. Moher and Johnson state that overall mortality could be reduced if more doctors gave aspirin.

B Ambulance service

The ambulance service should continue to improve training for control staff and to improve prioritisation of emergency and 'criteria-based response'. Ambulances should be sent on the basis of who is most in need rather than simply on a 'first come, first served' basis. By 1996 all ambulances would be staffed by at least one paramedic fully capable of advanced cardiac life support. All front-line ambulances carry either manually-operated or semi-automatic advisory defibrillators, an

49 Weston *et al.*, 1994, p. 769.
50 Weston *et al.*, 1994, p. 768.
51 Weston *et al.*, 1994, p. 767.
52 Moher and Johnson, 1994.

advantage of which is that operators require a relatively short training period to use them. Once an ambulance has been sent, the patient's GP should be informed, especially if the GP is responsible for initiating thrombolytic treatment. Cardiac monitoring must be introduced as soon as possible and direct communication developed between the ambulance and the admitting unit so that reception can be prepared.

C Hospitals

Hospitals should streamline their admission procedures to 'fast track' those with obvious myocardial infarction. If direct admission to a coronary unit is not possible then thrombolytic treatment should be started in the accident and emergency department. Senior hospital staff should note any delays and audit treatment. They should also help with the training of junior doctors and undergraduates so that overall treatment improves.

D Health authorities

The regional, district and family health service authorities should formulate policies and help develop the conditions in which to achieve the target of ninety minutes' time from first call to needle.

ADVANCES IN SURGERY

There have been many advances in surgery since Dr Christiaan Barnard carried out the first heart transplant. One of the problems in Britain at the moment is the waiting list for treatment. A Liverpool GP, Dr Jeff Featherstone, was quoted as saying:[53]

> We accept there will be a three month wait for coronary studies and that occasionally we will lose a patient during that time. On at least two occasions I have had patients on a waiting list for a coronary artery bypass graft who died before they could be operated on.

Stories of such deaths rarely become national issues, but often they become local ones. In January 1994 it was reported that the wife of a Golders Green pensioner died when two months into a three-month wait for a hospital appointment. He was reported to be furious that, although his wife was told she needed a full check-up and new medication for a heart problem, she was made to wait so long. He

53 Anonymous, 1994a.°

commented: 'We're a very rich country and we can and must have a properly organised NHS which we can and must pay for by proper taxation. We had expected to get an appointment within two or three weeks.'[54]

This kind of evidence shows the need for more resources so that people can have the treatment they need immediately. Other, European, evidence shows wide variation in the performance in operations. Britain is not the only country with delays. In January 1995 two Dutch reports suggested that the country needed to increase its expenditure on open-heart surgery by £4.5 million a year to bring the maximum waiting time down to three months. Dr Irene Hellemans, the medical director of the Dutch Heart Foundation, was quoted as saying that ideally there should be no waiting time but because of high cost a short wait for low-risk patients may be necessary to ensure maximum efficiency.[55]

There is also evidence of the need for people to specialise. In June 1994 the results of a study of 1,900 operations over six years were published. Malcolm Forsythe of the Centre for Health Studies at the University of Kent examined the outcome for aortic aneurism, a disease of the main artery which is a relatively common cause of death amongst smokers over the age of 65. The death rate was as high as 45 per cent where the surgeon had carried out fewer than ten operations, compared with 25 per cent amongst those who had completed more than ten. Forsythe suggested that there would be advantages in concentrating such surgical procedures on fewer sites so that surgeons were able to practice their skills and improve survival rates.[56]

STROKES

Strokes kill around 65,000 people each year and disable even more.[57] The carotid arteries, one on each side of the neck, are the main suppliers of oxygen and blood to the brain from the heart. In course of time fatty deposits may build up, especially at the site where the artery divides at the angle of the jaw. The greater the accumulation, the greater the narrowing and the potential for plaque to break off and travel to the brain to stop the flow of oxygenated blood. The result is a stroke.[58]

54 Liddell, 1994.
55 Sheldon, J., 1995.
56 Jones, 1994g.
57 Dennis and Langhorne, 1994, p. 1273.
58 Altman, L. K., 1994, p. 30.

Cerebrovascular disease accounts for around 12 per cent of all deaths in England and Wales and 5 per cent of those under the age of 65 years. There is some evidence that where the care of stroke patients occurs in specialised units there is much better survival.[59] Organised stroke care reduces early death rates by more than a quarter. Longer-term mortality is also lowered, with an improved survival of 21 per cent for patients in stroke units.[60] The evidence is that the most obvious factor leading to better survival in the stroke unit is the presence of a multidisciplinary team which has knowledge of the best treatment and the enthusiasm to administer it.

Carotid endarterectomy

A controversial operation, carotid endarterectomy, was introduced in 1954 to eliminate fatty deposits from a major artery in the neck. The operation is targeted at those who have no outward symptoms but are at risk of stroke through severe narrowing of either of the two carotid arteries due to a build-up of fatty substances from atherosclerosis. The early trials of effectiveness gave negative results. Despite this, increasing numbers of operations were carried out in the US, rising to a peak of 107,000 in 1985. Subsequently, doubts about the operation in terms of benefits and risks and wider use of aspirin and other drugs to prevent strokes led to a decline in numbers.

In 1994 the US National Institutes of Health reported that the operation reduced the risk of strokes from more than one in ten to fewer than one in twenty. Dr Michael Walker was quoted in the *New York Times* as saying that of the three million Americans who have survived a stroke, more than two million have major disabilities including paralysis, loss of speech and impaired memory. The *New York Times* commented that the operation could 'prevent many thousands of crippling and disabling strokes among the 500,000 to 600,000 people who now suffer a stroke each year'.[61] The National Institutes of Health's panel stressed the importance of using highly skilled vascular surgeons who have a proven rate for serious complications and death rates of below 3 per cent. The results are of interest, and a British study might provide useful results.

59 Sandercock, 1993, p. 1297.
60 Langhorne *et al.*, 1993, p. 395.
61 Altman, L. K., 1994, p. 30.

RECOMMENDATIONS

1   Many people can reduce their risks of a heart attack by improving their diet, taking more exercise and reducing their weight. These changes should be made easier to achieve through the widespread availability of recognised healthier foods at affordable prices and improved accessibility to fitness centres and exercise programmes.

2   Health education programmes in schools should promote healthy habits.

3   We have seen that the wide differences in heart disease and strokes according to ethnic groups suggest that there is useful research to be done. More data on this issue needs to be collected and possible differences in lifestyles should be analysed.

4   More research is needed to provide in-depth analysis of the effects of alcohol on heart disease.

5   There should be improvements in the care of stroke victims, using specialised units.

CHAPTER SIX

REDUCING CANCER

*The Netherlands, Luxembourg, Belgium, Ireland,
Denmark and France all had higher age
standardised incidence of breast cancer than Britain
but, nevertheless, lower death rates.*

Cancer was selected as a *Health of the Nation* target because of the toll that it takes in ill health and death and because some cases can be prevented. One in three people will develop cancer at some time during their lives and treatment in the form of surgery, radiotherapy and chemotherapy will cure between a third and half of these.[1]

There are four targets. Two of these relate to women, one to men and one to all. They are as follows:

- To reduce the death rate for breast cancer amongst those invited for screening by at least 25 per cent by the year 2000.
- To reduce the incidence of invasive cervical cancer by at least 20 per cent by the year 2000.
- To reduce the death rate for lung cancer under the age of 75 by at least 30 per cent in men and at least 15 per cent in women by the year 2010.
- To halt the year-on-year increase in the incidence of skin cancer by the year 2005.

International data were provided by two Swiss researchers and an Italian.[2] They considered data from fifty-five countries on the World Health Organization's database. Results are shown in Table 6.1.

---

1 Karp, 1994, p. 147.
2 Levi *et al.*, 1994, p. 109.

Table 6.1   *Britain's position in world mortality rates per million people 1985–9*

Country	Males	Country	Females
Hungary	237	Denmark	142
Czechoslovakia	229	Scotland	138
Luxembourg	212	Hungary	131
France	209	England and Wales	129
Belgium (1986–7)	206	Ireland	128
Uruguay	205	New Zealand	125
Scotland	202	Northern Ireland	124
Poland	202	Czechoslovakia	121
Netherlands	201	Uruguay	120
USSR	197	West Germany	118
Italy	196	Iceland	115
West Germany	187	Costa Rica	114
Denmark	185	Luxembourg	113
England and Wales	184	Canada	113
Singapore	183	Austria	112
Northern Ireland	179	USA	112
Switzerland	178	Netherlands	112
Hong Kong	177	Singapore	110
Austria	177	Belgium	108
Ireland	176	Poland	109
New Zealand	174	Colombia	107
Canada	170	East Germany	106
East Germany	169	Norway	104
Spain	167	Australia	103
Australia	165	Israel	102
USA	165	Switzerland	102
Finland	162	Italy	101
Costa Rica	157	Sweden	101
Argentina	155	USSR	100
Japan	155	Argentina	100
Yugoslavia	154	Cuba	98
Norway	151	Hong Kong	95
Malta	149	Malta	95
Greece	145	Finland	94
Portugal	141	France	93
Iceland	141	Yugoslavia	90
Bulgaria	138	Bulgaria	86

Source Levi *et al.*, 1994, p. 109.

The results show wide disparities in cancer deaths. Amongst men the highest rate in the world is Hungary, which is followed closely by the Czech Republic. These two countries have more than five times the death rate of the lowest countries, Sri Lanka and Egypt, which are not shown in Table 6.1. The rate for Scotland was the highest for the countries of the British Isles. The differences in death rates may partly be due to the average length of life in the various countries. As cancer is mainly a disease of elderly people, countries in which people generally do not live so long may well have much lower cancer levels. Furthermore, problems of validity and cancer death certification in certain developing countries may account for some of the variations.[2] However, there are clearly substantial differences in cancer rates and these offer a challenge to researchers to identify causes and to seek out ways of reduction.

Overall the death rates from cancer amongst women are much lower than amongst men. In England and Wales the death rate for women is 70 per cent that of men and in Scotland the rate is 68 per cent. These differences are likely to be partly because women smoke and drink less. The country differences show that the highest rate for cancer amongst women worldwide was Denmark, with Scotland second. England and Wales had the fourth highest death rate, Ireland the fifth and Northern Ireland the seventh. There appears to be a great deal of room for improvement.

Cancer rates not only vary according to countries, but also the kinds of cancer afflicting the different societies vary. This information may prove to be epidemiologically valuable, for it provides clues about how changes in diet or environment may reduce deaths. Information is shown opposite in Table 6.2.

2 Levi et al., 1994, p. 109.

Table 6.2   *Highest and lowest mortality rates for different cancer sites per 100,000, 1985–9*

	Male		Female	
	Highest	Lowest	Highest	Lowest
Mouth or Pharynx	Hong Kong 14.6	Egypt 0.6	Singapore 4.6	Eygpt 0.3
Oesophagus	Uruguay 11.9	Philippines 0.7	**Scotland** **4.0**	Thailand 0.2
Stomach	Costa Rica 48.6	Thailand 1.2	Costa Rica 22.6	Thailand 0.6
Intestines	Czech Republic 29.9	Sri Lanka 0.5	New Zealand 21.0	Sri Lanka 0.4
Pancreas	Czech Republic 10.4	Sri Lanka 0.3	Iceland 7.5	Thailand 0.1
Larynx	France 8.7	Sri Lanka 0.3	Cuba 1.0	Peru 0.1
Lung	Belgium 76.7	Sri Lanka 2.4	**Scotland** **27.2**	Sri Lanka 0.7
Skin	New Zealand 6.5	Mauritius 0.2	New Zealand 3.5	Mauritius 0.1
Breast			**England & Wales** **29.3***	Thailand 0.9
Uterus			Paraguay 22.1	Sri Lanka 1.9
Ovary			Denmark 10.0	Greece 3.0
Prostate	Switzerland 22.3	Thailand 0.2		
Bladder	Egypt 10.8	Sri Lanka 0.3	Iceland 2.7	Sri Lanka 0.1
Kidney	Czech Republic 8.3	Hong Kong 1.4	Iceland 4.5	Hong Kong 0.8
Leukaemias	Luxembourg 7.8	Thailand 1.2	Kuwait 4.8	Thailand 0.9

Source Levi *et al.*, 1994.

Note *Figures published in 1995 indicate that this rate has declined, as discussed below.

The results reveal major differences in all the common cancer sites. England and Wales had the highest rates of breast cancer and Scotland had the highest for the lungs and oesophagus. It should be pointed out that later figures, for 1991, show a higher death rate per 100,000 females in Denmark than in the UK as a whole.[3] On the positive side, people in the UK have the lowest rate of death from liver cancer and cancer of the larynx in the European Community.[4]

Coggon and Inskip[5] analysed the cancer rates for the period 1950–89 for different age groups. The evidence indicates that cancer is for the most part an illness associated with old age. As people continue to live longer, the number of cases will increase. Hazel Inskip of the Medical Research Council has kindly provided the figures for Table 6.3 below.[6]

Table 6.3   *Cancer death rates by age 1985–89 (per million per year)*

Age	Males	Females
0–4	43	47
5–9	46	37
10–14	43	34
15–19	66	42
20–4	77	56
25–9	107	99
30–4	156	229
35–9	278	441
40–4	514	775
45–9	1046	1367
50–4	2018	2191
55–9	3901	3445
60–4	6973	5115
65–9	10702	6687
70–4	15937	8630
75+	24840	13298

The data show several age- and sex-related trends. The first is that cancer is very uncommon in the youngest age groups. It is below one hundred per million in all groups up to and including the age group 20–4.

The sex differences show several trends. Cancer deaths are slightly more prevalent amongst women than men in the age group 0–4. For the age groups from 5–9 to 25–9 it is more common amongst men. In

3 OPCS, 1995, p. 132.
4 Esteve *et al.*, 1993, p. 25.
5 Coggon and Inskip, 1994, p. 305.
6 Private communication, 30 June 1994.

the age groups from 30–4 to 50–4 the cancer deaths are again more common amongst women. It is in the later age groups that cancer becomes far more common amongst men. Amongst those over the age of 75 the male death rates approach twice those of women. In fact over the age of 75 one man in forty will die of cancer each year, compared to one in seventy-five of the women.

These sex differences are due to the incidence of different forms of cancer at different ages. In the middle age groups the cancers which affect women are more important. These include breast cancer which is the commonest cause of death amongst women aged from 35 to 54, and ovarian cancer. At the older ages the effects of smoking on lung cancer become more important and affect men to a greater degree than women. Also male-specific complaints, principally prostate cancer, increase in importance.

In 1994 the *British Medical Journal* carried a series of articles considering the role of general practice in the reduction of cancer. It is instructive to look at the major forms of cancer and possible causes.

Stomach cancer

This has been declining. Until 1952 stomach cancer caused more deaths in England and Wales than any other form of cancer. Its incidence has fallen to the extent that mortality in the period 1985–9 was less than 60 per cent of that for the period 1950–4.[7] Other countries have also reported this trend. While the full reason is not known, one factor is likely to be the greater all-round availability of fruit and vegetables. It is also possible that salt intake is linked with stomach cancer and the reduced use of salt for preservation because of refrigeration may also be a factor. It has been shown that people with antibodies to the virus *Helibacter pylori* are two to six times as likely to develop the illness as those without. Other research has shown that this virus is more common in people brought up in crowded houses than in others. Long-term improvement in the housing stock could therefore be a factor.[7]

International data show that high rates of deaths from stomach cancer are found in Costa Rica, several other Latin-American countries, Japan, the former Soviet Union and several Eastern European countries. These all have rates of above 35 per 100,000 for men and above 17 per 100,000 for women. The lowest reliable rates for both sexes are in the United States, where death rates were only 5.3

7 Coggon and Inskip, 1994, p. 706.

for men and 2.4 for women. This is a sixfold to ninefold reduction in mortality over the high-risk areas. Researchers suggest that it probably reflects the earlier improvements in diet, storage and water supply with the consequent decline in *Helibacter pylori* infection.[8]

Breast cancer
The most prevalent form of cancer among women in the United Kingdom is breast cancer. Overall it is estimated that one in twelve will develop it some time during their lives. Breast cancer accounted for almost one in five (19 per cent) of deaths from cancer in 1992 and one in twenty (5 per cent) of all deaths amongst women.[9] We have seen that England and Wales had the highest death rate from breast cancer in the world for the period 1985–9. The rate of breast cancer deaths in England and Wales was 29.3 per 100,000. Denmark was second (28.1), Malta third (27.9), Scotland fourth (27.8) and Ireland was fifth (27.5). These rates were well above the rate of 19.5 in France, 18.9 in Norway, 18.5 in Sweden and 16.9 in Finland. An even starker contrast is with the rate of only 6.1 for Japanese women.[10] A report in *The Lancet* in June 1995 stated that the breast cancer death rates in England and Wales exhibited a welcome fall of 10 per cent between 1989 and 1993. The decline was greater in younger women; those aged 20–49 showed a 14 per cent decline. The authors, who were from the Cancer Epidemiology Unit in Oxford, concluded that 'earlier diagnosis and better treatment might be responsible for much of the recent fall in breast cancer'.[11]

Overall survival figures from the earlier period show that 62 per cent of women diagnosed as having breast cancer were alive five years later. This does, however, vary from 84 per cent of women with stage 1 breast cancer to 18 per cent of those with stage IV disease.[12]

Breast screening in randomised controlled trials with women over the age of 50 has shown a reduction in deaths. The combined estimate for all the randomised trials is 28 per cent. Non-randomised trials also point in the same direction. Randomised controlled trials of women under the age of 50 have been few and the results are not conclusive. Joan Austoker suggests that mammography detects different forms of cancer in younger and older women.[12]

....
8 Levi *et al.*, 1994, p. 113.
9 Austoker, 1994e, p. 168.
10 Levi *et al.*, 1994, p. 132.
11 Beral *et al.*, 1995, p. 1643.
12 Austoker, 1994e, p. 168.

The NHS breast screening programme started in 1988. Women aged 50 to 64 are invited to have a screening mammogram every three years. Targets set for the programme included:

A   Achieving attendance of 70 per cent or more of women invited.
B   Recalling fewer than 7 per cent of women screened to undergo further investigations.
C   Detecting more than five cancers for every hundred women screened.[12]

Although the 70 per cent target was achieved nationally there were very wide regional variations, ranging from 61.3 per cent in North West Thames to 78.9 per cent in the East Anglian Health Authority in 1992–3.

The NHS breast screening programme can be criticised in two major respects. First the data for 1992–3 show that the predictive value of a positive mammogram is very low, at 10 per cent. This means that 90 per cent of women (about 45,000) were asked to come for further investigations unnecessarily. This very high rate of false positives causes a great amount of unnecessary anxiety, pain and operative risk. The second major criticism is that the 50 to 64 age range for the programme is too narrow. Although over 30 per cent of breast cancer cases occur in women aged 65 and over, such women are not invited for screening. There is a case for offering screening to all women over the age of 50.[13]

The approach to reducing mortality from breast cancer could follow several different paths. Apart from screening improvements, one approach would be to track the epidemiology of the disease to try to identify further risk factors. It would, for example, be of relevance to discover the breast cancer rate of Japanese-born women living in Britain and relate this to their diet. If it were found that those who adopted food and drinking patterns similar to that of the indigenous population had higher rates, that might provide clues as to how changes in British habits could reduce incidence. US data show second and subsequent generations of Japanese women settlers have the same high rates of breast cancer as the host population.[14] This suggests that the wide differences between societies are due to diet and environmental factors.

....
12 Austoker, 1994e, p. 168.
13 Jatoi and Baum, 1993, p. 1481.
14 Cancer Research Campaign, 1991.

Information from the European Community suggests that the following risk factors are associated with an increased risk of breast cancer:

- Having a family history of the disease.
- Increased body size.
- A past history of benign breast disease.
- Reproductive factors including late age of first giving birth.
- Early menarche and late age at menopause.
- The use of oral contraceptives at a young age.
- Unopposed oestrogens for the relief of menopausal symptoms.
- Nulliparity.
- Exposure to ionising radiation.

In addition, a diet rich in fat and protein of animal origin and increased alcohol consumption have been suggested as factors.[15]

There may also be a case for improving the quality of care. In 1986 the King's Fund consensus conference published guidelines for treatment. A study of the management of breast cancer in South East England found a lack of consensus among clinicians in 1990 on the management of breast cancer. This led Choillet, Bell and Hiscox to comment as follows in the *British Medical Journal* on a sample of 417 cases resident in the Thames regions: 'The variation in management suggests that there is no consensus among clinicians on the optimal treatment, and that perhaps some clinicians may not be aware of the recommendations on diagnostic investigations and treatment options'.[16]

There was also evidence that the guidelines were only followed in 24 per cent of the cases. The article called for improved audit of the care of breast cancer patients as a way to improve the overall survival rate. Data for 1990 from the European Community suggested that the treatment in parts of the United Kingdom could be greatly improved. The Netherlands, Luxembourg, Belgium, Denmark, Ireland, Germany and France all had higher age standardised incidences of breast cancer than Britain but nevertheless had lower death rates.[17]

Cervical cancer

In England and Wales there were 4,467 new cases of invasive carcinoma in 1988, making it the eighth commonest cancer amongst

---

15 Esteve *et al.*, 1993, p. 30.
16 Chouillet *et al.* 1994, p. 170.
17 Esteve *et al.*, 1993, p. 30.

women. The age-specific death rate is highest amongst the older age groups. It is, however, the most common cancer in women under the age of 35, where it accounts for 25 per cent of the total.[18] The risks for those in the North of England and Wales are highest. Women in social class 5 have three times the level of risk of those in social class 1.

The aim of *The Health of the Nation* to reduce the incidence of invasive cervical cancer by 20 per cent by the year 2000 implies a reduction in incidence from 15 per 100,000 population to 12 per 100,000.[18]

Screening

This is safe and has the potential of reducing the incidence and mortality of cancer. It has the disadvantage of over-diagnosis. There are more women with abnormal smears than would be expected to develop invasive cancer over their lifetimes. The 1990 GP contracts set targets for screening and this incentive appears to have worked. In 1990 53 per cent of GPs met the 80 per cent target, but by October 1993 the screening rate had increased to 83 per cent.

There is evidence that cervical screening is beginning to reach those most at risk. At least one survey carried out in 1992 showed that the social class gradient in uptake had almost disappeared. However, inner London tends to have a lower uptake and nine health authorities showed an uptake coverage of less than 60 per cent. In the over 45 age group the death rates have fallen noticeably over the past thirty years, and the increase in death rates in the age group 40–4 which was evident in the late 1970s and early 1980s has now been reversed. There was a rise in mortality in the under-40 age group during the 1970s and 1980s. However, this now appears to be stabilising.[18] In fact a report from the Cancer Research Campaign published in May 1994 suggested that the death rates even for young women were falling for the first time. The number of deaths amongst women aged from 25 to 54 fell from 120 in 1987 to 81 in 1992. The Cancer Research Campaign suggested that this change was partly due to the doubling of the number of women given smear tests over the past five years and also possibly partly due to an increase in the use of condoms.[19]

In July 1994 the *British Medical Journal* gave advice to doctors on how to encourage women to attend for screening. It proposed that doctors should send a letter of invitation which would advise of the

18 Austoker, 1994f, p. 241.
19 Mihill, 1994a.

potential benefits and suggest a specific day when the woman could attend. Other relevant information to be included was the fact that 93 per cent of tests were negative, what a positive test would mean and how the results would be imparted. It suggested that the availability of a female doctor or nurse should also be mentioned. One survey has shown that 41 per cent of women would prefer a female doctor to take the smear; this percentage was higher for older women and lower socio-economic groups, which are particularly at risk. Overall the journal set out suggestions for setting up an effective service, as shown in Box One.[20]

Box One **Improving the cervical screening programme**
- Spread screening evenly across the age range.
- Ensure a high participation rate amongst the target population.
- Repeat tests at regular intervals, not exceeding five years.
- Ensure adequate facilities and quality control for taking and interpreting smears.
- Ensure a reliable fail-safe mechanism for the prompt follow-up of abnormal results.
- Ensure adequate facilities for appropriate treatment.
- Ensure systematic evaluation and monitoring.

Source Austoker, 1994f, p. 242.

The improving picture may be due to an increase in screening rates which seems to be effective, although no random controlled trials have been carried out. Screening in Iceland, Finland, Sweden and parts of Denmark was followed by a reduction in incidence and mortality.[21]

CANCERS THAT ARE ON THE INCREASE

We discuss below five forms of cancer which have been shown to be increasing in this country. It is important to consider possible reasons for the changes in order to aid preventative action.

Cancer of the prostate
In 1991 prostate cancer was second to lung cancer in mortality from malignant diseases in men, with 8,570 deaths. It is increasing in

---

20 Austoker, 1994g, 1994h.
21 Austoker, 1994f.

incidence in other Western countries and is now the most frequently diagnosed male malignancy in the United States, where the lifetime risk is 9 to 11 per cent. It affects predominantly an ageing male population and sufferers lose an average of nine years of life. In 1994 only 40 to 50 per cent of men in the UK presented with the disease at its early stages but this figure is expected to increase.[22]

It seems that some protection from the disease is afforded by a diet that is rich in yellow and green vegetables. This may act on the prostate by modifying the circulation of sex hormones. In contrast, a high fat diet may be positively linked with the disease. There has been some concern that the high prevalence of latent prostate cancer may mean early detection programmes could uncover disease which does not need to be treated. D. P. Dearnaley of the Institute of Cancer Research thinks this unlikely, however, and suggests that a balance must be drawn between morbidity, the anxiety caused by unnecessary investigation and the likely benefits of early detection to those with prostate cancer. He calls for rigorous research, including a control population to assess the effects of an early detection programme.[22] In August 1994 the US Food and Drug Administration approved a blood test for detecting cancer of the prostate, which is to be used in conjunction with a digital rectal examination.[23] The American Cancer Society recommends an annual examination for men over the age of 50. F. H. Schroder, a Dutch professor of urology, agreed that this would lead to the cancers being detected earlier. However, he said that it was not certain that those in whom cancer is found early would in fact benefit. In the United States the known incidence of prostate cancer has increased but the mortality has remained constant. This may change, and a reasonable proposal is that there should be randomised studies in which screening is compared with absence of screening. In fact such studies are beginning and could lead to improved prognosis.[24]

Melanoma (skin cancer)

We have seen that one *Health of the Nation* target is to stop the year-on-year increase in the incidence of this form of cancer by the year 2005. In the United Kingdom there are currently 40,000 new cases each year. Since 1974 the number of people dying of melanoma has increased by 73 per cent and the incidence has risen by 156 per cent.

....
22 Dearnaley, 1994, p. 780.
23 Schroder, 1995, p. 140.
24 Schroder, 1995, p. 141.

The disease is very uncommon before puberty but it is one of the few cancers to affect young adults. In fact 22 per cent of all melanomas occur in people under the age of 40. Amongst the age group 15 to 34 it is the third most common cancer in women and the seventh most common in men.[25] Overall 1,288 people died of malignant melanoma in 1991. Death rates for melanoma rose threefold for both men and women over the age of 40 during the period 1950–89; however, the increase in rates amongst the younger age groups has not been as marked.

The evidence linking melanoma to solar radiation is well developed. One suggestion is that a major reason for the change is the growth in package holidays to Mediterranean countries and the Canary Islands. The patterns of the tumours corresponds to the area of the body exposed to the sun, as shown in Figure 6.1. For women tumours of the leg are the more common, while for men tumours are more common on the trunk.

Figure 6.1   *Occurrence of melanoma*

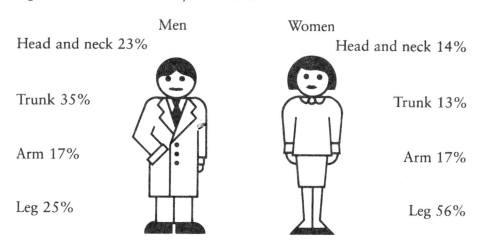

Men

Women

Head and neck 23%

Head and neck 14%

Trunk 35%

Trunk 13%

Arm 17%

Arm 17%

Leg 25%

Leg 56%

Source Austoker, 1994c.

The incidence of melanoma varies with latitude. For populations of the same skin colour, the nearer the Equator, the higher the incidence. In a major article in the *British Medical Journal*, Austoker set out the main risk factors and methods of protection against such tumours.[26]

25 Austoker, 1994c, p. 1683.
26 Austoker, 1994c.

The incidence of skin cancer is ten to twelve times higher in white-skinned people who have little protective melanin pigment than in black-skinned ethnic groups with the same lifestyle. Amongst white-skinned people, those who have fair skin that tans poorly and burns easily are most at risk.

It is not simply the case that those fair-skinned people who are exposed to more sunlight are at an increased risk of developing tumours. This is known from the fact that mortality is higher in people who work indoors and who experience intensive periods of sun exposure while on holiday than in those who normally work outside. This has led to the suggestion that it is intermittent exposure to sunlight that is most hazardous and that a regular tan affords a degree of protection. Comparative studies with people who have not developed the illness seem to support this theory. In particular, it seems that those with a past history of sunburn are at increased risk. A severe incident of sunburn, especially during childhood or infancy, can perhaps trigger melanoma in later life. An interesting finding comes from studies of emigrants to Australia and New Zealand. These indicate that those who arrived there after the age of 15 have a substantially reduced risk of melanoma compared to those born in the country. This supports the need for protection against exposure for children.

Manufacturers of sunbeds have an economic interest in promoting their use. An estimated eighty thousand machines for home use were sold in 1988 compared to five thousand in 1982.[27] Manufacturers may give incorrect information to boost sales. Writing in the *British Medical Journal*, Shuttleworth drew attention to a large manufacturer who was wrongly claiming that sunbeds can inhibit the development of both melanoma and internal cancers. Shuttleworth was concerned that use of sunbeds may activate and accelerate the growth of human viruses, including HIV. He said that potential sunbed users need to be better informed about the potential damage caused by continual exposure to ultra-violet A radiation.

A further article in the *British Medical Journal* gave advice to GPs about how to help prevent skin cancer amongst their patients. See Box Two.

27 Shuttleworth, 1993, p. 1508.

> *Box Two* **Guidelines for reducing the risk of malignant melanoma**
> - Ration exposure to strong sunlight.
> - Keep out of the midday sun, i.e. between 11 a.m. and 3 p.m.
> - Clothing, especially fine woven cotton, is an effective sun screen.
> - Use hats when out in the sun.
> - Use a sun screen to shield from ultra-violet B radiation, with additional protection against ultra-violet A.
> - Sun screen should be liberally applied and reapplied every two hours if exposure to the sun continues.
> - Protect children and infants against sunlight. Use a sun screen with a high sun protection (over factor 10) and additional protection against ultra-violet A radiation.
> - Avoid sunbeds and lamps.
> - Remember that there is no such thing as a safe or healthy suntan.
> - Recognise the cumulative nature of sun-induced skin damage.

Source Austoker, 1994c.

Testicular cancer

The incidence of testicular cancer has increased to such an extent that what was once an extremely rare form of cancer is now the most common form of malignancy found in young men. However, the good news is that there have been rapid advances in treatment which have made the disease largely curable.

Various explanations for the increase have been proposed but so far none has been confirmed. One suggestion has been a change in the type of underwear worn. A different and more likely explanation relates to maternal weight and changes in the environment of the developing fetus. It is known that those with maldescended testes have an increased incidence and are more prone to malignant changes. However, this can only explain a small part of the change.[28]

Cancer of the brain and nervous system

A fourth form of cancer which is increasing is primary cancer of the brain and central nervous system. There has been increased incidence for both men and women. It is most pronounced in the age group 70–4, where the rates rose sixfold during the period 1950–89.

Coggon and Inskip suggest that part of the increase may be due to

28 Coggon and Inskip, 1994, p. 707.

better diagnosis following the growing use of radioisotope scans and other diagnostic tools. However, this is unlikely to be the total explanation as similar trends have occurred in the United States, France, Italy and West Germany.[29] Clearly research is needed to try and identify the reasons for the increase with a view to making changes that will reduce incidence.

Diet and cancer

Austoker[30] claims that, although the evidence linking diet and cancer is not conclusive in many areas, there is growing evidence that modifications in diet may reduce the risk of cancer by one-third or even two-thirds. Diet is likely to be a major factor in the aetiology of cancers of the large bowel and stomach and it may also be a major factor in the aetiology of breast and prostate cancer. Box Three gives some information about this.

Box Three **Diet and cancer**

Possible protective factors

- Fruit
- Vegetables
- Fibre
- Antioxidant nutrients
- Fish oils
- Plant-derived oestrogenic compounds
- Calcium

Possible risk factors

- Meat
- Total fat
- Saturated or animal fat
- Preserved foods
- Alcohol
- Salt

Source Austoker, 1994b.

International comparisons of patterns of food consumption and the differences in the incidence of cancer have led to the formulation of many hypotheses about diet.

Fruit and vegetables

There is strong and consistent evidence that a high intake of fruit and vegetables protects against various cancers, in particular against tumours of the respiratory and digestive tracts. Although no effect is

29 Coggon and Inskip, 1994, p. 708.
30 Austoker, 1994b, p. 1510.

found on hormone-related cancers, the evidence is sufficiently strong to justify public education about the value of increasing the intake of fruit and vegetables, especially raw or lightly cooked ones. In Britain fruit intake is below that of other European countries.

A random controlled intervention study in Linxian, China, showed that those who received a supplement of B Caroten, Vitamin E and selenium showed a reduction in mortality from cancer, in particular stomach cancer. However, this was a population with a relatively poor diet and the results cannot be directly related to Western populations.

There have been suggestions that salt intake may be a risk factor for gastric cancer – and that reduction in its consumption may be beneficial in reducing blood pressure. Increased fibre intake and decreased meat eating are associated with a decreased rate of cancer of the colon and rectum, as we shall see in the next section.

Vegetarianism and cancer

A major study of 6,115 non-meat-eaters and 5,015 controls who were meat-eaters was published in the *British Medical Journal* in June 1994.[31] Over two thousand of the main sample were members of vegetarian societies. In order to identify a group of controls who were similar to the vegetarians in all lifestyle factors except diet, participants were asked to nominate friends and relatives. The controls were reasonably well matched for cigarette smoking and social class, but the meat-eaters tended to have a higher body mass.

The study noted that the diet of vegetarians differed from that of meat-eaters in other respects than the avoidance of vegetables. Because they have a high intake of vegetables, fruit, cereals, pulses and nuts, their diet is high in unsaturated fats and low in saturated fats. It is also high in carbohydrate and dietary fibre.

The sample was followed up for a period of about twelve years. Both groups were relatively healthy, with less than half the expected number of deaths compared to the national Standardised Mortality Ratio. This is in part to be expected, for volunteers for studies tend to be healthier than the general population. The study found that vegetarians and fish-eaters had significantly lower death rates for all causes, and for ischaemic heart disease and cancer. For cancer the reduction in mortality was roughly 40 per cent. Overall the mortality amongst the non-meat-eating group was 20 per cent lower than amongst the meat-eaters. Heavy smokers had significantly higher

31 Thorogood *et al.*, 1994.

deaths from all causes and from ischaemic heart disease, and also higher deaths from cancer.

The authors of the study said that their data did not provide a justification for encouraging meat-eaters to alter their diet. However, the results confirm that those who choose not to eat meat can expect overall reductions in mortality. They indicate a protective effect of 40 per cent for cancer and 20 per cent overall. The advice of the study is therefore that people should adopt many of the dietary practices of vegetarians even if they continue to eat some meat.

SMOKING

Each year about 110,000 deaths are related to smoking, representing 17 per cent of all deaths.[32] Approximately 30 per cent of all deaths are from cancer. The major form is lung cancer and 90 per cent of those deaths are caused by smoking. People who smoke fifteen to twenty-four cigarettes a day are thirteen times as likely to develop lung cancer as non-smokers, while those who smoke twenty-five or more cigarettes a day have twenty-five times the chance of developing lung cancer as non-smokers. Interestingly, there is evidence that smokers who have a high intake of vegetables sufficient to substantially increase their plasma concentration of B carotene have 60 per cent less risk of developing lung cancer than other smokers.[33]

Other cancers which are linked to smoking are cancers of the oral cavity, bronchus, trachea, pharynx, larynx, oesophagus and bladder. There are also possible links to cancers of the kidney, pancreas, nose, stomach, and cervix and to leukaemia. Regarding the last named, in August 1993 it was reported by the United States Office on Smoking and Health that the risk of developing myeloid leukaemia was 50 per cent higher for smokers than non smokers.[34]

Persuading and assisting people to give up smoking

People in the higher social classes have been the first to stop smoking. Consequently there is now a strong social class gradient in prevalence. Men and women in social class 5 are nearly four times as likely to be smokers as those in social class 1. Working-class men are three times as likely to die of lung cancer as middle-class men.[35]

32 Austoker et al., 1994, p. 1478.
33 Austoker, 1994b, p. 1610.
34 Headlines, 1993.
35 Austoker et al., 1994, p. 1478.

GPs are able to persuade about 5 per cent of smokers to give up each year through giving brief advice. This compares with a cessation rate of 1 per cent in those not advised. The evidence indicates that the advice is more likely to be heeded when it stresses short-term benefits rather than long-term dangers. It seems that more could be done by GPs to persuade people to stop smoking. Only 22 per cent of smokers report that they have been advised to give up by their doctor.[36]

There are indications that longer-term and more intensive courses are effective in helping people stop smoking. The use of nicotine patches seems to help some. In a randomised placebo-controlled trial, it was found that one in five (19.4 per cent) of heavy smokers using patches gave up smoking for at least three months, compared to one in eight and a half (11.8 per cent) of the control group. About half of those abstinent at the end of the three months would be able to keep it up for a year.[37] This confirmed an earlier randomised study.[38] Law, Tang and Wald[39] analysed interventions intended to help people stop smoking. It included only randomised controlled trials where the duration of follow-up was at least six months. They found that 24 per cent gave up after hypnotism, 14 per cent after psychological methods including aversion, 11 to 12 per cent after a nicotine patch or gum if they were self-referred, and 2 per cent if advised once to stop smoking by their doctor.

Marks considered efficiency in terms of cost effectiveness, measured in terms of cost per ex-smoker for three methods for achieving cessation.[40] These were as follows:

1   GP advice and encouragement supported by health promotion clinics run by practice nurses.
2   Nicotine patches.
3   Intensive psychological therapy in groups in the form of the 'Quit for Life' programme.[41]

Table 6.4 presents the results for these three interventions.

36 Austoker et al., 1994, p. 1481.
37 Yudkin et al., 1994, p. 1476.
38 Russell et al., 1979.
39 Law et al., in press.
40 Marks, 1994.
41 Marks, 1993.

Table 6.4   *Cost effectiveness of three methods of helping people stop smoking*

Variable	GP	Patches	Quit for Life programme
Efficacy	7%	12%	23%*
Net-efficacy			
Cost/ex-smoker	£1103.00	£3063.33	£558.82
Cost effectiveness	0.91	0.33	1.79

* This figure is an estimate based upon an unpublished pilot evaluation in the UK.

This analysis suggests that the Quit for Life programme is at least five times more cost effective than nicotine patches and twice as cost effective as GP health promotion clinics. In spite of their cost effectiveness, intensive smoking cessation programmes are not yet available within the NHS because smoking is seen as a matter of individual choice and responsibility.

Persuading teenagers not to start smoking
For every thousand young persons who take up smoking, one will be murdered and six will die on the roads. Five hundred will die before their expected age as a result of tobacco use.[42]

One sub-target of *The Health of the Nation* was to reduce the prevalence of cigarette smoking in young people aged 11–15 by at least 33 per cent by 1994. This was the first *Health of the Nation* target not to be achieved. There is obviously a need to think again about the best strategies for reducing teenage smoking. The evidence is that by the age of 15 one in four young people are regular smokers. By the age of 19 about 30 per cent of the population are smokers. Children are twice as likely to smoke if their parents do so.

One of the problems in preventing teenagers from starting smoking is the existence of an anti-school or youth sub-culture. There is a group of teenagers who reject health education messages, which are based on middle-class values of thinking for the future and restraint, in favour of a youth culture based on immediacy and enjoyment of the moment.[43] This culture is very strong. It may prevent the young from studying and it encourages smoking. During the course of the interviews for this

42 Department of Health, 1992.
43 Francome, 1976.

book we engaged in some instructive conversations with young people on social pressures. A 14-year-old who had only tried cigarettes on one or two occasions said: *'These days I never feel bad if I tell people I don't smoke.'* This was an important comment. It illustrates the conflicts that teenagers face between a youth culture based on immediate gratification and an education system base on deferred gratification. A 12-year-old, who was already a regular smoker, explained that he smoked 'out of habit'. He was 'already addicted', having been a regular smoker for three years. A 9-year-old told one of us that he wouldn't become a smoker but then continued: *'But what if my best friend is a smoker?'*

In the key health areas of sex, pregnancy, smoking and drinking it is important to take into account the effect on teenagers of the anti-school culture. One suggestion we have been making to the health authorities is that health education should come not only from schools but also from outside agencies. These can more easily educate those who are alienated from school.

DRINKING

Excessive drinking leads to increased risk of high blood pressure and stroke, liver cirrhosis and deaths from accidents. The International Agency for Research on Cancer states: 'Epidemiological studies clearly indicate that drinking alcoholic beverages is causally related to cancers of the oral cavity and pharynx.'[44]

British research suggests that alcohol consumption leads to 28,000 deaths each year in England and Wales alone and that it is second only to smoking as a cause of cancer. Three per cent of all cancer deaths are related to excess alcohol consumption. This is around 4,300 deaths a year. In conjunction with smoking, alcohol may be responsible for 10 per cent of all cancer deaths.[45]

There are a number of cancers that are definitely related to alcohol consumption. These are cancers of the mouth, pharynx, larynx, oesophagus and the liver. The *British Medical Journal* has published data on the relative risks of developing oral or pharyngeal cancer both amongst non-smokers and smokers. The more people drink, the greater the potential for harm. Research has shown that if non-smoking men drink between five and twenty-nine units a week, their risk of oral or

44 Llewelyn, 1994, p. 1508.
45 Austoker, 1994d, p. 1549.

pharyngeal cancer is increased by 50 per cent. If they drink over thirty units a week their risk is nearly six times that of a non-drinker. The risks seem to be multiplied for those who both drink and smoke. Amongst those drinking over thirty units a week, the risk is twenty-four times greater than those who neither drink nor smoke.[46]

Cancers possibly related to alcohol consumption are tumours of the breast and the rectum. Drinkers who also have a low fruit intake have higher risks of oral, pharyngeal and oesophageal cancer.[46] There is evidence that alcohol in a mouthwash can increase the risk of oral cancer.[47]

The recommended limit for alcohol consumption advised by the Royal College of Medicine in 1987 was twenty-one units a week for men and fourteen units for women. A unit is defined as half a pint of beer or one measure of spirits. There were some doubts about the reliability of the recommendation. Subsequently the government set up a working party to consider whether recommended safe drinking levels should be increased. The director of Alcohol Concern said that he did not believe that the guidelines needed to be changed, but commented that it was important to clear up the matter urgently as eight million people were drinking amounts above the recommended limits.[48] At the end of 1995 the recommended limits were changed to twenty-eight units a week for men and twenty-one units for women.

There is a tendency for people to underestimate the amount of alcohol they consume. Some insurance companies have told us they multiply the stated amount of alcohol intake by a figure of 4.[49]

However, if, in general, people underestimate their alcohol consumption, then the figures can over-estimate the harm that it causes. So we must use caution in interpreting the raw data. However, it was estimated in 1992 that men in the United Kingdom aged 18 or over drank an average of 15.9 units or the equivalent of eight pints of beer a week. Women drank only a third of this – about two and a half pints. Overall, almost three in ten men and one in ten women admit to drinking above the recommended limit. One of the factors is that alcohol has become relatively cheap; it is just about half of its real cost in the 1950s. Consumption doubled between the 1950s and late 1970s.

The *Health of the Nation* target is to reduce the proportion of men drinking more than 21 units of alcohol per week from 28 per cent

46 Austoker, 1994b, p. 1610.
47 Llewelyn, 1994, p. 1508.
48 Mihill, 1994b, p. 3.
49 Personal communications.

in 1990 to 18 per cent by 2005, and the proportion of women drinking more than fourteen units per week from 11 per cent in 1990 to 7 per cent by 2005.

The negative effects of alcohol consumption in terms of increased cancer risk may be partially offset by the reduced risk of heart attacks. However, as we saw in Chapter 5, this remains controversial. One problem is that while the latter factor is given a great deal of publicity, the true risk factors are given minimal publicity so as not to affect sales.

OBESITY

This subject has been dealt with more fully in our discussion of heart disease. Obesity is an established risk factor for endometrial and post menopausal breast cancer.[50]

TREATMENT OF CANCER

There have been some improvements in the treatment of cancer. A study based in Oxford showed that for children, the five-year survival of cancer patients was only 26 per cent during the period 1962–70. The rate increased from 57 per cent in 1980–2 to 65 per cent in 1986–8. The percentage of patients still alive ten years after diagnosis has increased from 53 per cent to a projected 63 per cent. It is expected to improve further so that around two-thirds of children diagnosed with cancer will survive for ten years. There are now over ten thousand survivors of childhood cancers and the number is increasing by five hundred a year.[51]

In relation to cancer treatment, some observers have reported unacceptable delays in the provision of health services. They suggest patients with cancer are having to wait for up to two months to start radiotherapy or chemotherapy. Such delays have been criticised by the Joint Council for Clinical Oncology. It argued that for urgent cases the treatment should begin within a day and that there should be a maximum of two weeks' wait for patients with mild symptoms that would be relieved by radiotherapy.

A report compiled by the Royal College of Physicians and the Royal College of Radiologists said that oncologists all over the country who

---

50 Austoker, 1994b, p. 1611.
51 Stiller, 1994, p. 1612.

were telephoned complained about the quality of service they were able to provide for their patients. Clearly this is a problem that has to be dealt with urgently. Dr Jill Bullimore, chair of the Joint Council, made it clear that for many patients a two-month wait may well mean a worse outcome. Furthermore, not only could a delay lead to a worse physical outcome, there are also psychological problems involved. Dr Robert Hunter, the medical director of the Christie Hospital Trust, stated: 'Patients get very worried if they don't start radiotherapy within three to four weeks of being seen by an oncologist, every extra week they have to wait is hell for them.'[52]

There has not been the necessary input of funds to change this situation and it is something that needs to be given priority.

One of the points made by several consultants is the advisability of setting up specialised units concentrating on specific kinds of cancer. These units would have many more cases, which would make it easier to monitor the efficacy of different kinds of treatment. There is also a need for much greater rationalisation. Professor John Smyth, director of clinical oncology at the Western General Hospital, Edinburgh, told a meeting organised by the Marie Curie Cancer Care and BACUP – the cancer information charity – that the treatment of lung cancer was a 'cock up' and far more could and should be done for patients. Not enough doctors were referring patients to specialised units, and this was because they believed little could be done:[53]

> I am sick and tired of the arrogance of the medical profession in refusing to refer patients to people who know what they are talking about. There is so much that could be achieved with relatively simple clinical research, but there is a reluctance by patients to ask for specialist referral and a reluctance by the medical profession to take the treatment of lung cancer seriously. We should rationalise treatment on a regional basis.

A similar point was made by a specialist in the treatment of cancer of the oesophagus. He reported improvements in survival in his unit but then commented more generally.[54]

> The treatment of cancer generally is patchy in Britain. It is encouraging that the government has recognised this and is

52 Tonks, 1993.
53 Mihill, 1993a.
54 Salama et al., 1994, p. 126.

trying to do something about it. Cancer of the oesophagus, like any other cancer, should be treated in specialised units, where the patient stands the best chance of a cure. The future must lie with agents which kill the tumour but spare the rest of the body. Until then the best advice for patients with oesophageal cancer is to find a good surgeon.

In May 1994 an expert advisory group on cancer called for an overhaul of diagnosis and treatment to ensure that each person received the best treatment. We welcome the fact that in April 1995 the government accepted the recommendation that rarer forms of cancer should be treated at specialist units. Peter Selby – professor of cancer surgery at St James's Hospital, Leeds – said that numerous studies had shown that when patients were provided with treatment by specialised units, about 9 per cent more were still alive after five years and 7 per cent after ten years compared to patients treated at general units.[55] Karol Sikora, professor of cancer studies at Hammersmith Hospital, drew attention to disparities in treatment and then commented:[55] 'There are still a few lone surgeons doing just one or two breast cancer operations or one or two bowel cancer operations. We all recognise that this is wrong and should come to an end.'

Since 1993 NHS acute hospital providers have been required to make a return on each patient with cancer as part of a common dataset for cancer registration. The Calman Report also argued for Regional Centres of Excellence which would be able to provide the best possible treatments and improve the survival rates of patients. These regional centres could remove the variability in the quality of care, which currently resembles the National Lottery.

RECOMMENDATIONS

1   Improvements in diet, reductions in obesity, smoking and drinking, increased activity levels and improved screening are all factors in the incidence of cancer. A comprehensive strategy is needed at societal level for the achievement of changes in relation to these. They cannot be left to rely solely on the provision of information and the delegation of responsibility to individual 'healthy choices'.

2   It is clear that there is a need for improvements in the treatment of cancer. Once it is diagnosed, treatment should begin immediately, so once again we are looking for an injection of funds. The setting

55 Mihill, 1995b, p. 5.

up of regional centres and careful monitoring of all treatment is also important.

3   More epidemiological research is necessary to consider the reasons for national differences in incidence of different forms of cancer and to identify lifestyle factors which affect prevalence. We should especially consider the reasons why certain cancers have an increased incidence.

4   Creative new methods for reducing smoking and drinking by young people and cost-effective methods of achieving smoking cessation within the NHS are needed. Although helpful, increases in price are an inadequate mechanism for reducing the prevalence of smoking. Only a complete advertising ban combined with reliable educational messages about smoking will ensure that young people are provided with consistent information.

CHAPTER SEVEN

COPING WITH MENTAL ILLNESS

The number of beds in mental hospitals fell from 91,000 in 1978 to 58,000 in 1992 but only 11,000 places were found in the community.

The care and treatment of people with mental health problems is very different to the treatment of those affected by other *Health of the Nation* areas because of recent radical developments. The last forty years have seen tremendous changes in the perception of mental health problems and of what services are required. Research has led to a shift from social theories to biological and more integrated biopsychosocial formulations. New treatment strategies for both neuroses and psychoses have developed at a rapid rate, particularly in the cognitive behavioural area. The result is that the way services are delivered is now radically different. In particular, case management has become the core component of comprehensive care in much of the Western world and is now the mainstay of community approaches. It must be stated at the outset that the *Health of the Nation* strategy for mental illness is not a short-term initiative.[1] The strategy will develop and evolve over at least the next ten years. There is virtually universal agreement among mental health professionals that services are starved of financial resources. Although there are clearly ways forward and a great strength and potential for improving effectiveness, unless new financial resources are found there will be insufficient capacity and human resources to face the numerous challenges ahead.

TARGETS FOR MENTAL HEALTH

The strategy set out in the original *Health of the Nation* document was developed in detail in the key area handbooks published in January 1993 and October 1994.

This key area has these targets:

1 Jenkins, 1994.

- To improve significantly the health and social functioning of mentally ill people.
- To reduce the overall suicide rate by at least 15 per cent from the 1990 levels of 11 per 100,000 by the year 2000.
- To reduce the lifetime suicide rate of severely mentally ill people by at least 33 per cent by the year 2000.

Mental illness was chosen as a target because it affects many people. The government believed there was much that could be achieved by an improvement in services.

The first year's experience
The Department of Health's publication *The Health of the Nation: One Year On* showed that there was an increase in the suicide rate of 0.9 per cent.[2] In analysing the reasons for this, correspondents to the *British Medical Journal* said that although factors such as education, housing and employment are important factors in mental illness, the changes in the organisation of mental health care may also have implications. The experience within one intensive care unit was that there had been a considerable increase in the number of patients admitted after deliberate self-harm or an overdose in the past three years. Admissions increased from nine in 1990 to twenty-two in 1992 and fifty-one in the first eleven months of 1993. The rate of increase was therefore 566 per cent over three years. The authors stated that there were great costs involved with the policy and that social and economic issues would need to be considered before the government's targets could be achieved.[3]

THE CAUSES OF SUICIDE AND MENTAL ILLNESS

The classic work by the sociologist Durkheim published in 1897[4] distinguished three kinds of suicide based on the integration of the individual with the social group. The first is *egoistic* suicide, which results from the lack of integration of the individual. Durkheim pointed out that Protestants have more suicides than Catholics or Jews because the latter groups have more close-knit communities. For the same reason divorced and single people had higher suicide rates. At the

2 Department of Health, 1993d.
3 Marsh *et al.*, 1994.
4 Durkheim, 1964.

other extreme is *altruistic* suicide, where pressure from the group may encourage a person to commit suicide. Examples of this type are Hindu widows who by tradition committed suicide (*suttee*), Japanese fighter pilots (*kamikaze*) and Bobby Sands and other members of the IRA who committed suicide for their political beliefs. The third form is *anomic* suicide, resulting from some social crisis, such as an increase in divorce rates, which challenges the established norms of society. Durkheim suggests that one way to reduce suicide is to improve social cohesion in order to give people extra support. This is an important point for those who have been sent out of mental hospitals into the community. Many such persons have not had sufficient care, as we shall see.

The average age in most developed societies for suicide is over 55 years. However, in a very useful table, UNICEF published the suicide rates for young people aged from 15 to 24 years. See Table 7.1.

Table 7.1   *Annual suicide rate per 100,000 population aged 15–24*

Country	1970	1987–90
Australia	8.6	16.4
Norway	6.2	16.3
Canada	10.2	15.8
Switzerland	13.7	15.7
USA	8.0	13.2
Sweden	13.3	12.2
France	7.0	10.3
West Germany	13.4	9.6
Denmark	9.0	9.2
UK	4.3	7.2
Japan	13.0	7.0
Netherlands	4.9	6.7
Spain	1.7	4.3
Italy	2.9	3.2

Source UNICEF, 1993, p. 45.

The results show that the suicide rate for young people aged from 15 to 24 in the UK increased substantially from 4.3 to 7.2 per 100,000 between 1970 and the period 1987–90. It was still below the average, however, for over this period the suicide rate for this age group rose in eleven of fourteen industrial countries. Those in which it fell were

Sweden, Japan and the former West Germany.[5] An analysis of the reasons for these changes could provide some useful results.

In a booklet produced to publicise the *Health of the Nation* targets in 1993, the government discussed the fact that one in ten people, and up to one in five children, suffer from mental illness.[6] In 1990/1 more than 91 million working days were lost through mental illness, compared to under a million lost in strikes. The report drew attention to the difference between psychosis, in which people's ability to distinguish between the real and the imaginary may be seriously affected; and neurosis, which is a broad term to describe anxiety and depression. In addition it identified seven kinds of mental illness. These are briefly considered below:

1 *Schizophrenia* This affects the most basic functions which provide people with their sense of individuality. It may cause them to hallucinate or believe that their innermost thoughts are known to others. It is possible to recover from the illness, although for some the symptoms persist or return.

2 *Manic-depressive illness* This causes large swings in mood from elation to deep depression. The polarisations affect a person's ability to function in normal personal relationships.

3 *Depressive disorder* This may lead to people's lives becoming full of despair and is often accompanied by loss of interest and reduced energy. People affected may feel disproportionately guilty and harbour thoughts of suicide.

4 *Anxiety states* These include phobias, panic attacks and general anxiety symptoms such as worry, tension and giddiness. Phobias may lead to people avoiding certain situations which cause them difficulty, such as shopping or even going out.

5 *Dementia* Dementia leads to a decline in a person's intellectual functioning and memory. Recollection of current events may be impaired but long-term memory remains clear. Dementia is rare in those under the age of 65. It becomes more common with increased age and 20 per cent of those over the age of 80 are affected by it.

6 *Eating disorders* The two best known are anorexia nervosa, a condition which causes severe weight loss; and bulimia nervosa, which leads to compulsive over-eating followed by vomiting. Both disorders are characterised by the extreme fear of being fat and are most common in young women, which suggests they may be linked with problems in gender role identification.

5 UNICEF, 1993, p. 45.
6 Department of Health, 1993c, p. 4.

7   *Personality disorders* These are characterised by inconsistent and inflexible responses to a broad range of personal and social situations. There are several kinds of disorder. Some sufferers are so shy that they cannot develop friendships.

When we consider mental illnesses we need to recognise that some are due to genetic causes. There is, however, important evidence that some are almost certainly the result of social causes. George Brown found that depression is essentially a social phenomenon but he could not make the same claim for schizophrenia, although its beginnings and development seem to be strongly influenced by social factors.[7] There is evidence that eating disorders are closely related to social stress. The improvement of social conditions is likely to be one important way to reduce the incidence of mental illness.

COMMUNITY CARE IN THE HISTORICAL CONTEXT

Historically, many mentally ill people used to be hospitalised even when there were doubts about the necessity of that. In 1955 the population of mental hospitals in the UK was about 160,000 and the population of mental hospitals in the USA was in excess of 600,000, which was roughly the same proportion of the population.[8] The alternative of community care emerged from the Royal Commission on the Law Relating to Mental Illness and Mental Deficiency 1954–7: 'The whole approach should be a positive one offering help and obtaining the co-operation of the patient and his family.' The Royal Commission also reported that for mentally handicapped people, belonging to a family may be important.[9]

Policy changes in the direction of community-based care were marked by the Community Mental Health Centres Act in 1965 in the USA and inspired by President John F. Kennedy and by a speech made by Enoch Powell in the UK in 1961. The changes were greatly influenced by studies such as those of Wing and Brown[10] who highlighted the poverty of the lives of the residents of long-stay wards in hospitals.

In 1961 Richard Titmuss said that he doubted the country's commitment to carrying out a community care policy.[11] In 1979 a

7 Brown, G. W., 1984, p. 76.
8 Mosher and Burti, 1994.
9 Jaehnig, 1979, p. 2.
10 Wing and Brown, 1970.
11 Jaehnig, 1979, p. 2.

Fabian pamphlet 'A Family Service for the Mentally Handicapped' was produced. This made a number of points, as follows.

A   It suggested a social rather than medical pattern of care.
B   Care should be integrative, enhancing the individual's links with his or her home, neighbourhood and community.
C   Care should be preventative, aiming to support the family of the handicapped person so that admission to a segregated institution could be prevented or deferred.

At this time about half of the severely handicapped lived with their families or in the community.[12]

For over thirty years, then, there has been universal agreement among mental health professionals that the end-point of a policy shift should be that the care and treatment of the seriously mentally ill should be firmly located in the community and that minimal services only should be based in hospitals. Indeed, there has been a considerable effort directed towards the development and testing of community-based treatment. The first community-based service was set up in Madison, Wisconsin by Stein and Test.[13] It was followed by similar initiatives elsewhere. Examples are Sydney, Australia;[14] Ladbroke Grove, London;[15] and Auckland, New Zealand.[16] All of these services have used case management as a central vehicle for delivery. This concept utilises the principle of comprehensive health and social care which is usually, but not always, the responsibility of one person, the case manager. Over the years various models of case management have evolved and a detailed description of them is provided by Andrews and Teesson.[17] Case management may involve various mixtures of some or all of the following: advocacy, networking with other agencies, brokering of services, assertive outreach, interventions with symptoms, medication management, employment counselling, skill training in daily living, housing support, family education, family stress management and problem solving. While such services have the primary purpose of allowing people to stay in their own homes, there is a virtually universal consensus that some residential facilities are required.

12 Jaehnig, 1979, p. 4.
13 Stein and Test, 1980.
14 Hoult, 1990, 1993.
15 Onyett, 1992.
16 McGeorge, 1993.
17 Andrews and Teeson, 1994.

The Griffiths Report, *Community Care: Agenda for Change*, was published in March 1988.[18] It proposed that local authorities should take the leading role. Following this, the NHS and Community Care Act became law in July 1990 with key objectives as follows:

- Promote and develop domiciliary, day and respite services.
- Ensure service providers make practical support a high priority.
- Make a proper assessment of need.
- Promote a flourishing independent sector.
- Clarify the responsibilities of agencies.
- Secure better value for taxpayers' money.

This was to be implemented in several stages. First a new local authority complaints' unit was set up, inspection units were developed for residential care, and grants were made towards drug and alcohol units. At the second stage community care plans were to be produced jointly between the local authority and the health authority. Thirdly, by April 1993 there were to be contracts with providers, assessment procedures for all clients and the transfer of funds from DSS to local authorities over three years. In keeping with the government's preference for using the private sector, 85 per cent of funding was to be spent with private providers.

Commenting on the changes, the Socialist Health Association said the government had succeeded in removing from itself the problem of a DSS budget that was out of control and presented local authorities with the task of rationing care.[19]

Others have been more positive about the changes. Kevin Gournay[20] states that the approach contains three central strands:

1   Improvement of information and understanding.
2   Development of comprehensive community services.
3   Development of good practice.

Gournay proposes that each strand should contain a number of initiatives, many of which will need some years to develop. When they are in place each will then probably require further innovations for successful outcomes to develop. A particular problem is funding. On this issue the Mental Health Foundation points out:[21]

18 Griffiths, 1988.
19 Socialist Health Association, 1994, p. 1.
20 Personal communication.
21 Mental Health Foundation, 1994, p. 23.

> Successive Governments have failed to make the financial provision required to make community care policies succeed for people with severe mental illness...It is very easy for every report to argue for additional funding directed to its particular professional concerns. Yet there are some situations where such a call is fully warranted. We feel strongly that mental health services are such a case.

In the likely event that there are not large increases in the total sums available for mental health care, it is important to develop a strategy which uses existing resources in creative and cost-effective ways. Although the key area handbooks contain some very useful information regarding rates of various mental illnesses and suicide, there is no doubt that there are major gaps in our knowledge. These are most obvious at a local level. Gournay argues that, although some progress seems to have been made by purchasers and providers, many local services are still unable to provide the crudest of information regarding the number of people receiving services and the diagnostic categories to which they belong.[22]

At a national level, there are several very important initiatives. One is the confidential enquiry into homicides and suicides conducted by the Royal College of Psychiatrists; another is the national survey of the prevalence of mental illness and social disability commissioned by the Department of Health. Arguably the most important aspect of mental health care is the development of valid and valuable measures of health and social function. An initiative relating to this has been led by the Royal College of Psychiatrists' Research Unit. Such measures are intended as both instruments of assessment and change, and will be used by individual clinicians. For the first time it should be possible to collect hard outcome data routinely in the context of local district services rather than having to conduct special research studies. This innovation will enable the assessment of outcomes and progress towards achieving targets.

As a corollary to developing an information base, the Department of Health has launched a number of initiatives which are intended to improve public attitudes and reduce the stigma of mental illness. It is universally accepted that this area is problematic and it is difficult to see how major changes could be effected in a short period of time. It must be added that improving public knowledge regarding mental illness is not necessarily the same as improving public tolerance of the

....
22 Personal communication.

mentally ill. The tolerance dimension is perhaps the ultimate factor in determining both how far we can proceed with deinstitutionalisation and where we should site our community resources. To put it simply, there is still a great reluctance on the part of the public to live 'cheek by jowl' with those with mental health problems.

EVALUATING THE EARLY EXPERIENCE OF COMMUNITY CARE

Reports suggest that the number of beds in mental hospitals fell from 91,000 in 1978 to 58,000 in 1992, but only 11,000 places were found in the community. The government policy of emptying hospitals restarted in 1992.

Since that time there has been increasing concern about releasing into the community people who do not have the resources to cope. Some point out that many have committed suicide. Others estimate that mentally ill people have killed forty people in two years.[23] One was Jonathan Zito, who was stabbed in the eye by schizophrenic Christopher Clunis at Finsbury Park tube station on 17 December 1992.

Clunis was an ex-Friern Barnet patient. This hospital was closed in March 1993. Clunis became ill in 1986 and had a history of violent activity. He had missed an out-patient visit for the third time. Janet Sergeant, the psychiatrist in charge of his case, arranged an assessment visit to decide whether he was a danger to the public. However, he walked away when the visiting team arrived and nobody on the team knew what he looked like.[24] In 60 per cent of cases in which disturbed patients killed people, the event followed a period during which patients refused to co-operate with their carers. A week before Jonathan Zito's death, Clunis was reported to have threatened people with a screwdriver and a bread-knife. Malcolm Weller, a psychiatrist who worked at Friern Barnet, said 'It gives me no comfort to know that we were right all along'.[25] Since Clunis's trial and detention, the Minister of Health has announced measures designed to improve the supervision of mentally ill people in the community, including registers of discharged patients considered at risk.[26]

There are signs of recognition by Parliament that serious mistakes

23 Lonsdale and Cicatti, 1993.
24 Evans, M., 1994.
25 Anonymous, 1993.
26 Brindle, 1994d.

have been made. In April 1994 a report from the House of Commons Health Committee said that people with serious mental illness were being discharged into the community with inadequate preparation and supervision. It also stated that there was a lamentable lack of information on care in the community and that many people had either lost touch with the services or had not been registered with them.[27]

Another problem is that there is some wrangling between government departments over responsibility for homeless mentally ill people. The committee said that, while short-term housing was provided by the Department of Health, there was confusion about who was responsible for permanent accommodation. Housing associations, local authorities and the Housing Corporation were not clear about their responsibilities at a time when there were increasing numbers of mentally ill people on the streets.

In addition, there is a shortage in the number of secure units for mentally ill offenders. Since the deinstitutionalisation process began, some have spoken as if we would need few, if any, residential facilities for people with serious mental illness. This view has been reinforced by the positive outcomes of case-management-based services delivering home treatment in Wisconsin,[28] Sydney[29] and London.[30] However, the reality of the situation is that appropriate residential facilities are desperately needed. Lelliott, Wing and Clifford[31] in describing their National Audit of the New Long Stay Patients have cited three main reasons for this continuing requirement. First, there is a group of people who are so handicapped by their psychiatric state and possibly also by concomitant physical illnesses and disabilities that they will need skilled nursing and medical care. Secondly, there is a group of people whose behaviour is such that they are unsuitable for community facilities. Thirdly, there is a group who remain in hospital simply because no suitable community facilities are available. The audit showed[32] that 61 per cent of new long-stay patients would be better placed in a non-hospital setting, and 47 per cent were thought to require a community-based residential setting. Sadly, the authors concluded that many patients remained in hospital solely because of the lack of suitable community services. This conclusion brings us back

27 Dillner, 1994.
28 Stein and Test, 1980.
29 Hoult, 1990.
30 Marks et al., 1994.
31 Lelliott et al., 1994.
32 Lelliott and Wing, 1994.

to the issue of resources, which are obviously badly needed to provide satisfactory residential facilities.

A deficiency of acute hospital beds is also a problem in some, but not all, parts of the UK. A recent study of London services by a group from the Royal College of Psychiatrists revealed a situation in which bed occupancy rates were routinely in excess of 130 per cent.[33] Furthermore, there seemed little doubt that some people with serious mental illness were being discharged into the community in a most vulnerable state. It should be added that the situation is not the same throughout the UK and there are various anecdotal accounts of many acute facilities with under-occupancy.

The type of acute provision that exists is also providing concern. For example, although the last twenty years have seen the widespread development of units attached to district general hospitals, there is some uncertainty about whether these surroundings are the most appropriate ones. The recent Mental Health Nursing review[34] has recommended that this provision should be re-examined for its suitability.

Despite the efforts of researchers and clinicians in developing comprehensive, humane and user-orientated services for the seriously mentally ill, there have been inhibitory processes which have prevented these systems having an impact. Such processes need to be considered when one looks at how the new strategy is succeeding. One major problem has been the increasing emphasis placed on working with people with less serious mental health problems and the consequent abandonment of the seriously mentally ill. By 1990 the 4,500 community psychiatric nurses in the UK had begun increasingly to base themselves in primary health care settings and move away from people with severe and enduring mental illness. By 1990 only 27 per cent of the caseloads of community psychiatric nurses comprised people with schizophrenia, and 80 per cent of people with schizophrenia in the UK did not have the service of a mental health nurse.[35] Increasingly, the nurses were working with people with depression, anxiety and relationship problems. Their preferred method of treatment was client-centred counselling. Gournay and Brooking[36] examined this phenomenon by carrying out a randomised controlled trial in six health centres in north London, involving a total of thirty-six GPs referring to

33 Lelliott, 1994.
34 Department of Health, 1994b.
35 White, 1991.
36 Gournay and Brooking, 1994.

eleven community psychiatric nurses. In this study 231 patients were referred by their GP and randomly allocated to continuing GP care; immediate community psychiatric nurse intervention; or they were placed on a twelve-week waiting list, after which time they were offered community psychiatric nurse intervention. The authors used a range of measures of symptom and social functioning. Ratings were carried out at assessment and twenty-four weeks later. The study – which included an examination of process and economic analyses – showed that, while patients improved on all measures over time, there were no differences between the group of patients receiving GP care and patients seen by the community psychiatric nurses. Improvements also seemed to occur regardless of the amount of contact. Drop-out rates from the community nurses were high (50 per cent). The process analysis confirmed the predominant use of counselling. The economic analysis showed that work with this population of people, who were mainly suffering from anxiety, depression and other less serious mental health problems, was very expensive compared with work with people with schizophrenia for a comparable health gain. Furthermore, the intervention by community psychiatric nurses did not seem to save GP time. Their results were passed on to the first review of mental health nursing held since 1968.[37] It made forty-two recommendations, but most notable was the proposal to concentrate on people with serious mental health problems. This refocus by mental health nurses on the population which is undoubtedly the most vulnerable is in accord with the *Health of the Nation* strategy and other initiatives integral to and alongside the approach.

Despite the results described above, evidence available in 1994 showed that community psychiatric nurses continue to be attached to primary health care settings in large numbers. Mutale[38] carried out a random survey of 300 fundholding practices in the UK and found that 83 per cent had regular meetings with such nurses and 77 per cent had related clinics. Unfortunately, the survey did not provide information regarding the diagnostic categories of the people who used these services. Given what is already known of this area of work (e.g. White[39]), it seems likely that these fundholders are using the community psychiatric nurses to deliver services which have outcomes of uncertain value. The current situation – which gives fundholders 'wild card'

37 Department of Health, 1994b.
38 Mutale, 1994.
39 White, 1991.

status, allowing those GPs to function outside national or local strategic frameworks – obviously gives major cause for concern. These GPs may well be diverting resources from the people with serious and enduring mental illness who most need them. GP fundholders may be an impediment both to achieving the *Health of the Nation* targets and to implementing the recommendations of the review of mental health nursing which emphasised the need for mental health nursing services to refocus effort on people with serious mental illness.[40]

The situation in psychiatric nursing reflects many of the problems of mental health services in the past. The service in many areas was, and still is, driven by idiosyncratic interests which are very often not in accord with the needs of the local population.

GENERAL PRACTITIONERS' VIEWS ON THE QUALITY OF COMMUNITY CARE

We decided to investigate GPs' views on the quality of community care as they may have a good idea of what their patients are experiencing. Some carers whom we interviewed expressed the view that their GP may under-estimate the problems they face. A total of 250 doctors responded to the survey in 1994, a 72 per cent response rate. We were concerned with care for the mentally ill, the long-term sick and the elderly.

GPs were asked the following question: '*Are the community services in your area coping well with the extra patients they are meant to care for?*' The results were as shown in Table 7.2.

Table 7.2   *General Practitioners' views of community care*

All doctors	Coping well	Coping moderately	Not coping well	All
1992	49 17.7%	146 45.8%	82 29.6%	277
1994	26 10.7%	127 52.5%	89 36.8%	242
	6.8–14.6%	46.2–58.8%	30.7–42.9%	

Note Small figures show 95 per cent confidence intervals.

The results show that in 1994 over a third (36.8 per cent) of doctors said that the community services were not coping well. Only 10.7 per cent said they were successful. This latter percentage had fallen from

40 Department of Health, 1994b.

17.7 per cent in 1992 and the difference is statistically significant. The fact that such a large minority of doctors said the community services were not coping well raises the question of whether some patients were being placed into stressful situations.

The second question regarding community care was: *'Is the policy of community care placing a strain on any of your patients?'* The results are set out in Table 7.3.

Table 7.3   *Is community care placing a strain on patients?*

All doctors	Placing strain		Not placing strain		Other		All
Fundholders	37	70%	13	24%	3	6%	53
Non-fundholders	133	67%	41	21%	23	12%	197
All	170	68%	54	21.6%	26	10.4%	250
		62.2–73.8%		16.5–26.7%		6.6–14.2%	

Note 95 per cent confidence intervals are in small figures.

The results show that around seven out of ten of both fundholders and non-fundholders said that a strain was being placed on at least some of their patients. Just under a quarter said that there was no strain. One of these was a fundholder from the South West Region. He commented, *'Not now the one who was released inappropriately has killed himself.'*

The questionnaire invited respondents to give further comment on community care.

Comments made by the doctors on community care

One answered by saying there was no strain at present, but added: *'I am sure there will be.'* Another said that the movement to community care had caused strain *'for some'*. A doctor from Wiltshire said the policy is *'improving the lot of the few'*.

The general quality of community care was criticised by some. A doctor from the South West said, *'there have been instances of poor organisation'*. Another said *'there is a thin spread of services that only just copes and any extra load causes a collapse'*. A doctor from the North East and Yorkshire Region made a similar point: *'The waiting times for social workers to respond and to react are increasing. Home carers spend minimal time with patients.'* A similar point was made by a Scottish fundholder who said: *'There are long waiting lists for social work initial assessment especially.'* A doctor from the Trent Region said: '*Response by community services are slow.*' A doctor from the Home Counties said: '*The social services are not good at urgent referrals and if no simple solution can be produced they tend to "ignore the problem" and hope...*' Another doctor from Trent said: '*Things take longer. It is what is likely to happen over the next ten years that is very worrying though.*' Other doctors made similar points, including the comment that it is difficult to get social workers to respond within two weeks.

Some doctors did not see any benefits at all. A fundholder from the North West said: '*It has led to no material improvements in patient care.*' A doctor from Wales said: '*There is a lot of theory of community care but unfortunately not enough personnel to carry it out. The GP seems to be the dumping ground for many problems.*' A doctor from the Trent Region spoke of the situation being too bureaucratic: '*There is too much fuss and meetings for no real extra benefit.*'

Other doctors made more specific comments and it is instructive to consider these under a number of headings.

Finance and care
Several doctors mentioned financial problems in connection with care. One from Berkshire said of the new policy: '*The burden on carers is increased and the financial burden on patients has risen.*' A doctor from Trent said: '*They cannot afford to pay for help.*' A respondent from the East Anglia and Oxford Region said: '*There is sometimes strain when they should be in residential care but community care is cheaper.*' A doctor in Wales said: '*There is inadequate funding of home help service in particular.*' Similarly a fundholder said: '*Inadequate financial backup for community care in all specialities appears to be the cause of the strain.*' A Scottish fundholder spoke of the '*cost to some patients of equipment*'.

Staffing problems
A doctor from the West Midlands commented: '*There are insufficient caring professionals in the community.*' Another doctor said, '*There are inadequate community care facilities with a lack of trained staff.*'

A doctor from South London commented:

'*It is very difficult to obtain home helps and bathing attendants. So patients often go long periods without baths. Sometimes appointments are very slow coming through and patients are at risk if disabled whilst waiting for aids to daily living.*'

Families and caring

A number of doctors reported that families found it difficult to cope. A doctor from the North East and Yorkshire Region complained: *'There are problems especially for families of long term psychiatric patients.'* A fundholder from London talked of problems *'especially home care of mentally ill patients'*. Another doctor from South London said:

> *'There is a strain mostly on relatives who are expected to shoulder more of the burden. Social services are trying hard but do not have the money or resources. Quite often relatives are not given the help in making decisions by social services.'*

A doctor from the South West commented: *'I have several instances where relatives cannot cope and I would formerly have placed the patient directly in a nursing home.'* A north London doctor talked of one of her patients whose relatives were far away; so she was awaiting a crisis so the patient could be readmitted.

The elderly and mentally ill

Many reported problems for their geriatric patients. A fundholder from Somerset said: *'More elderly are forced to cope alone at home when it is not necessarily appropriate.'* A doctor from Glasgow said: *'It is mainly elderly patients who need nursing home care – some are inappropriately kept at home and in sheltered nursing.'* Several mentioned financial concerns. A doctor from Aberdeen said: *'Many elderly patients are not prepared to pay for the services they need and would rather do without placing extra demand on carers'*, while a doctor from the Trent Region talked of *'the fear of having to use up their savings or sell their home'*.

The mentally ill inevitably had some problems. One GP from the North West commented: *'I have recently had a patient after six months in psychiatric hospital on a section and no proper arrangement for her depot injections.'* A doctor from North East and Yorkshire said: *'Many patients are discharged from mental hospitals into flats and expected to look after themselves.'*

Difficulties in obtaining residential care

A number of doctors reported difficulties in getting patients into hospital or home. A Scottish doctor spoke of the *'difficulty in getting rapid access to residential care. Many elderly are struggling to cope despite full support services.'* Similarly a doctor from the North West

Region commented: '*A number of patients muddle through at home when they would be better off in an institution.*' A fundholder from Derbyshire talked of the '*time taken to get the appropriate care*'. Others reported delays in assessment. A doctor from the North East and Yorkshire Region said: '*Patients requiring admission to nursing homes are left for days or even weeks without being assessed.*' One from South London said: '*There is uncertainty of getting patients into a respite home or nursing home when needed. Furthermore social services assessment often leads to a request for hospital assessment to try and pass the buck into another budget and delay the final decision.*' A doctor from the North West spoke of '*delays in assessment even for especially urgent residential care admissions*'. A similar point was made by a doctor from the West Midlands: '*In the case of the elderly and of mental illness we cannot get them into hospital in time of crisis.*' Another doctor from the Trent Region said: '*It is more difficult to get places as there are longer waiting lists for the best establishments.*'

Early discharge from hospital

A doctor from the North East and Yorkshire Region said: '*We need an appreciation of the fact that community care requires staff and facilities including GPs. That discharging patients early is not community care but rather trying to achieve high bed occupancy.*'

One doctor, commenting on returning patients home from hospital too early, said that '*extra and unnecessary visits are demanded by patients discharged too soon and still in pain*'. A Trent doctor similarly commented: '*Occasionally early discharge from hospital causes anxiety in the elderly.*'

The government response to the problems of community care that have reached the media is that they are teething troubles or that they are relatively isolated incidents. However, the fact that seven out of ten doctors are reporting that their patients are suffering strain indicates that there is a need to review the overall policy.

THE FUTURE OF COMMUNITY CARE

The key area handbooks provide detailed guidance for local managers and clinicians on how to develop appropriate services. There are several obstacles which inhibit comprehensive development. Most importantly, there are separate budgets for the mentally ill within social service and health areas and staff are still managed separately.

Obviously, comprehensive services need unitary funding and common operational management. Even within the health area, separate management structures exist. For example, clinical psychology services often maintain a separate identity from mainstream mental health services, claiming to be members of the multidisciplinary team but also demanding the freedom to take referrals and deliver interventions as they wish, eschewing central strategic action. Allowing such a situation to exist leads to a maldistribution of precious resources. Remedial action is needed not just in clinical psychology services but also in nursing and to a lesser extent in occupational therapy.

In order to assist in the development of comprehensive and integrated services, the Mental Health Task Force has been in operation since January 1993. The task force is to be applauded for its active use of support from a range of statutory and voluntary agencies as well as an increasingly active user movement.

Improving practice

This is an area which should always be a priority. There is always a need to question one's method and style of working with regard to people with serious mental illness. As stated above, the care programme approach is the most important central method; there is a consensus that care programming is the most important strategy in the care of people with serious mental illness. However, as many (e.g. Kingdom[41]) have pointed out, it is much harder to agree how to put the principles of the care programme approach into practice.

First and foremost, care programming is designed to ensure that people with serious mental illness do not fall through gaps in the service. Essentially it contains four major components. These are:

1   That people with serious mental illness should have their health and social care needs assessed.
2   That there is a named key worker for each patient.
3   That a clear care plan is designed for each patient.
4   That this care is reviewed at predetermined intervals.

One of the most difficult aspects of the care programme is that it has become overly bureaucratic in many ways. This may be indicative of a situation in which the health service, now dominated by a management culture, has forgotten to focus on people with serious mental illness and become obsessed with paperwork processes.

....
41 Kingdom, 1994.

A step forward in the care programme approach is the targeting of the most vulnerable people with serious mental illness and of those who pose the most risk to themselves and others. This is currently the subject of a great deal of controversy because of the proposed implementation of supervision registers, a topic which will be referred to again below.

There is obviously a need to develop acceptable standards of care to guide local services and in this regard some progress is being made.

Standards

One initiative has been the work of the Schizophrenia Committee of the Clinical Standards Advisory Group, which has been charged with the development of comprehensive standards of care and treatment for people with schizophrenia. This committee was set up to meet part of a ten-point plan for safe and effective community care promoted by the Secretary of State for Health in 1993. The work of the committee has been wide ranging. It includes the commissioning of visits to services throughout England, Wales, Scotland and Northern Ireland to identify good (and bad) practice; a study of purchaser/provider contracts; and a review of relevant literature and the taking of information from other initiatives. This work has been assisted by the Health Advisory Service and by a team of researchers located in the Royal College of Psychiatrists' Research Unit. From April 1995, services in the UK have had a comprehensive set of standards to assist them in reaching the target of improving the health and social function of people with serious mental illness in general and with schizophrenia in particular. Such standard setting will need several years of careful implementation before reaching the target can become a reality.

Some contemporary issues

There are several other new developments which are of interest. There is obviously a need to improve mental health awareness and education across all health care professionals. An example of a wide-ranging initiative is to be found in the 'Defeat Depression' campaign. This is run jointly by the Royal College of General Practitioners and the Royal College of Psychiatrists and is supported by the Department of Health. The campaign recognises that GPs need further education in the recognition and management of depression. Perhaps it is now timely to subject all mental health professions to scrutiny and establish ways to improve their practice. In its recent review, mental health nursing began this process but clearly this was only a beginning. The review process could profitably be applied to psychiatry, clinical psychology and occupational therapy.[42]

Training and education

A negative consequence of establishing a purchaser/provider framework and the ensuing preoccupation with cost has been the widespread reduction in training budgets. Training and in-service education have been targets for savings in most financially pressed provider units. This state of affairs will undoubtedly have a major impact on the quality of services and on clinical and social outcomes.

The training of staff is crucial. At present there are few training/education initiatives for staff working with those with mental health problems. The Sainsbury Centre has provided some excellent training in the original case management sites and is continuing to develop other initiatives in community-based services.[43] Additionally, two other programmes are providing comprehensive training in problem-oriented case management. The Thorn programme is training mental health nurses in London and Manchester in a diploma programme and Middlesex University offers a master's level course for nurses, social workers, occupational therapists, psychologists and non-professionals. Both programmes teach skills in cognitive behavioural intervention; medication management; and family approaches involving problem solving, family stress management and education; as well as the traditional case management skills of advocacy, networking, brokering and assertive outreach. While such initiatives will produce graduates with the necessary skills to improve the quality of services thereby helping to meet the *Health of the Nation* targets, the current number of these people is very small. The Thorn programme is currently producing twenty-four graduates per year and Middlesex University produces fifteen graduates every two years. Furthermore, there is ample evidence from all over the country that trainees on in-service programmes are often expected to pay their own fees and may not be given time off to undertake their studies. To make a real impact through the appropriate training of staff, we need to 'ring fence' substantial sums to ensure the adequate preparation of our workforce in meeting the contemporary challenges of mental health care.

42 Department of Health, 1994a.
43 Ford *et al.*, 1993.

Supervision registers

Part of the *Health of the Nation* strategy, integral to the ten-point plan for successful and safe community care, is the aim of protecting the most vulnerable group of people, those with serious mental illness. These are the people who are most at risk to themselves or others and who need most support. In this context, in February 1994 the NHS Executive issued guidelines concerning supervision registers. However, this initiative produced substantial opposition from the professions. The president of the Royal College of Psychiatrists, Dr Fiona Caldicott, listed in a letter to the Secretary of State, ten major concerns about this policy. These included issues of confidentiality, problems of definition and cost.[44] Although there have been continuing attempts to reconcile the policy with professional concerns, it appears that its implementation will increase the already immense burden on some services. Given the general shortage of resources, it is unlikely that targeted individuals will receive the necessary high quality and intensive attention without depriving other parts of the service. Holloway has taken a balanced look at the issues and concludes:[45]

> It is possible to argue that supervision registers will turn out to be a bold policy initiative which will be of practical benefit to patients and offer essential reassurance to a public opinion that has become nervous of community care. It is equally possible to assert that the register is a mistaken policy that yet again proposes a bureaucratic solution to what is essentially a problem of inadequate resources. Time will tell.

At present there is no objective commentary available on this initiative and therefore the question of whether supervision registers will assist in meeting the *Health of the Nation* targets must remain open.

Resources

In 1958 15 per cent of NHS spending was on public health, compared to 10 per cent in 1993.[46] Though 75 per cent of expenditure is on in-patients, 90 per cent of the severely mentally ill live in the community. In 1995 the Mental Health Foundation released data suggesting that there is a £540 million shortfall in funds and that as a result 300,000

44 Caldicott, 1994.
45 Holloway, 1994.
46 Waterhouse, 1995, p. 12.

people are being denied adequate community care. An extra £1,700 per person would improve services such as housing, daytime occupation, respite care and specialist psychiatric care. The foundation called upon the government to ensure savings made from hospital closures are reinvested in community services.[46]

As the report regarding Christopher Clunis has indicated, not all of the problems in the mental health services can be attributed to a shortage of financial resources.[47] However, the lack of resources must impede progress. Notwithstanding this reality, there is no doubt that if two particular situations were modified, the flow of resources could be changed. First, as the Association of Metropolitan Authorities' report[48] indicates, the resources realised from the sale of mental hospital sites are not currently returning to fund new services in the community. The other factor is that a disproportionate amount of the mental health care budget is being spent on hospital facilities.[49] The proportion has remained at approximately 90 per cent despite the process of deinstitutionalisation referred to above. Other, more successful, systems in Madison, Wisconsin and Kansas have reduced this proportion drastically, yet have still been able to maintain a more than adequate infrastructure of residential accommodation catering for the widest spectrum of need.[50]

CONCLUSION

The key area status given to mental health within the *Health of the Nation* strategy gives an opportunity for mental health care that should not be missed and it should be owned by everyone, not just the mental health professions. Alongside this opportunity there are major problems with services, some of them attributable to poor resourcing. Given the possible continuing shortage of resources, the priority should be to mobilise the mental health workforce to improve services within the limits of economic constraints and to foster public tolerance towards mental illness. Any alternative to this course of action would only mean even greater impoverishment in the lives of people with mental health problems.

46 Waterhouse, 1995, p. 12.
47 Ritchie, 1994.
48 Association of Metropolitan Authorities, 1993.
49 Department of Health, 1994a.
50 Rapp, 1993; Stein and Test, 1980.

RECOMMENDATIONS

A   Greater care needs to be taken to ensure the population is not placed at risk by violent patients. This requires an increase in the number of beds for the mentally ill and the provision of more effective supervision in the community. As in many other areas, extra resources are needed, along with more effective communication between all relevant parties – including the social and health care professionals, the police, families and patients.

B   More attention should be given to the seriously ill patients, who do not at present receive sufficient resources.

C   We should appoint a Minister for Community Care so that someone has the responsibility for pulling the different strands together. This was a recommendation of the Griffiths Report.

D   There should be increasing emphasis on prevention of mental health problems by policies which improve social cohesion and introduce such services as well-person clinics for the elderly.

E   We need further research into the reasons why the suicide rate in some countries has increased in recent years while in others it has fallen.

CHAPTER EIGHT

HIV/AIDS
AND SEXUAL HEALTH

*I said Angie don't get sick and die and leave these
kids for me to look after.*
AIDS – America's Ideal Death Sentence

The issue of sexual health is especially problematical. First of all, the
Health of the Nation target of measuring gonorrhoea has very little, if
any, relevance to the issue of AIDS, as we saw in the introduction
(p. 7). Secondly, there has been a dearth of accurate information for
heterosexuals. Thirdly, there has been evidence of a lack of
commitment to sex education.

The *Health of the Nation* targets are as follows:

- To reduce the incidence of gonorrhoea amongst men and women
  aged 15–64 by at least 20 per cent by 1995, as an indicator of
  HIV/AIDS trends. This would mean a reduction from sixty-one new
  cases per 100,000 population in 1990 to no more than forty-nine
  new cases per 100,000.
- To reduce by at least 50 per cent the rate of conceptions amongst the
  under-16s by the year 2000. This would be from 9.5 per 1,000 girls
  aged 13–15 in 1989 to no more than 4.8.

AIDS is perhaps the greatest new threat to public health this century.
HIV infection has increased from an estimated 100,000 cases
worldwide in 1980 to nearly twenty million by 1993.[1] At the Tenth
Annual International AIDS conference in Tokyo in August 1994 the
delegates were told that the HIV virus was spreading more rapidly in
India, Burma and Thailand than anywhere else. The World Health
Organization estimates that in some parts of northern Thailand one in
five young men is infected.[2] Thailand is known to be a major centre of
the vacation sex industry for heterosexual males.

In considering AIDS we shall be looking at the position of groups

1 Mann and Wilson, 1993, p. 1575.
2 Headlines, 1994a.

which up to now have been most at risk. These are homosexuals, intravenous drug users and sexually active heterosexuals. The safety of haemophiliacs should be secured in the future by the now mandatory heat treatment of blood, before which they have been greatly affected. The consideration of heterosexual transmission will lead to a discussion of young teenage pregnancy.

HIV AND AIDS

In 1959 an anonymous person from Zaire had serum taken which was later identified as HIV positive. In 1966 three members of a Norwegian family fell ill and died. The father, who had a history of sexually transmitted diseases, the mother and one daughter died from illnesses which were later found to be AIDS related. The daughter was thought to have been infected in the womb or through breast feeding, making this the earliest known case of paediatric AIDS. Two other daughters were unaffected.[3] It is possible that earlier cases will be uncovered following further research.

There are suggestions that the media were slow to react to AIDS as it was thought to be primarily a gay disease. To quote Altman:[4]

> In its early days the media tended to shy away from AIDS, seeing it as a gay story they should not touch. Once the illness appeared among infants, and those who received blood transfusions, this attitude changed dramatically, and from 1983 on, AIDS has been a continuing preoccupation of the media.

The lack of concern earlier is a reflection of an anti-gay bias among the health care professions, especially medicine. The prognosis for AIDS patients was dismal and has improved only a little.

INTERNATIONAL DATA

A study reported in the *British Medical Journal* in 1994 provided data on the survival of 6,655 patients diagnosed with AIDS between 1979 and 1989.[5] They were in fifty-two centres from seventeen countries and represented 22 per cent of cases reported to the World Health Organization from the participating countries during the study. At the

3 Garfield, 1994, p. 6.
4 Altman, D., 1986, p. 16.
5 Lundgren *et al.*, 1994, p. 1068.

time of the report 73 per cent of the patients had died. They had a median survival of seventeen months with an estimated survival rate at three years of 16 per cent. There was an improved survival rate for those diagnosed in or after 1987 but it was mainly at the earlier stages and the three-year survival was still below one in five. Those contracting AIDS from sources other than bisexual/homosexual contact or injecting drugs had a slightly lower survival rate. There were no sex differences in survival. The statistics are shown in Table 8.1.

Table 8.1   *AIDS in ten European countries 1979–89*

Country	Median age	% men	% homo-sexual	% inject drugs	Total
Belgium	35	74	38	7	258
Denmark	38	96	81	3	452
France	36	93	75	10	610
Germany	40	98	85	6	448
Italy	30	83	20	71	1009
Ireland	30	85	36	62	55
Netherlands	38	98	92	3	317
Portugal	37	94	58	14	194
Spain	30	92	27	69	823
United Kingdom	36	99	93	2	1239
Total	24	91	60	27	6578

Source Lundgren *et al.*, 1994, p. 1068.

Note The totals at the foot of the table are based on eighteen countries. The ten most important ones have been chosen for this table.

This table shows that nine out of ten patients diagnosed with AIDS were men. Only Belgium (26 per cent) and, to a lesser extent, Italy (17 per cent) had a substantial minority of women. In the United Kingdom 93 per cent of the cases were homosexuals, the highest proportion of the ten countries listed. Part of the reason may be that gay men from Ireland tend to travel to England because the lifestyle is more amenable to them. That would in part explain why only 36 per cent of Irish cases of AIDS were homosexual men. Garfield suggests that probably only 60 per cent of British cases of HIV were due to sexual intercourse between men and 16 per cent were due to heterosexual intercourse.[6] In

6 Garfield, 1994, p. 8.

fact the 1994 figures show that the percentage of new cases of AIDS due to homosexual intercourse was down to 56 per cent of the total.[7]

The figures for 1994 show that the number of AIDS cases had passed the 10,000 mark for the first time, and 68 per cent of the people affected had died. This is an annual rate of increase of 11 per cent – less than some had feared but this rate will lead to a doubling of cases in five years.[7] The number of women with AIDS reached 890, which is 8.6 per cent of the total. However, 3,201 women (13.9 per cent of the total) are known to have contracted the HIV virus.

Let us consider some country differences in more detail. In Britain one AIDS death was reported in 1981. On US Independence Day the next year Terrence Higgins became one of seven men to die of AIDS that year. Later in 1982 a fund for information, advice and research was set up in his name. In the early days there was a great deal of ignorance. The first leaflet produced by the Terrence Higgins Trust contained no suggestion that anal sex might be a high risk activity, did not mention incubation time and made no mention of condoms. It said, 'Have as much sex as you want, but with fewer people and with healthy people.' In 1983 the Cabinet minister Kenneth Clarke stated that 'there is no conclusive evidence that AIDS is transmitted by blood products'.[8]

Things began to change a little, however. The government started an educational programme in March 1986 which resulted in the postal delivery of a leaflet to every household in January 1987. The Health Education Authority then took over the programme of education, which included advertising the dangers of infection and the routes by which HIV is transmitted. In 1988 the AIDS hospice London Lighthouse opened, and the number of AIDS cases in Britain reached 1,900. By the end of September 1994 the total number of AIDS cases in Britain was 9,865, of which 837 (8.5 per cent) were women.

In the Netherlands the first case of AIDS was diagnosed in a homosexual man in 1982. By 1988, 487 cases had been reported of which 413 were homosexual men.[9] The Dutch reported great changes in sexual behaviour over the period. For those who were HIV positive the number of men with whom anoreceptive sex was practised fell from a mean of 10.6 to 1.4 in successive cohorts from 1981 to 1987. For those negative for the antibody, the number of people with whom

7 Brindle, 1995a.
8 Garfield, 1994, p. 62.
9 van Griensven et al., 1989, p. 218.

anoreceptive intercourse occurred fell from a mean of 3.7 to 0.5 partners.[9]

In the United States there were 1,361 confirmed cases of AIDS by 8 May 1983 and 520 of these were dead.[10] In 1985 the proportion of AIDS cases in the USA attributed to male to male contact was 66.5 per cent. By 1993 this had fallen to 46.6 per cent.[11] A 1994 report in the *New York Times* stated that as the AIDS epidemic spread across the United States a number of grandmothers were being thrust into a new role. They were caring for adult children dying of AIDS and for the grandchildren left behind. In some cases the children were also dying. One grandmother was quoted: 'I said Angie don't get sick and die and leave these kids for me to take care of [but] I realised that she was going to die before me.'[11] In 1992 a total of 865,000 children under the age of 18 were being cared for by grandparents and in 1993 the number jumped to over a million. Studies in the USA suggest that 30 per cent of the children of HIV positive mothers are themselves HIV positive.[12]

HOMOSEXUALITY AND AIDS

The issue of AIDS has raised the level of controversy about homosexuality. There was a time in the later 1960s and the 1970s when homosexuality was promoted by some as an alternative lifestyle.[13] Altman commented, 'One of the basic demands of the gay movement has been to "get government off our fronts".'[14] This seemed to be happening, but, 'AIDS came along just when the old religious, moral and cultural arguments against homosexuality seemed to be collapsing'.[15] Some of the right-wing moralists thought the disease a godsend. An editorial in the *Southern Medical Journal* commented, 'Might we be witnessing, in fact, in the form of a modern communicable disorder, a fulfilment of St Paul's pronouncement: "the due penalty of their error"?'[16] Similarly at Stanford University across a poster for a gay organisation was scrawled the message: 'AIDS – America's Ideal Death Sentence'.[17] When the Australian state of New

9 van Griensven *et al.*, 1989, p. 218.
10 Garfield, 1994, p. 8.
11 Lee, 1994, p. B6.
12 Lee, 1994, p. 1.
13 Plummer, 1975.
14 Altman, D., 1986, p. 166.
15 Altman, D., 1986, p. 14.
16 Fletcher, 1984.
17 Altman, D., 1986, p. 59.

South Wales decriminalised homosexuality in 1984, a member of the Liberal party on the front bench attacked homosexuals as being responsible for AIDS and commented, 'I hope they do not find a cure for it.'[18]

The appearance of HIV and AIDS came at a time when there were increased opportunities for casual sex amongst the gay community in the Western world. Altman comments:[19]

> We don't know in real quantitative terms, what really changed in homosexual behaviour in the 1970s, but it is possible to identify three major areas of change: the expansion of homosexual bathhouses and sex clubs which facilitate numerous sexual contacts in one night, the emergence of sexually transmitted parasites as a major homosexual health problem especially in New York and California and a boom in recreational drugs.

There were moves to close the bathhouses. One of them placed an advertisement in the gay press. If what it said were anywhere near the truth, it would be worthy of note:[20]

> If AIDS is indeed sexually transmitted, why have there been so FEW cases? Yes I say few because if an estimated 20,000,000 gays have an estimated 200 'contacts' per year this means that in 4 and a half years we have seen 1279 cases in 4,000 million contacts or odds of 3,127,443 to 1 against getting AIDS during a given contact. With all this gay-play going on why aren't we all getting AIDS instead of only 1279 of us?

It seems that few took notice of such comments. Gay sexual behaviour changed rapidly in California. In 1983 there were reports of a sharp decline in the numbers of partners and rapidly declining venereal disease amongst homosexuals. Dr Mervyn Silverman, head of San Francisco's Health Department, stated that he was seeing a more dramatic change in sexual behaviour than he had seen in his career in public health.[21] A report in 1984 stated that two-thirds of gay men in San Francisco had changed their sexual behaviour to reduce the risk of AIDS. However, in other parts of the US the business interests of those

18 McKie, 1984
19 Altman, D., 1986, p. 14.
20 Altman, D., 1986, p. 121.
21 Altman, D., 1986, p. 155.

making profits from casual sex were such that they opposed any controls. A handbook distributed at a number of bathhouses in 1984 included an article entitled 'How to Enjoy a Night at the Baths'. The only health advice was 'thoroughly clean yourself after contact, and you have little to fear, despite what you've heard'.

Altman suggests that behaviour was slow to change; indeed:[21]

> some men may have even increased high risk sex as a means of denying the reality of the epidemic. The scene in New York's St Marks Baths reminded me of stories of people during the Black Death turning to sex as a way of warding off the disease.

However, in due course new expressions of sexuality began to be practised. There was the expansion of 'jerk off' clubs in large American cities. The participants practised masturbation as safe sex.[22] Altman further reports that many Europeans believed that AIDS was a US import:[23]

> AIDS seemed to have spread from the new gay meccas of New York and San Francisco. Epidemiologists speculated about the role of air stewards as carriers of the disease, and there was considerable discussion of the travel patterns of gay men.

He notes that the fact that the disease seemed to be most prevalent amongst gay men led to some conspiracy theories from left-wing groups. A leaflet distributed by the Communist cadre in 1983 proclaimed 'AIDS is political germ warfare by the US Government'.[24]

Changes in homosexual behaviour

Altman gives evidence of some casual attitudes in the 1980s in the United States. This is probably the reason why in 1993 the percentage of young men aged 20–9 who were HIV positive in San Francisco approached the HIV-positive rate of young men of the same age in 1984. This led Ron Stall of the University of California to comment that some people assume that raising the level of knowledge of AIDS will in itself lead to changes in behaviour. His view was that the evidence for this is not supported by behavioural risks to health,

21 Altman, D., 1986, p. 155.
22 Altman, D., 1986, p. 157.
23 Altman, D., 1986, p. 15.
24 Altman, D., 1986, p. 43.

especially where sexual relations are concerned. He suggested that interventions must address the context within which high risk behaviour occurs. One of the crucial problems to which he drew attention was the difficulty of maintaining safe sex over a long period. He argued that the evidence showed that by the mid-1980s homosexual men had made 'the most profound response to a health education campaign ever detected'. This meant, however, that attention went elsewhere. Although in the 1990s the male gay community accounted for 85 per cent of the deaths from AIDS in California, that state received only 8 per cent of state funding for prevention.[25]

In Britain a research project set out to study whether the spread of HIV infection could be reduced by changes in sexual practices, and looked at the effectiveness of government-inspired information in changing behaviour. The study occurred between 1984 and 1987 amongst a sample of 1,050 HIV-positive homosexual men who were presenting for the first time for HIV testing. They were not known to have been individually counselled about safe sex beforehand.[26]

The results showed that over the period the percentage of the men testing positive for the HIV antibody reporting casual sex fell from 88 per cent to 50 per cent. The percentage of homosexuals reporting 'more than twenty partners in the past year' fell from 23 per cent in the 1984–5 group to 8 per cent in the group presenting in 1987. The percentage reporting more than fifty partners over their lifetime fell from 76 per cent in 1984–5 to 50 per cent in 1987.[27] There was also a fall in the proportion engaging in high risk sexual activity such as anoreceptive intercourse with a casual partner. However this reduction was only from 90 per cent in the earlier group to 70 per cent in the final group.[28] The changes in sexual behaviour, despite being somewhat limited, had been a probable cause of the reduction in HIV infection from 35 per cent of those presenting in 1984–5 to 21 per cent in 1987. Over the same period the percentage reporting syphilis fell from over a third (37 per cent) to less than a quarter (24 per cent).

The study also showed that the proportion of patients who had had heterosexual intercourse in the past year was 10 per cent, while if the past three years were considered the figure rose to 20 per cent. Actively bisexual men showed a much smaller risk of HIV infection: only 5 per

25 Altman, D., 1986, p. 686.
26 Evans et al., 1989, p. 215.
27 Evans et al., 1989, p. 216.
28 Evans et al., 1989, p. 215.

cent of 57 bisexual men were infected compared to 30 per cent of 375 exclusively homosexual men.

The authors found that the statistically significant but moderate changes in behaviour had largely occurred before the government's education programme occurred. They noted a reduced trend in safe sex practices in later years which, they said, 'may be attributable to the Government's reluctance to target the homosexual community in its subsequent publicity'. They concluded by calling for more effort to reduce risky behaviour to a minimum. So observers on both sides of the Atlantic are identifying the failure to maintain adequate support to help the male gay community to maintain safe sex practices.

From the comments of those closely involved in the field, the following proposals can be identified:[29]

- Stronger efforts should be made to help people maintain safe sex practices.
- Interventions to promote safe sex must address the context within which high risk sex occurs.
- Young gay men have a different developmental and social history from older ones in that they came of age at a time when AIDS was visible. Their needs and perspectives are likely to be different. They need to be closely involved in the development of safe sex projects and to have useful proposals to help them survive the epidemic.
- It is important to remember that the gay community is very heterogeneous. They are not all well-educated white, middle-class people and it is important to have programmes of action which cater for the less educated, the very young and the different ethnic groups.
- Vigilance, risk reduction and support need to be maintained.
- The evidence of AIDS shows global vulnerability to a new pandemic. There is a need for aggressive and appropriate responses in an age where the enormous mobility of people, the high number of sexual partners and an international epidemic of drug misuse can lead to the rapid spread of sexually transmitted diseases. New global responses are needed for AIDS and for other possible or actual threats.
- Books such as Peter Tatchell's explicit *Safer Sexy*[30] give hard-hitting advice and photographs. Quotes include: 'Love won't protect you from HIV – rubbers will.' Advice on alternatives to sex – such as 'Toys are sexy, and they don't throw tantrums and leave you for another guy' – provide helpful options to traditional penetrative sex.

29 Stall, 1994; Mann and Wilson, 1993.
30 Tatchell, 1994.

We might wish to argue the case for preventing the spread of AIDS on humanitarian grounds. However Ron Stall of the Center for AIDS Prevention in California stresses initially the financial factors:[31]

> Western societies can either support efforts to promote long term sexual safety within gay communities now or pay for the medical care of dying men later. Worse, the costs of the AIDS epidemic among gay men will be more than financial. The continuing diminution of the contributions of men at the height of their productive lives will be an incalculable and irreplaceable loss.

Drug use and AIDS

In New York 120 people die of AIDS each week. Most of these are intravenous drug users or their partners.[32] A longitudinal study in Edinburgh found that of 330 men who were injecting drug users, 172 (54 per cent) were HIV positive. In all but eight cases it was judged that the cause of the spread of the virus was the sharing of needles. All these infections occurred between 1982 and 1986 and during the early 1980s there was a great amount of publicity about HIV transmission through shared needles. The campaign showed success in that from 1987 to 1993 there were no cases of transmission from shared needles and all eight new cases during this period were judged to be by heterosexual intercourse.[33]

The British data included Scotland within the overall figure for the United Kingdom. However, we do have other information as since 1985 the Communicable Diseases (Scotland) Unit has maintained a register, based on laboratory reporting, of all people known to be infected with HIV in Scotland. Although it is voluntary and so will not be complete, it is the basis of official action on the epidemic. The data do, however, show that both the virus and full-blown AIDS are transmitted in a very different way in Scotland than in the United Kingdom as a whole. The results from selected years can be tabulated as shown in Table 8.2.

....
31 Stall, 1994, p. 686.
32 Lee, 1984, p. B6.
33 Ronald et al., 1993, p. 1184.

Table 8.2   *Causes of HIV in Scotland*

Year	Homosexual or bisexual	Heterosexual	Injecting drug use	Total
1985	26%	1%	59%	275
1990	40%	30%	20%	134
1991	35%	26%	32%	162
1992	36%	38%	19%	137
1993	37%	25%	32%	153

Source Davies, 1994, p. 538.

Note The percentages do not reach 100 because of other sources such as blood transfusions.

The results show that in 1985 the major cause of transmission of the virus was injecting drug use, which accounted for three fifths of all cases. With better education and needle exchange programmes this has fallen to just over three cases out of ten. Transmission through heterosexual intercourse rose from 1 per cent of cases in 1985 to 38 per cent in 1992, when it was the major source of transmission. However, in 1993 it fell back to a quarter of all cases. Since 1990 the percentage caused by homosexual/bisexual transmission has been in the 35 to 40 per cent range.

There is a link between drug use and prostitution, which may be a factor in the spread of the HIV virus amongst the heterosexual population. A study at the Glasgow Drop In Centre, a health care and social work facility for female street prostitutes, asked fifty-two consecutive women visitors to complete a questionnaire. Fifty-one did so. Of these, forty-four (86 per cent) were injecting drug users.[34]

Heterosexuality and AIDS
In Britain by June 1993 there were 780 people (451 men and 329 women) who had contracted AIDS from sexual intercourse between men and women. Commenting on the figures, *Social Trends* said that most people infected by heterosexual intercourse were probably infected abroad.[35] Data for 1994 indicate that heterosexual sex was the cause of 28 per cent of the 2,411 new cases of AIDS, which is a significant increase from the figure of 17 per cent overall since counting began in 1984.[36]

....
34 Carr *et al.*, 1994.
35 OPCS, 1994d, p. 97.
36 Brindle, 1995a.

In the United States in 1993 there were 9,288 AIDS cases attributed to heterosexual transmission. This was a 130 per cent increase from 1982. In some part this increase was due to a change in definition. However, the *New York Times* reported that experts estimate that as many as 125,000 children will lose their mothers to AIDS by the year 2000.[37]

One of the problems in identifying the extent of heterosexual transmission of AIDS is finding out about sexual behaviour. This is an issue of great concern. It is important to identify the number of sexual partners people have had in order to estimate the transmitability of the HIV virus in society. Researchers have consistently found that men report more partners than women, despite the fact that the number of heterosexual partners must be equal overall. If these figures are taken at their face value, we could misunderstand the situation. For example, if the data underestimate the number of sexual partners for women, that could lead to an overestimate of the likelihood that women would be infected by the HIV virus with each new partner. D. I. Smith[38] pointed out that the number of partners within gender groups has clear implications for HIV prevention programmes. Furthermore, commenting on the US sex surveys, Lewontin stated:[39]

> Because AIDS is spread largely through certain sexual practices, an accurate estimate of the frequency of such practices, the way they are distributed through the population, and what the network of sexual partners looks like, are all important variables in any model of the spread of the disease. If we are really interested in a useful epidemiological model of AIDS, not to speak of one that does not make the situation worse, we had better get the answers right.

However, we shall see that the information from the sex surveys has been misleading and this is a problem that needs to be addressed.

In order to assess the variety of findings, we shall begin with Kinsey's classic studies and move on to the most recent ones. Kinsey's analysis of male sexual behaviour was published in 1948 and that of women in 1953.

....
37 Garfield, 1994, p. 8.
38 Smith, D. I., 1992.
39 Lewontin, 1995, p. 25.

The Kinsey reports

Margaret Mead[40] argued that the double standard of sexual behaviour was much stronger in the United States than in Britain and our own research points in the same direction. We would therefore expect Kinsey[41] to find that men claimed a great deal more sexual activity than women. Indeed this was the case. Kinsey found that even excluding intercourse with prostitutes, in the age group 16–20 males said they had seven times as much premarital intercourse as females. Men aged 21–5 claimed to have had four times as much intercourse as the equivalent group of females. However, the most remarkable figures came from the males in the under-16 group. They claimed to have intercourse four times as often as women aged 16–20 and even twice as often as women aged 21–5. Kinsey realised that his information for men and women was inconsistent. He and his colleagues commented as follows:[42]

> Comparison of the frequency data for premarital coitus reported by the females and males in the sample show discrepancies of considerable magnitude. Quite consistently in every educational level and for every age group the males reported incidence and frequencies which were higher and in some cases considerably higher than those reported for females.

Kinsey concluded that women covered up part of their sexual activity and that there was over-statement by the young males. Although Kinsey was sceptical of his own figures, other researchers have largely accepted them as accurate. An excellent study by Hollingshead based on participant observation amongst Elmstown's youth was first published in 1949 and reprinted in 1961. He found that more young girls were having sex than boys, yet he concluded that his sample must have been unrepresentative:[43]

> Although the few figures given here involve about four times as many girls as boys, we do not want to give the impression that high school girls are more likely to have sex relations than boys, the contrary is the case as Kinsey has indicated.

....
40 Mead, 1944.
41 Kinsey et al., 1953.
42 Kinsey et al., 1953, p. 80.
43 Hollingshead, 1961, p. 239.

However, his sample may not have been unrepresentative, although we know there was a tradition in the US of young men using prostitutes to gain experience at an early age. As boys usually date girls younger than themselves, it is logical that as a rule women begin sex as part of a relationship at an earlier age. Despite the fact that the findings were to some extent inaccurate, Kinsey's report had a tremendous social effect. For example, he shocked Americans with his finding that half the women who married after the First World War were not virgins on their wedding day.

The Wellcome sex survey
The early results of this British survey were published in the journal *Nature* in December 1992.[44] It found that British men reported 9.9 sexual partners while British women only reported 3.4. This is a finding which could only be accurate if British men were having a great number of foreign sexual partners. This was pointed out in letters to the *British Medical Journal* and to the quality newspapers.[45] The finding came as no surprise; in 1986 one of us explained the sociological reasons why men were likely to report more partners than women.[46] One factor was that young men can obtain higher status within their peer group by claiming sexual prowess, so at younger ages they are inclined to over-state their experience. The classic British study of coalminers provided another reason:[47]

> Any display of tenderness or affection seems to be regarded as 'soft'. If one of the group of young males at this early stage does begin to take a girl seriously he finds himself the butt of constant 'kidding'. Only a convincing and jealousy-provoking claim that he is intimate with his girlfriend will save him from ridicule.

Peer group pressure was found also in our research. As we previously reported, a 19-year-old man said: 'After we'd taken girls home on a Saturday night, we'd get together and ask each other, "Did you have it last night?" and we'd all claim to, whereas really none of us had.'[48] In our research we found that it was casual sex that was likely to be least accurately reported.[49]

----

44 Johnson *et al.*, 1992.
45 Francome, 1993; Smith, D. I., 1992.
46 Francome, 1986, p. 10.
47 Dennis *et al.*, 1956, p. 222.
48 Francome, 1976, p. 155.
49 Francome, 1986, p. 9.

Sex in America

This is the title of a book based on a random sample of 3,432 adults over the age of 18. The project began in 1987 as a response to the spread of HIV.[50] The researchers were concerned about the accuracy of their data and for this reason asked about the number of partners twice during the interview. The first time was as a simple question early in the interview. To reduce potential embarrassment the respondents were asked to write down the figure privately and place it in a sealed envelope. The second time was about an hour later, when reviewing the person's lifetime sexual history. The researchers commented, 'We found that the numbers came out essentially the same both ways, increasing our confidence that people were telling the truth.'[51]

However, just as in other surveys, there was a tendency for men to claim many more partners than women. The results were as shown in Table 8.3.

Table 8.3   *Number of sexual partners since the age of 18*

Gender	0	1	2–4	5–9	10–20	21+
Men	3%	20%	21%	23%	16%	17%
Women	3%	31%	36%	20%	6%	3%

The results in the table show that 33 per cent of the men in the sample said they had more than ten partners, compared to only 9 per cent of the women. The book does not give an overall average figure but from the table we can make a reasonable estimate. If we make a rather conservative assumption of an average of thirty heterosexual partners for those who said they had had intercourse with more than twenty-one people, we can predict the average figure for each sex. For men it is 9.9 and for women 4.6. The men's figure is therefore identical to the British figure, although the respondents were counting from the age of 18 in the US as against from birth in Britain. The women's figure is for a higher number of partners than for Britain but it is still below half that of the men.

50 Robert *et al.*, 1994.
51 Robert *et al.*, 1994, p. 34.

French sex survey

The interviews for this study took place between September 1991 and February 1992 and a total of 20,055 responses was available for analysis.[52] The survey found that the average number of sexual partners for women was 3.3. This is slightly less than the British figure, but for men it was 11.0, which is 1.1 per cent higher than in Britain. The authors commented that this difference between the sexes is reported in all surveys of this type and is presumed to stem from both female under-statement and male over-statement. They reported that the discrepancy was less than it had been twenty years previously, when the ratio between men and women for the total number of partners was reported to be about six to one.[53] This finding led to the conclusion that the double standard had lessened.

Swedish sex survey

This study was based on four annual surveys of about four thousand people aged 16–44 between the years 1986 and 1989.[54] Two factors would lead us to expect that Swedish figures might be different from those for other countries. First, in 1987 a nationwide information campaign was started which had as one of its main objectives the reduction of the number of sexual partners. Secondly, the greater openness of Swedish society towards sexuality might lead to fewer gender discrepancies. In fact this seems to be the case. Although the average number of lifetime partners was not published, the comparison of the ratio of the number of partners does not reveal as much difference as for other countries. Three or more partners in the past year were only claimed by 10 per cent of the men, compared to 5 per cent of the women. However, a striking finding from Sweden was that women reported a greater amount of sexuality at the younger ages. At the ages of 16–17 only 18 per cent of men had a regular sexual partner compared to 38 per cent of the women. At the ages of 18–19 26 per cent of the men had a regular sexual partner compared to 53 per cent of the women. As mentioned earlier, men date younger women on average, and it is therefore normally the case that women begin regular sexual relations at an earlier age than men. The findings from the Swedish survey are unusual in that other sex surveys have suggested that women begin sexual activity at an older age than men.

52 ACSF Investigators, 1992.
53 ACSF Investigators, 1992, p. 408.
54 Herlitz, 1993.

Recommendations for future sex surveys

In summary, in these five studies from four different countries there are clear gender differences in the number of partners reported. A key question for the future is how questions should be asked and how the results should be analysed and presented. In previous studies researchers have presented their results even when they realised they were inaccurate and, as we have seen, have acknowledged as much in the text. This is not very helpful, especially as we need accurate data in order to combat the threat of AIDS. There is a case for taking an alternative approach – not simply acknowledging where the results are wrong but reweighing the data. Some guidelines may help future researchers.

1 We should use the raw data to see what they tell us about the double standard of sexual behaviour. This will vary between countries and between ethnic groups within countries. The double standard provides us with very useful background data; we saw that the French used the change in the number of partners reported to comment on the reduction in the double standard. Of course, consistency in the way the questions are asked is very important here. The techniques used in the United States survey conducted by Robert et al.[55] might be more generally adopted.

2 In some areas of behaviour people will feel able and willing to give accurate information and the information can be used direct. However, we know that some people will cover up behaviour that they feel is socially unacceptable. We can use the whole range of information to hand in order to present a best estimate of the true situation. For example, we know that the number of heterosexual partners worldwide is bound to be equal between men and women, and we should use this to reweigh data. Only figures which have some kind of internal logic should be presented to policy makers and to the media.

3 We should use participant observation and small-scale surveys to try to obtain a picture which is as near as possible to the actual situation. If there had been more studies in the United States like the Hollingshead one for Elmstown's youth, then people might have begun to realise much sooner that it is generally the case that women begin their sexual behaviour at an earlier age than men.

Since the Wellcome study was published, we have engaged in a number of in-depth interviews and discussions with close friends

55 Robert et al., 1994.

and colleagues to try to ascertain whether women covered up part of their behaviour or whether the discrepancy was due rather to men over-stating their number of partners. One surprising finding is evidence that older men sometimes tend to rewrite their early history. Another factor is that many people forget previous relationships. We have evidence that when people researched into their number of partners by consulting documents from their past such as diaries and photographs, they found evidence of a number of sexual relationships which they had overlooked and would not have reported in an interview. They needed to increase their estimates of the number of partners substantially.

From discussions and from the Wellcome data we estimate that the average number of lifetime partners amongst heterosexuals is around eleven for each sex. This figure, even if it is not quite correct, has the merit of being consistent with all the evidence available to us. It could serve as the basis for rational discussion and be revised in the light of any new evidence. Such a best estimate provides information which could be useful to policy makers. Our data would have the merit of giving a basis of information about areas where there is a lack of knowledge.

4   We should ask questions in such a way as to be able to get nearer to the truth. The use of private envelopes to be opened only by those coding the data is one innovation. Another point that could be very useful in future studies would be to ask not simply about the number of sexual partners but also to distinguish between casual and serious relationships. In countries with a strong double standard we would expect to find men claiming many more casual partners than women. The discrepancy between the sexes in terms of the number of partners is likely to be less in relation to people who are married or in long-term relationships. We should also follow Kinsey in distinguishing intercourse with prostitutes as separate data.

5   Variations between social classes and ethnic groups are likely to be instructive. One of us (Francome) has been working with students of different ethnic groups whose parents were born abroad. The studies include Africans, Hindus, Sikhs, Muslims and Greek Cypriots. What is becoming clear is that the norms in some of these sub-cultures reveal great differences between men and women. To varying degrees it is acceptable for men but not women to have casual sex. Preliminary results indicate that Greek Orthodox students are more likely to believe in a double standard in which

premarital intercourse is acceptable for males but women should be virgins, or relatively sexually inexperienced, upon marriage. It has been found that some female Indian students have been very concerned in case any sexual activity would harm their marriage chances. Detailed knowledge of sub-cultures can provide insight into patterns of sexual relationships.

6   We should accept that the fear of disclosure may depend on region. This fact can be useful in estimating the extent of disclosure. The Wellcome study found that men in London were more than twice as likely to report homosexual experience as those living in the country. The researchers attributed this in part to a greater willingness to disclose such behaviour in the more tolerant atmosphere of the capital.[56] This kind of information could be used to reweigh raw data to give a more accurate prediction of the extent of homosexuality and other behaviour.

In sum, it is necessary to weld together a variety of information to provide the best estimate of the current position. By looking behind the face value of what people are willing to disclose, with all the other background information that is available, it is possible to build up a more accurate picture of sexual behaviour in different societies, social classes and ethnic groups. This information could be most useful in combating AIDS and sexually transmitted diseases.

TEENAGE PREGNANCY

We have seen that the government's target is to reduce the rate of teenage conception from a national average of 9.5 per thousand girls aged 13–15 to no more than 4.8 by the year 2000. The Chief Medical Officer's annual report for 1990 estimates that almost half of all conceptions were unwanted or unintended.[57]

The historical information for England and Wales shows that the age of the mother at the birth has been recorded only since 1938.[58] At that time known teenage pregnancies were relatively rare and the number of abortions is also not known, although one estimate suggested that there were about 100,000 a year.[59] In the 1940s and 1950s the number of teenage births was still relatively low and those that did occur were

---

56 Field et al., 1994, p. 9.
57 Department of Health, 1992, p. 94.
58 Bury, 1984, p. 7.
59 Glass, 1940.

predominantly within marriage, although in many cases conception was before the wedding day.[60] In 1951 there were twenty-one births per thousand teenagers aged 15–19. This figure rose to twenty-seven in 1956, thirty-seven in 1961 and a peak of fifty-one in 1971.[61] From then on improvements in birth control and to a lesser extent the legalisation of abortion led to a reduction in the rates so that by 1977 they fell to thirty, at which level they stayed for several years until falling to twenty-eight in 1982.[62]

One of the problems with statistics in the early years is that analysts, in comparing abortions to births, did not allow for the fact that the latter occur about six months later than the former. In recent years data have included the date of conception as well as the outcome, allowing it to be taken into account that many who become pregnant under the age of 16 will be over 16 by the time they have their babies.

The changes in conception rates for all teenagers and for those aged under 16 can be tabulated as shown in Table 8.4.

Table 8.4   *Teenage pregnancy rates by year for England and Wales*

Year	All teenagers Conception rate per 1,000 aged 15–19 yrs			Under-16s Conception rate per 1,000 aged 13–15 yrs		
	Total	Maternities	Abortion	Total	Maternities	Abortion
1980	58.7	40.5	18.2	7.2	3.3	3.9
1985	61.7	40.8	20.9	8.6	3.8	4.8
1989	67.6	43.5	24.0	9.4	4.5	4.9
1990	69.0	44.4	24.6	10.1	5.0	5.1
1991	65.1	42.7	22.4	9.3	4.6	4.8

Source OPCS, 1993, 1994a.

Table 8.4 shows that the overall conception rate for teenagers rose by nearly a fifth during the years 1980–90 but then fell slightly in 1991. For the under-16s the increase was 40 per cent over the same period until again there was a fall in 1991. The figures also show that in 1991 52 per cent of conceptions among the under-16s ended in abortion. Amongst all teenagers 34 per cent of conceptions ended in abortion.

60 Carstairs, 1962.
61 Francome, 1983a, p. 4.
62 Francome, 1983b.

This may reflect the fact that more of the older teenagers will be married or in a stable relationship. It should be noted also that evidence from Asian ethnic groups suggests that some members of those groups will have arranged marriages and begin childbearing in their teens.[63]

A book published in 1993 presented international data on teenage births.[64] The data related to the years 1984–5 and discussions with the Alan Guttmacher Institute (who produced the book) indicate that it wishes to collect new information. The data do, however, show that of the countries studied the teenage birthrate per 1,000 was as follows: Japan 4.1, Netherlands 6.8, West Germany 8.6, Canada 23.2, Australia 26.5, England and Wales 31 and the USA 52.0. Very wide variations are evident.

It has been noted by previous researchers that there is a link between social inequality and levels of teenage conception. In Glasgow it has been reported that teenage births made up 2 to 4 per cent of all births in areas characterised by high proportions of professional and managerial residents and 20 to 25 per cent in areas of high unemployment and social deprivation.[65] A study in the North Thames Regional Health Authority found that there was a wide discrepancy in pregnancy rates according to social status. In 1990 Tower Hamlets, an area of high social deprivation, had a conception rate amongst 16–19-year-olds of ninety-five per thousand. This contrasted to thirty-seven per thousand in Hampstead. The study also found that teenagers in deprived areas were much less likely to obtain an abortion; a pregnant teenager in Tower Hamlets was four times as likely to continue the pregnancy as a pregnant teenager in Hampstead. This study concluded by saying that a cycle of deprivation is being perpetuated and that teenage mothers and their offspring are becoming a substantial part of an urban underclass.[66]

In the light of this information, it is instructive to consider the statistics of young teenage pregnancy. The regional and district data published in 1994 were for the three-year period 1989–91.[67] These show that the national rate was 9.6. Details are shown in Table 8.5.

63 Francome, 1994d.
64 Lawson and Rhode, 1993, p. 60.
65 Rosenberg and McEwen, 1991, p. 173.
66 Garlick et al., 1993.
67 OPCS, 1994b, pp. 15–18.

Table 8.5   *Conceptions and outcomes by region – data for combined years 1989–91*

Area	Number	Rate/1000, age 13–15	Maternity rate	Abortion rate
England and Wales	28,844	9.6	4.7	4.9
Northern	1,967	12.3	6.7	5.6
Yorkshire	2,137	11.2	5.9	5.3
Trent	2,654	11.0	5.5	5.5
East Anglia	866	8.1	3.2	4.9
North West Thames	1,128	6.6	2.7	3.9
North East Thames	1,592	8.6	3.6	4.8
South East Thames	1,647	9.2	4.2	5.0
South West Thames	891	6.2	2.5	3.7
Wessex	1,288	8.8	3.6	5.2
Oxford	1,036	7.5	3.2	4.3
South Western	1,348	8.2	3.6	4.6
West Midlands	3,064	11.1	5.3	5.8
Mersey	1,236	9.7	5.2	4.5
North Western	2,538	12.1	7.0	5.1
Wales	1,444	9.7	5.4	4.2

Source OPCS, 1994b.

Table 8.5 shows that the Northern Region had the highest young teenage pregnancy rate at 12.3, almost double that of South West Thames which had a rate of 6.6 per thousand women aged 13–15. In 1990 North West Thames had been the region with the lowest under-16 pregnancy rate but its rate rose slightly in 1991. One of the reasons for low rates in some areas may be a high proportion of Asian teenagers. A study published by the Health Education Authority shows that the percentage of teenagers admitting to intercourse according to ethnic group was white 53 per cent, Afro-Caribbean 51 per cent and Asian 24 per cent.[68]

Out of 178 health districts in England, only five met the government's target. These were Tunbridge Wells with 3.6 per thousand women aged 13-15, Northallerton with 4.2, South West Surrey with 4.3, Harrow with 4.3 and Wycombe with 4.4. All these are areas with little poverty. At the other end of the scale two districts had

68 HEA, 1990.

rates four times the *Health of the Nation* targets. These were North Manchester with a rate of 19.9 and Hull with 19.2. Other districts had rates exceeding 15, which is more than three times the target. These were Grimsby 16.9, West Lambeth 16.7, South Manchester 16.5, Hartlepool 16.0, Doncaster 15.7, Central Manchester 15.4, Camberwell 15.4, Salford 15.3 and Sandwell 15.3. In Wales none of the nine districts met the targets. The lowest rate was in Powys (6.1), that had a rate which was less than half that of Mid Glamorgan (13.1).[69] We do not have comparable data for Scotland. Overall many districts with excessively high rates must be considering what action to take to meet the targets.

OUR SURVEY OF YOUNG TEENAGE MOTHERS

In August 1993 one of us (Francome) was requested by the Family Planning Association to carry out some research into teenage pregnancy for a report and presentation on the television programme *World in Action*. The programme duly appeared on 4 October 1993 under the title 'Children who have Children' and a preliminary report was published by the association at the same time. We present here a more detailed survey based on a larger sample and with the questions analysed in greater detail.[70]

The sample was made up of young women aged 17 and under who had recently had babies or who were pregnant and continuing the pregnancy. The questionnaires were administered by the heads of special units providing education for pregnant schoolgirls. In all we asked 130 young women to fill in the questionnaire and 129 did so. This gives a response rate of over 99 per cent and is indicative of the women's wish to co-operate with the study. The questionnaires were collected in several towns throughout Britain. Although a high proportion of young mothers could see a benefit in carrying on with their studies, and indeed the younger ones had a legal obligation to do so, the less frequent attenders were inevitably under-represented. The sample must therefore be expected to contain a disproportionate number of young women who were more motivated to co-operate with the education authorities. There is a strong possibility that the sample may be skewed towards the young mothers who were least alienated from the education system.

69 OPCS, 1994b, p.18.
70 Francome and Walsh, 1995.

Characteristics of the sample

This is a study of 129 young women. Seventy-two were aged 15 or under and fifty-seven were aged 16 or 17. Of these seventy-nine had given birth to their baby and forty were still pregnant. In the younger age group nine were aged 14 and sixty-three were aged 15. In the older age group thirty-four were aged 16 and twenty-three 17. The questionnaires were completed between 12 September and 19 September 1993. They were supplemented by further interviews with young women and their partners during the period from February to May 1994.

Table 8.6   *Parents' marital status*

Parents' status	Teenagers age 14–15	Teenagers age 16–17	All	Percentage
Married	34	26	60	46.9%
Divorced	20	20	40	31.3%
Separated	13	7	20	15.6%
One deceased	2	1	3	2.3%
Single mother	2	0	2	1.6%
Living together	1	2	3	2.3%
Total	72	56	128	100.0%

Table 8.6 shows that just under half the sample's parents were married, and a further 2.3 per cent were living together. In all 46.9 per cent of the parents were divorced or separated. This is a higher percentage than we would expect in the general population and so our sample seems to have experienced a higher proportion of social dislocation than average. We also asked the young women if they had spent any time in the care of the local authority, and 15 per cent had done so. This is a relatively small minority but again it is higher than would have been expected on average.

Parental support

We asked the sample: '*Which of the following members of your family are you in contact with at least once a month?*' The results were as shown in Table 8.7.

Table 8.7 *Contact with parents*

Parents' contact	Age 14–15	Age 16–17	All	Percentage
Contact with father	45	45	90	69.8%
Contact with mother	70	56	126	97.7%

Note Three women did not respond to this question.

The results show that virtually all the young women were in contact with their mother. Possibly more surprising is the fact that seven out of ten said they had been in contact with their father. However, the level of contact is not necessarily high.

We also asked the young women: '*What kind of accommodation are you in?*' The results were as shown in Table 8.8.

Table 8.8 *Living conditions of the young mothers*

Living conditions	Age 14–15	Age 16–17	All	Percentage
Parent(s)	60	31	91	72.2%
Living with partner	0	12	12	9.5%
Foster parents	4	3	7	5.6%
Alone/Friends	1	9	10	7.9%
Single mothers' hostel	3	0	3	2.4%
Grandparents/Aunt	2	1	3	2.4%
Total	70	56	126	100.0%

Note Three women did not respond to this question.

The results show that the younger women were more likely to be living with their parents. In all 86 per cent of the younger women were living with at least one parent. We asked a further question about where they planned to live in the future. The exact wording was as follows: '*When you first became pregnant where did you plan to live (e.g. council flat, with parents)?*' In response to this 83 per cent of the younger teenagers and 70 per cent of the older teenagers said they planned to live with their parents. Only three of the sample specified that they planned to live in a council flat.

Parents and birth control

We asked: *'Which of the following people have you discussed birth control with (if any)?'* Table 8.9 shows the response.

Table 8.9   *Discussions of birth control within the family*

Family member	Age 14–15	Age 16–17	All	Percentage
Father	4	10	14	11.2%
Mother	51	41	92	73.6%
Brother(s)	3	2	5	4.0%
Sister(s)	5	12	17	13.6%
Non response	3	1	4	

The results show that overall nearly three-quarters of the sample had discussed birth control with their mother. However, in some cases it was clear that happened only after the girls became pregnant. There was a big divide between fathers and daughters in this respect. Only one girl in nine (11.2 per cent) had discussed birth control with her father. Evidence of participant observation of the youth culture indicates that mothers and daughters may collude to keep the fathers from knowing about their daughters' sexuality. For example, a father interviewed to give a parent's view said: *'I was looking for something in my daughter's room when I came across birth control pills. I was shocked as she was only 18. I then found out that she had been on the pill for two years and my wife had known all about it.'* A more surprising finding is that there was little discussion of birth control with a sibling.

One important issue is the quality of sex education and we asked: *'Which of these topics were you taught about in school and how good was the information?'* The responses are tabulated in Table 8.10.

Table 8.10   *Quality of sex education received by the young mothers*

Subject	No information		Little information		Good information	
Periods	16	13.6%	55	46.6%	47	39.8%
Pregnancy	33	28.0%	60	50.8%	25	21.2%
HIV	48	41.0%	44	35.8%	31	25.2%
Condoms	36	30.8%	48	41.0%	33	28.2%
Other birth control methods	36	30.5%	54	45.8%	28	23.7%
Relationships	46	37.4%	53	43.1%	14	11.4%

The results show that the best information was provided on periods with nearly two in five having good information. However, 13.6 per cent had no information. Just under three in ten (28.2 per cent) reported having good information about condoms. The lowest approval rating from the young women was on the matter of relationships; only one in nine said that she had received good information on these.

The comments are revealing. A pregnant 15-year-old girl said simply: *'Catholic school – no information.'* A 15-year-old with a baby of 3½ months said the information was: *'not very good at all. They should have sex education as a proper lesson starting when you are little.'* Several mentioned the fact that the teacher did not like the subject: *'We receive hardly any information and what we did get the teacher got embarrassed over and so the subject was changed.'*

Experience of first sexual intercourse
We asked about the reasons for starting sex. The question wording was as follows: *'Could you please think back to when you first had intercourse and tell us the reason why?' – Circle as many of the following that apply to you.'* Table 8.11 shows the responses.

Table 8.11 *Reasons for first experience of sexual intercourse*

Motivating factor	Age 14–15		Age 16–17		All	
In love	47	66.2%	27	50.9%	74	59.7%
Curiosity	15	21.1%	20	37.7%	35	28.2%
Pressure from partner	1	1.4%	8	15.1%	9	7.3%
Drunk	9	12.7%	5	9.4%	14	11.3%
Rape	4	5.6%	0	0.0%	4	3.2%
Wanted to get pregnant	1	1.4%	1	1.9%	2	1.6%
All my friends were doing it	10	14.1%	7	13.2%	17	13.7%
Got carried away	21	29.5%	15	28.3%	36	29.0%
To please my partner	11	15.5%	5	9.4%	16	12.9%
To find out about it	12	16.9%	14	26.4%	26	21.0%
Total number	71		53		124	

The teenagers gave an average of 1.9 reasons each. By far the highest one mentioned was 'in love'. This was the reason stated by three in five overall and by more than two-thirds of the younger girls. The second highest mention was 'got carried away', with nearly three in ten mentioning this factor. Almost as many mentioned 'curiosity', which appears to be a crucial supplementary reason.

In the younger group 12.6 per cent said that they were drunk and 5.6 per cent said they were raped. Overall, however, very few said that they were under pressure from their partner.

We were interested in the age at which sexual intercourse began for our sample and so we asked: 'How old were you when you first had intercourse, and how old was your partner?' The responses are shown in Table 8.12.

Table 8.12   *Age of woman and partner at first intercourse*

| Age | Girls aged 14–15 | | Girls aged 16–17 | |
	Age at which first had intercourse	Partner's age	Age at which first had intercourse	Partner's age
11	1 1.4%			
12	6 8.5%		4 7.1%	1 1.8%
13	16 22.5%		13 23.2%	1 1.8%
14	38 53.5%	7 10.4%	21 37.5%	3 5.3%
15	10 14.1%	15 22.4%	14 25.0%	10 17.9%
16		10 14.9%	4 7.1%	9 16.1%
17		13 19.4%		7 12.5%
18		6 9.0%		10 17.9%
19		4 6.0%		7 12.5%
20+		12 17.9%		8 14.3%
Total	71 100%	67 100%	56 100%	56 100%

The results show that the partners of the young girls were much older than they themselves were. If we consider the youngest group, who were aged 15 and under, we see that two-thirds (67.2 per cent) of their partners were over 16 and almost one in five (17.9 per cent) were over 20. If we consider the older group aged 16 and 17 only 7 per cent waited until 16 for their first experience of intercourse, yet 57 per cent of their partners were over the age of 16.

Birth control use at first intercourse

We asked the sample: '*When you first had sex did you or your partner use any form of contraception? If so what?*' The results are tabulated in Table 8.13.

Table 8.13   *Birth control use at first intercourse*

Method	Aged 14–15		Aged 16–17		All	%
Pill	3	4.3%	4	7.3%	7	5.6%
Condom	31	44.9%	24	43.6%	55	44.4%
Withdrawal	4	5.8%	4	7.3%	8	6.5%
None used	31	44.9%	23	41.8%	54	43.5%

The results show that the teenagers used largely 'male' methods of birth control; over a half said that they used either the condom or withdrawal. Over two in five of the sample did not use a method of birth control at all, but about one in ten of these wanted to get pregnant or were ambivalent about it. So a 16-year-old living with her partner and her 4½-month-old baby said, *'I knew if I got pregnant it wouldn't bother me, as I knew he would stay with me.'* Less than 6 per cent used female methods of birth control. Typical comments on non-use were: *'It just happened'*, *'I thought it would be alright.'* Some mentioned non-availability of condoms: *'It just happened and we didn't have anything on us.'*

General Practitioners and contraception
We asked the respondents if they had been to their GP for advice on birth control. In all twenty-seven (22 per cent) said that they had and ninety-seven (78 per cent) said that they had not. Three of those who went to their doctor were refused access on the grounds of their age. In one of these cases the doctor had told the girl she could have the pill when she was 13. However, by that time she was pregnant.

Of those who had not received birth control assistance from their doctor, ninety-one gave reasons. These are tabulated in Table 8.14.

Table 8.14   *Reasons for not obtaining birth control from General Practitioner*

Reasons	Age 14–15	Age 16–17	All	%
Didn't think of it	30	13	43	47%
Too embarrassed	18	16	34	37%
Thought it illegal for under-16s	25	14	39	43%
Thought parents would be told	21	14	35	38%
Thought parent would be present	2	4	6	7%
GP male and did not want to talk to him	14	7	21	23%
Did not know could get from GP	6	1	7	8%
Total	47	34	91	

Note The percentages add up to more than 100 per cent because of multiple responses.

The results show that overall the major reason for not obtaining birth control from their GP was that they 'did not think of it'. This fits in well with the fact that the highest mentioned reason for pregnancy was that they 'had intercourse unexpectedly'. The second highest reason was the mistaken belief that birth control is illegal for the under-16s. In fact over half of those aged 14 and 15 gave this as a reason. The young women also often expressed concern that their parents would be told of their visit; over two in five mentioned this.

Young people and family planning clinics

We asked our sample: *'Before you were pregnant did you ever attend a family planning clinic?'* The responses are shown in Table 8.15.

Table 8.15   *Attendance at a family planning clinic*

Attendance	Age 14		Age 16 and 17		All	
Yes	11	15%	14	26%	25	20%
No	60	85%	39	74%	99	80%
Total	71		53		124	

In all eleven (15 per cent) of the younger girls and fourteen (26 per cent) of the older teenagers had visited a family planning clinic. One of the attenders, a 16-year-old with a 9-month-old baby, was adversely affected by the visit. She commented: *'My clinic shouted across the waiting room that I was pregnant. I would not go there again.'* Those who had not attended a clinic and did not want to get pregnant were asked the reasons for non-attendance. These are shown in Table 8.16.

Table 8.16   *Reasons for non-attendance at birth control clinics*

Motivating factor	Age 14–15		Age 16–17		All	
I did not think of it	43	74%	18	49%	61	63%
I was too embarrassed	12	21%	8	22%	20	21%
Thought illegal for clinics to give advice to under-16s	12	21%	11	30%	23	24%
Thought clinic tell parents	10	17%	8	22%	18	19%
Didn't know where there was an FPA clinic	15	26%	9	24%	24	25%
Base number	58		37		95	

The results show that of the younger teenagers almost three-quarters said that they 'did not think of it'. With the older group this was again the major factor; it was mentioned by half. This ties in with our other findings about the lack of birth control awareness amongst many of those in this sample of young people.

Overall the second highest reason for non-attendance was that the young women did not know where there was a birth control clinic. One in four of the young women said this was a reason for her non-attendance. Some of the young women said that they did not even know that clinics existed. A 15-year-old said: *'I did not know there was a clinic.'* Another said: *'I did not know whether it was open at night.'* A 17-year-old with an 11-month-old baby who was pregnant with her second child commented: *'I didn't know about it till after I was pregnant and a friend told me about it.'*

The third most important reason, which was mentioned by almost a quarter of the sample, was that the young women thought it was illegal for a clinic to give advice to those under the age of 16. This is despite the Gillick decision in the House of Lords that gave permission for such advice. So for many of the young women their lack of knowledge of the current legal position was a bar to using birth control.

Over one in five of the sample said they were too 'embarrassed' to attend a birth control clinic. For some of them there may also have been some fear of not knowing what would happen. As they clearly had little knowledge about the clinics they would not have known whether to expect a physical examination or, if there was to be one, what it would entail. Also they would not know whether to expect a male or female doctor. The assumption is generally made that women prefer a woman doctor for a gynaecological examination. However, this is not the case for all. The final reason for non-attendance was the fear that their parents would be told. This was mentioned by 19 per cent of those not attending. Although this is under one in five of the total sample, it reveals another gap in information for some of the teenagers.

Partners in pregnancy
A second question on the age of partners asked about the partner's age at the time of the pregnancy. Of 129 girls in the sample 126 responded to this question. One of the three non-respondents said she did not know the age of the father.

Table 8.17   *Age of teenagers and their partners at pregnancy*

Girl's age	14	15	16	17	18	19	20	21	22	23	24	25	27
13		5	2	2	1	1	1			1	1		
14	5	5	5	12	6	5		4	1		2	2	
15	2	5	7	11	6	9	4	2	2	3	1	1	2
16		1		1	2		1			2			
17								1	1	1			
All	7	16	14	26	15	15	6	7	4	6	4	3	2

Note In addition one young woman became pregnant at the age of 12. Her partner was aged 15.

The results show that in 113 (90 per cent) cases the male was older than the female. In ten cases they were the same age (in completed years) and in three cases only the boy was younger. The average age of pregnancy for the girl was 14.5 years while the average age of her partner was 18.2 years.

The results show that for the 117 girls who became pregnant before the age of 16, over four out of five (81 per cent) of their partners were over the age of 16. Indeed over a quarter (26 per cent) were over the age of 20 and two were aged 27. Given the fact that condoms were most often mentioned as the method of birth control, this finding suggests that great inroads could be made into young teenage pregnancy if young men aged 15–30 could be convinced of the necessity of taking precautions, the most efficient method being the wearing of condoms. A much greater use of condoms among young couples has the potential to provide significant reductions in unwanted pregnancies. It would also reduce sexually transmitted diseases and would help to limit the transmission of HIV.

Beliefs, reasons and intentions relating to the pregnancy

We asked the young women: *'Did you plan to get pregnant?'* In reply eight of the younger women said they did and sixty-four said that they did not. In the older group five said they intended to get pregnant and forty-nine said that they did not. The other three did not respond. So overall only 10.3 per cent planned to get pregnant.

Those not wishing to be pregnant were asked: *'Did you use any method of birth control?'* In reply eighteen of the younger girls and seventeen of the older ones said that they had. The rest were asked the reason for non-use and the replies were as follows:

Table 8.18   *Reasons for not using birth control*

	Age 14–15	Age 16–17	All	
Did not know enough about contraceptives	6	10	16	19.8%
Did not know where to get contraceptives	2	5	7	8.6%
Couldn't get contraceptives quickly enough	8	5	13	16.0%
Had intercourse unexpectedly	31	22	53	65.4%
Didn't like to talk about it with partner	8	4	12	14.8%
Partner refused to use condom	6	3	9	11.1%
Forgot	9	10	19	23.4%
Stopped taking the pill	5	2	7	8.6%
Tried to get the pill from doctor but was discouraged or refused	4	3	7	8.6%
Intended to use but had not made appointment	4	4	8	9.9%
Stopped using because of side effects	3	4	7	8.6%
Hoped pregnancy would lead to marriage		2	2	2.5%
Did not intend to have intercourse any more	2	5	7	8.6%
Thought boyfriend would leave if refused sex	3	1	4	4.9%
Total*	46	35	81	

* This is calculated by leaving out those wishing to get pregnant and those using birth control. The percentage adds up to over a hundred because of multiple replies.

The results show that by far the most frequent reason for non-use of birth control methods was that they 'had intercourse unexpectedly'. This reason was mentioned by nearly two-thirds (65 per cent) of those at risk. In fact, it has consistently been the most frequently stated in previous surveys in the United States, Britain and Ireland.[71] The second most frequent reason for non-use was that they 'forgot' and the third most often mentioned was that they 'did not know enough about contraceptives'.

Reasons for continuing the pregnancy

Once they had become pregnant, the young women faced the choice of having a baby or seeking an abortion. To find out why our sample decided to continue their pregnancies, we asked: *'What were the reasons you continued with the pregnancy?'* The results are tabulated in Table 8.19.

Table 8.19   *Why they decided to continue the pregnancy*

	Age 14–15	Age 16–17	All	
Did not believe in abortion	14	21	35	30.2%
Did not want an abortion	21	9	30	25.9%
Decided to keep the baby after finding out about the pregnancy	16	9	25	21.6%
Too late when pregnancy discovered	5	5	10	8.6%
It is my own responsibility	1	5	6	5.2%
I had a great amount of support	3	1	4	3.4%
Not believe in abortion or adoption	3	0	3	2.6%
Other reasons	3	1	4	3.4%
Did not give a reason	12	7	19	16.4%

Note The number excludes the eight younger girls and five older ones who wanted to become pregnant.

The results show that three in ten said that they did not believe in abortion and a further one in four said that they did not want one. The comments are instructive and show a variety of feelings. For example, one young woman said, *'I would feel that I had killed someone'* and another commented, *'I do not believe in killing our future.'* A 15-year-

71 Francome, 1986, 1991.

old said, *'I don't believe in abortion unless it is necessary and I like children.'*

Over one in five said she decided to keep the baby after finding out she was pregnant. One commented: *'I couldn't face giving my baby up when I saw what she would look like in a magazine.'* A second said: *'After seeing the heartbeat and seeing the movement I could not give up the bump for anything.'* A 15-year-old said: *'I did not want to get rid of something that was part of me and was mine.'*

A 17-year-old from Sussex said: *'I decided I wanted a child and I knew I could love and care for it. This is the same as any mother who has an unplanned pregnancy. Unplanned does not mean unwanted.'*

One of the younger women and five of the older ones said that they did not feel the fetus should face termination when it was their responsibility. One commented: *'I couldn't go through abortion as it was my fault and not the baby's.'*

The 'other reasons' for continuing the pregnancy were: *'parents against termination'*, *'mother would have turned against me'*, and *'did not like the other options'*.

One factor that in some cases influenced the decision to continue the pregnancy was the fact that it was discovered late. We have further details on this issue as we asked: *'How many weeks pregnant were you when you found out?'* The results show that over a third (35 per cent) were over eleven weeks' pregnant when they realised their situation. In fact one in twenty was over twenty weeks when she discovered the pregnancy and one of the young women in our sample was thirty-six weeks pregnant before she realised.

A 15-year-old knew she was pregnant at five weeks but said: *'I did not tell my parents until five and a half months. This was too late for an abortion and I had become emotionally attached to the baby.'* Another discovered her pregnancy at six weeks but still said: *'I was too late to have an abortion unless I had a private one but I could feel the baby moving about and so I didn't have one.'*

This information supports the other evidence we have obtained of the poor quality of much sex education in this country.

IMPLICATIONS OF THE RESULTS OF OUR SURVEY

Scapegoating the ill-informed
Of those who had not intended to become pregnant, 31 per cent stated that they had used a method of birth control. The most common reasons for non-use were that they had not anticipated having

intercourse (65 per cent), that they forgot to use contraception (23.4 per cent) and that they did not know enough about contraceptives (19.8 per cent).

We have seen that national figures show that 34 per cent of those under 20 years of age who become pregnant undergo termination of pregnancy. This figure rises to 52 per cent for those under 16 years.[72] The reasons for continuing with the pregnancy given by young women who had not intended to become pregnant are instructive; it is clear that many regard abortion as unacceptable and wrong not only for themselves, but in principle.

Twenty per cent of children are brought up by a lone parent, usually the mother, but only 5 per cent of lone mothers are teenagers.[73] An article in *The Lancet* argued that despite this kind of evidence, single mothers are suitable scapegoats for the government:[74]

> The government is in trouble with a record deficit (£50 million), a record crime rate, and a record low in the opinion polls. What better tactic than to divert attention – and blame – on to a group who will find it difficult to fight back.

Those in society who are sympathetic with the struggle of single parents to bring up their children adequately in difficult financial circumstances would have been happy to find that Virginia Bottomley, the Health Secretary, defended lone parents. She argued that there was never a golden age of the family, and also stated that the vast majority of lone parents provide good care for their children.[75] These comments would strike a chord with many of the young women in our sample who, while receiving some help from families and male partners, were primarily responsible for the care of their children.

Reducing unwanted pregnancy
There has been an almost continuous debate concerning what kind of sex education programmes we should be pursuing. Sue Lees, writing on sexuality and adolescent girls, drew attention to a 1992 survey in which the Sex Education Forum found that, while 70 per cent of schools had a written policy on sex education, almost a quarter did not. A further 6 per cent had decided not to include sex education as

72 Francome and Walsh, 1995.
73 Mihill, 1993c; Waterhouse, 1993.
74 Dean, 1993, p. 978.
75 Brindle, 1994c.

part of the curriculum.[76] This was despite the 1987 statutory obligation to develop such a policy.[77]

New government guidelines have been issued to schools covering changes made by the Education Act 1993. Sex education must now be provided within all maintained secondary schools to all registered pupils, while maintained primary schools have a responsibility to decide whether and when to offer sex education. All maintained schools must have a written and updated policy on sex education, which is to be made available to parents.[78]

These guidelines propose that teachers should not give advice on contraception to individual young people under the age of 16 (the legal age of consent for heterosexuals) without parental knowledge and consent. This ruling, if it stands, could cause great difficulty. As David Hart, the general secretary of the National Association of Head Teachers, said: 'Teachers are placed in a very difficult, if not impossible, position in relation to pupils seeking advice but do not wish their parents to be informed.' He suggested that most schools would continue to provide sex education as before. The government guidelines are likely to prove counter-productive to sex education, bearing in mind the evidence presented here that suggests that young people are very poorly educated about sex and birth control.[79]

In many ways this issue exemplifies the difficulties for those who wish to provide sex education. How should we provide young people with the improved information and understanding they require to make choices about sexual behaviour and contraception *without* contravening the law or creating conflict between teachers, young people and parents?

The Sex Education Forum recommends that a specialist trained teacher should be available in each school.[80] Perhaps the most problematic aspect of sex education is the need to develop and implement a consistent strategy which overcomes the existing dichotomies in beliefs to which teachers, parents and school governors are all subject.

The traditional position
This is that sex education should encourage chastity or very restricted sexuality before marriage and fidelity within marriage. This view

76 Lees, 1993, p. 205.
77 Department for Education, 1987.
78 Department for Education, 1994.
79 Meikle, 1994.
80 Lees, 1993, p. 206.

regards sexuality outside family relationships as a problem and a possible threat to the social order. To those who take this line it appears that there are great dangers that sexual education will lead to greater problems. Thus Bishop Joseph Bernadin said that he very much doubted whether:[81]

> more and better contraceptive information and services will make major inroads in the number of teenage pregnancies...[for]...It will motivate them to precocious sexual activity but by no means to the practice of contraception. In which case the 'solution' will merely have made matters worse.

Educators
These argue that a significant proportion of young people will engage in sexual activity outside marriage and therefore we should enable them to protect themselves against its risks and empower them to make and implement informed choices about sexual relationships. They also argue the case for enabling young people to understand more about the nature of social relationships, so that they can be better prepared for the potential sequelae of sexual relationships, such as pregnancy and parenthood.

Both sides in this debate can marshal some facts in support of their case. It is true, for example, that the increased sexual activity of the 1960s led to a large increase in teenage pregnancies and births. We have seen that in 1951 the birth rate amongst all teenagers was only twenty-one per thousand; by 1971 it had risen to fifty-one.[82] This led to newspaper reports with headlines such as 'We got it wrong' and the argument that increased sex education had been a great mistake.[83]

However, changes in the 1970s included the development of free birth control services and the extension of such services to single people through GPs, family planning clinics and Brook Advisory Centres. Such developments enhanced the accessibility of birth control advice and supplies, resulting in a great reduction in teenage births. In the space of only six years they dropped from fifty-one per thousand to thirty per thousand teenage women, despite evidence that the rate of sexual activity among teenagers had increased.[84] Less than one-seventh of that

81 Francome, 1984, p. 11.
82 Francome, 1983a.
83 Bogle, 1981.
84 Farrell, 1978; Francome, 1979.

decline could have been due to an increase in abortion rates, so the conclusion must be that teenage use of birth control had become much more effective during this period.[85]

By far the most frequently cited reason for non-use of birth control in our sample was that the women 'had intercourse unexpectedly'. Such a finding has diverse implications for the provision of sex education. This evidence certainly indicates that the only sensible way forward is to ensure universal provision of good quality sex education which acknowledges the reality of teenagers' lives and the situations they are likely to face. Only in this way will all young people acquire the necessary knowledge and skills with which to protect themselves from unplanned pregnancy and parenthood. For young women to be permitted and educated to anticipate sexual behaviour and its sequelae requires a total paradigm shift in social mores. Young women should be able to plan for the possibility of sex without being labelled as promiscuous or feckless. Furthermore, the onus of responsibility should not be placed on women. Young males must take an equal share of the concern and this sharing of commitment should be central to sex education.

Both when they first had intercourse and when they became pregnant, the young women usually had partners who were older than they were. In fact the average age of the unmarried fathers was 18 years, almost four years older than the average age of the sample. Such evidence suggests that current sex education provision for boys and young men inadequately addresses issues of responsibility for self and partner. The findings also indicate that sex education for girls currently fails to equip them with the necessary skills to assert themselves and to negotiate for safer sex in relationships where a power differential almost certainly exists. Sex education messages such as 'No condom, no sex' need to become part of the curriculum if the current situation is to be significantly improved.

This survey did produce some encouraging findings. For example, when the young women had intercourse for the first time, 44 per cent of their partners wore condoms. If this percentage were increased it could have a dramatic affect in reducing teenage pregnancies and sexually transmitted infections among young people. A report in the *British Medical Journal* told of a Danish law whereby those who are HIV positive and do not wear a condom during sex or do not tell their partners could be imprisoned for a period of up to four years. The Danish Parliament added an amendment to a law that prohibits

85 Francome, 1983b.

reckless behaviour 'by spreading a life threatening and incurable disease'.[86]

Sue Lees calls for feminist sex education which challenges the traditional roles and the double standard of behaviour: 'Young men's traditional attitudes to sex should be questioned and links between sexism and sex education drawn.'[87] Lees argues that the Swedish sex education programme succeeds not only in teaching the mechanics of sexuality but also the value of responsibility and care for others. She is right to draw attention to the great amount of sexism amongst young men and women. An important part of sex education could be to engender anti-sexism through the promotion of attitudes of caring for each other.

Previous research into youth culture has shown the existence of sub-cultural attitudes within schools.[88] In opposition to the traditional school values of planning for the future, using restraint and deferring gratification, there are contrary attitudes of immediacy, excitement and spontaneous enjoyment. If sex education is closely wedded to a pro school ideology, it is likely to fail to impress those who are not committed to the school ideology. There is therefore a case for introducing outsiders into schools or having special sex education classes at family planning clinics, allowing students to claim credits for their attendance. Another idea might be for representatives of GPs or health districts to meet teenagers reaching the age of 14 or 15 in order to provide them with some general health education in which there would be discussions on smoking, alcohol and other drugs. Discussions on relationships and birth control would be a part of the programme, which could also include some elementary first aid. Among helpful changes would be for doctors to begin to give free condoms to men, just as they provide free birth control to women. Those using condoms could also be given an emergency tablet for after-sex birth control in case they have birth control failure in a situation where they cannot easily go to their GP or family planning clinic because, for example, they are abroad or have urgent engagements at work or as students.

Surveys of women with unwanted pregnancies have shown that while 70 per cent knew about emergency after-sex contraception, only 3 per cent tried to use it.[89] This has led for calls for it to be deregulated. Overall the evidence indicates that we need to overcome the traditional

----

86 Headlines, 1994d.
87 Lees, 1993, p. 219.
88 Francome, 1976; Willis, 1977.
89 Drife, 1993.

ambivalence towards sex education that is apparent in the government and begin to educate young people effectively about sexuality, sexual behaviour and the nature of relationships. 'Living skills' are at least as important as academic knowledge and the basics of mathematics, grammar and information technology.

RECOMMENDATIONS

1   We have set out a number of suggestions for reducing AIDS (pp. 181–3). These include helping gay men to be vigilant, realising that not all gay people are wealthy well-educated people, and involving young gay men in developing safe sex projects.

2   We have shown up some for the weaknesses of the sex surveys in providing information on which to base AIDS policy. We need to re-analyse the data along the lines proposed on pages 181 to 183.

3   On teenage pregnancy, we need to develop a comprehensive and coherent policy for sex education within an effective programme of health promotion for young people. We also need to ensure as far as possible that there are suitable work roles even for the less academically able, so that there are fewer attractions in conceiving a baby when under the age of 16.

CHAPTER NINE

ACCIDENTS

Cars are only one tenth as safe as buses or coaches.
Trains are four times safer than cars. These figures
identify the value of promoting public transport.

Accidents were included in *The Health of the Nation* because they are an important cause of disability and death, especially in the very young and the elderly, and many accidents could be prevented. The targets are as follows:

- To reduce the death rate for accidents among children under the age of 15 by at least 33 per cent by 2005. This would be a reduction from 6.6 per 100,000 population in 1990 to no more than 4.4 per 100,000 in 2005.
- To reduce the death rate for accidents among young people aged 15–24 by at least 25 per cent by 2005. This would be a reduction from 24.0 per 100,000 population in 1990 to no more than 18.0 per 100,000 in 2005.
- To reduce the death rate for accidents among people aged 65 and over by at least 33 per cent by 2005. This would be a reduction from 55.8 per 100,000 population in 1990 to no more than 37.4 per 100,000 in 2005.

Although we are concerned in this section with all accidents, some of the most complete information is for road accidents. The overall position for different countries in Europe showed wide differences in 1992. See Table 9.1.

The international data show that England does very well, with the lowest death rate per 100,000 population and the second lowest number of deaths per 10,000 vehicles after Norway. A number of countries have a death rate per 100,000 population that is more than double that of England. These include the USA, Belgium, Spain, Hungary and Portugal. In fact Portugal has a death rate more than four times that of England.

Table 9.1   *International comparisons of road deaths: selected countries*

Country	Road deaths per 100,000 population	Deaths per 10,000 vehicles
England	7.3	1.6
Wales	7.6	1.8
Netherlands	8	1.8
Norway	8	1.4
Scotland	9.0	2.4
Northern Ireland	9.3	2.6
Sweden	9	1.7
Denmark	11	2.7
Ireland	12	3.7
Japan	12	1.9
Germany	13	2.3
USA	15	2.0
Belgium	17	3.3
Spain	20	4.2
Hungary	20	8.2
Portugal	34	–

Source Department of Transport, 1994b, p. 126.

THE EARLY RESULTS

The government's report *The Health of the Nation: One Year On*[1] showed that there had been some progress towards the *Health of the Nation* targets. In 1992 death rates fell by 6.8 per cent among children. In fact data for OECD countries show that Britain's child road death rate is very good compared to other countries, only Sweden and Norway having better records for 1992. A total of thirteen countries had a worse record. However, in terms of pedestrian accidents Britain has not kept pace with reductions in death rates in other countries. In 1992 it had three times the death rate of Norway and was well above the OECD average.[2]

Other data show a reduction in death rates of 16.2 per cent in young adults and 6.8 per cent in older people. When these annual figures are

1 Department of Health, 1993b.
2 Department of Health, 1994b, p. 35.

incorporated into the three-year moving average for 1990–2 it can be seen that there has been a movement towards the achievement of the targets.

The government published data for the first year. They showed some progress as follows:

- 9.0 per cent towards the 33 per cent reduction sought for children;
- 4.8 per cent towards the 25 per cent sought for young adults;
- 5.0 per cent towards the 33 per cent reduction sought for older people.

In the early 1990s the government announced a number of initiatives to reduce the number of accidents. Some of these were primarily educational. One was to try to reduce the number of accidents which are alcohol related. Another was an initiative to explore how work could contribute to accident prevention, and a third was to set up the Children's Traffic Club to try to prevent road accidents. A road safety campaign entitled 'Kill your speed not a child' was launched.[3] Safety helmets were made compulsory for child horse riders. In addition, in July 1993 over a million road safety leaflets were prepared for distribution among older people by primary health care teams.[4] There has been a considerable amount of research to identify factors which contribute towards accidents.

Other action by the government has been more specific. During 1992 came the introduction of buildings regulations to improve fire safety; requirements included the installation of fire detectors in all new dwellings. Furthermore, the Health and Safety Executive is carrying out a number of initiatives to improve safety in industries which previously were identified as having the bulk of fatalities. These include offshore oil and gas, mining, construction, agriculture and the railways.

In addition to direct action the government has also supported voluntary organisations such as the Royal Society for the Prevention of Accidents. One initiative from this was the publication of a guide on the accident prevention needs of ethnic minorities. Age Concern has developed a programme called 'Ageing well in the UK'. It aims to produce innovative programmes for peer-group health counselling for older people using trained volunteers. Four out of eight pilot projects are aimed at accident prevention.[5]

3 Department of Transport, 1994b, p. 8.
4 Department of Health, 1993b, p. 104.
5 Department of Health, 1993b, p. 106.

The 1993 figures showed a further fall in road accidents. For the under-16s the number of deaths fell slightly, from 310 to 306. At this level it was well below the 1981–5 average of 563 and this was despite an overall increase in traffic of 40 per cent.[6] There was a more substantial fall for those aged 16–59, from 2,752 to 2,382, which was a 10 per cent reduction.[7]

OTHER ACCIDENTS

Other types of accident have shown a continuing decline. Accidents at home and in communal establishments fell from 7,045 in 1971 to 4,717 in 1991 and 4,521 in 1992. Accidents occurring outside the home also fell. There were 3,807 in 1971, falling to 2,427 in 1991 and 2,307 in 1992.[8]

For the purposes of our analysis we have considered these reductions in deaths by accidents under two main headings: first, measures taken to decrease the number and severity of accidents; and, secondly, measures to improve the quality of treatment when accidents do occur. Particularly important in this respect are the accident and emergency units and we have therefore made a special study of these.

Table 9.2   *Passenger fatality rates by mode of travel*

Mode of transport	Deaths per 100 million kilometres	Change in passenger travel since 1985/6
Car	0.4	+30%
Van	0.2	+16%
Motor cycles etc.	9.7	-26%
Pedal cycle	4.3	-12%
Foot	5.3	-13%
Bus or coach	0.04	-11%
Rail	0.1	+7%
Water	0.6	
Air	0.03	+107%

Source Department of Transport, 1994a, pp. 13, 35.

6 Department of Health, 1994b, p. 34.
7 Department of Transport, 1994b, p. 17.
8 OPCS, 1995, p. 133.

Reducing accidents

In examining the British performance with regard to accidents, it is instructive to look at the fatality rates for different kinds of transport. These are shown in Table 9.2.

These figures identify the value of promoting public transport for passengers. The results show that cars are only one-tenth as safe as buses and coaches. Trains are four times safer than cars. However, the third column shows that in recent years there has been a great increase in car transport; it rose by 30 per cent over the most recent six-year period. In contrast, bus transport has declined and rail travel has increased by only 7 per cent. One figure that does seem high is the death rate for pedestrians, which is more than twelve times that of car passengers. Cars are the main danger to pedestrians, so a move from cars to public transport would help improve pedestrian safety.

The death rate for cyclists is much higher than that for car transport but below that for pedestrians. This high figure shows the need for bicycle lanes and, as far as possible, separate bicycle routes. The death rate for motor cycles, scooters and mopeds is the highest rate for all modes of transport. As we know from comparative insurance rates, this danger is especially high for young people. Between 1985/6 and 1991–3 the percentage of total distance travelled by motor cycle fell by 26 per cent, which will have led to improvements in death rates for this category. Finally, it is perhaps surprising that water transport was six times more dangerous than rail.

Young people

One of the main locations for accidents among young people is on the roads. A report published in May 1994 stated that sixteen child pedestrians are killed every day.[9] Overall the number of deaths from accidents fell from 6,922 in 1963 to 3,858 in 1993. However, Michael Evans, chairman of the Royal Society for the Prevention of Accidents, noted that British child pedestrian casualty rates are among the worst in Europe. He said that 30 per cent of accidents involving child pedestrians involve journeys to and from school. One problem he identified was that parents were driving their children almost everywhere:[9]

> Much of the early road safety training no longer takes place. Today, unless people live in the centre of a town

9 MacLeod, 1994, p. 6.

most young children are taken everywhere by car. They go to school by car and shopping expeditions are either to out of town supermarkets or in town-centre shopping precincts. It is not unusual to find an 11 year old with absolutely no idea of how to behave safely as a pedestrian.

In a major article on the risks of accidents to 5,334 children aged 11–14, the Department of Transport stated that in England childhood unintentional injury is a major public health problem, but the injuries are both predictable and preventable.[10] It drew attention to the fact that *The Health of the Nation* advocated the setting of local targets. However, the only information routinely available is that for deaths and this is inadequate because, fortunately, death is a relatively rare event.[11] The evidence from the research also revealed that, in general, boys, older pupils, and pupils from poorer households were exposed to the most risk when travelling back and forth to school and to places of recreation. Subsequent research not surprisingly showed that a major cause of accidents is children running out into the road. Furthermore, there is a higher number of accidents among ethnic and lower socio-economic groups.[12]

After reviewing the evidence MacLeod made a number of suggestions about how the number of accidents could be reduced.[13]
- Pre-school groups should be taught about road safety so that by the time children go to school, they are prepared to cope with traffic.
- Parents should leave their cars at home and walk their children to school so that they can teach them kerb drill.
- There should be something in the National Curriculum about road safety.
- The Green Cross Code is out of date and needs to be revised.

Improvements in the environment for walkers and cyclists would also reduce the number of accidents. There is a need for protective helmets to be worn. An article based on a study of 445 children presenting with bicycle-related incidents in Queensland showed the benefits of helmets. It showed that 52 per cent of the children had simply fallen from their bicycles and only 7 per cent had contact with a motor vehicle. Head injuries were more likely to occur on paved areas than on grass, gravel or dirt. Wearing a helmet reduced the risk of head injury by 63 per cent

10 Department of Transport, 1990.
11 Towner *et al.*, 1994, p. 449.
12 Department of Transport, 1994b, p. 37.
13 MacLeod, 1994.

and of loss of consciousness by 86 per cent. The report recommended that legislation to enforce the wearing of helmets should be considered.[14]

The reduction in deaths from traffic accidents in recent years follows the introduction of seat belts and other safety measures. The improvement in statistics also suggests that motorists are being more careful and not drinking and driving as commonly as formerly. However, Guppy stated that there was a need for a reduction in the amount of alcohol that should be legally allowed for safety.[15] Drinking and driving is an area which is capable of improvement.

IMPROVING CARE BEFORE PATIENTS ARRIVE AT HOSPITAL

With the decline in the number of accident and emergency units since the NHS reforms, there is a need for improvements in pre-hospital treatment in cases of accidents. In an important study of 152 pre-hospital deaths (110 males and 42 females) from accidental injury, death was found to have been potentially preventable in 39 per cent of cases. The average age of those dying was 42 years. In many cases death was through airway obstruction. All the pre-hospital deaths occurred before medical help arrived and so if death was to have been prevented in those cases it would have required action by members of the public. The researchers called for training in first aid for everyone, and especially for motorists as traffic accidents were the cause of eighty-six of the deaths.[16]

IMPROVING CARE IN ACCIDENT AND EMERGENCY UNITS

The Department of Health has revealed that the number of NHS trusts and directly managed hospitals with accident and emergency units declined from 301 in 1988 to 213 by the middle of 1994. The largest single yearly reduction occurred between 1991 and 1992 when the number of sites with units fell by 56. This has meant that instead of serving 150,000 people, each unit must now look after 225,000 people. The change is viewed with equanimity by some. Dr Keith Little, president of the British Association of Accident and Emergency Medicine, which is in favour of increased specialisation, was quoted as saying:[17]

14 Thomas *et al.*, 1994.
15 Guppy, 1994, p. 1056.
16 Hussain and Redmond, 1994, p. 1077.
17 Dixon, 1994, p. 1.

> It tends to happen in centres of population where there are several or multiple A&Es which are geographically close. There is a finite budget so if you have three departments which are close together your resources are split three ways. If you amalgamate those departments on one site, you have three times the staff. Also staff become more adept in the treatment of major trauma.

However, others have been critical. David Blunkett, the shadow Health Secretary, said that the decline in the number of accident and emergency units is occurring at an increasing rate and commented that it was very worrying that there was a loss of casualty units without clear evidence of alternatives.[17] It is clear that the closure of units has meant that many people now need to travel much further to get their care, and it seems that closures have not been rationally planned or well executed. The town of St Albans, for example, had a new accident and emergency unit which was promptly closed. At the time of writing (September 1995) the accident and emergency unit at Edgware Hospital in north London is under threat of closure in 1997. If this is carried out there will be greater distances for people to travel and increased congestion on the roads, and people will have to wait longer before they are treated.

A letter in the *Hendon Times* drew attention to the problems that could be caused for families by such a closure.[18]

> Twenty one years ago my son Darren was born with asthma. Recently Darren suffered an extremely bad asthma attack. It was 5.30 am when I had to rush him to hospital. Fortunately there was no traffic on the roads so our journey was made shorter. However, 30 yards from the hospital's main entrance Darren slumped on the dashboard. His breathing had stopped and he turned a strange colour. I drew to a halt outside the main entrance where a male and female nurse were getting some early morning air. They both rushed to my car to assist me. The male nurse took Darren under the arms, the female nurse turned to find a trolley when the male nurse shouted 'forget the trolley, he's dead on arrival.' The female nurse took hold of Darren's feet, and he was rushed into the A&E.

17 Dixon, 1994, p. 1.
18 Caulfield, 1995.

After several attempts to revive him Darren responded to the doctor's efforts and made a full recovery. My family and I have much to thank Edgware General Hospital for. Who would we thank if the A&E at Edgware is closed and Darren suffers another major attack and we have to travel further miles to enable Darren to keep his life. In these cases time is of the essence. Next time Darren may not be just 30 yards short of his future.

Another potential closure in north London of the accident and emergency unit at Chase Farm Hospital, was abandoned in 1995 after a fierce campaign of protest in the local community.

In 1992 a major report was published in the *British Medical Journal* on the outcome of major trauma.[19] It aimed to give an overview of the effectiveness of treatment in the United Kingdom by considering the data from thirty-three hospitals. In order to measure the severity of impairment the abbreviated injury scale is now widely used. This gives scores for over 1,200 injuries. Those patients with multiple injuries are scored by adding together the squares of the highest scores in up to three body regions. The injury severity score ranges from 1 to 75 (3×25). The lower the score, the better the chance of survival. Only 2 per cent of those with a score of 9 to 15 died within three months, compared to 80 per cent of those with a score of 50 to 66.[20] The results showed that British hospitals did not compare very favourably with their counterparts in the United States. A study of 14,648 patients admitted for more than three days showed that over 21 per cent of seriously injured patients (numbering 1,299) took longer than one hour to reach hospital. Only 46 per cent of patients (165 of 355) judged to require an early operation arrived in theatre within two hours. The report also stated:[21]

> Many participating hospitals were unable to provide information on journey times – just one example of the inadequate integration of trauma services in the United Kingdom...The 36% of cases where these data were supplied show long intervals before many seriously injured patients reach hospital...The limited information available suggests that there is a considerable delay between arrival in hospital and first operation.

19 Yates *et al.*, 1992, p. 737.
20 Yates *et al.*, 1992, p. 738.
21 Yates *et al.*, 1992, p. 740.

It concluded by saying that the management of major trauma in the UK remains unsatisfactory, with delays in providing experienced staff and necessary operations. It also pointed out that mortality rates varied inexplicably between hospitals.

OUR SURVEY OF ACCIDENT AND EMERGENCY UNITS

In the light of problems existing in 1992 in accident and emergency units, we wanted to consider the results of the NHS reforms on a large sample and to ask those responsible to identify what they needed to improve their services. The raw figures give the impression that there were likely to be further problems. There were some fourteen million attendances at accident and emergency units in England and Wales in 1992–3. New attendances in England increased from 197 per thousand population in 1980 to 230 in 1992 (an increase of 17 per cent). The average number of daily available beds for all specialities fell from 8 per thousand population in 1978 to 5 in 1991/2. The rise in new attendances combined with the fall in the number of beds available has clear implications for waiting times spent in accident and emergency departments. A report by the Royal College of Nursing showed that a third of all accident and emergency units had patients waiting overnight for a bed, most of them on trolleys. The problem seems to be worse in London. One respondent in the Royal College of Nursing's study reported: 'Two to eight people stay overnight in the department every night: the waiting room has become a mini ward. Most patients wait 24 hours for a bed.'[22]

The evidence of those working in the service is that the reduction in the number of beds was based on funds and not on need. In 1993 Professor John Ward, clinical director of medicine at Central Sheffield University Hospital, wrote that he had been forced to close forty-eight medical beds and, with inadequate funds to compensate for the reduction in junior doctors hours, there were shortages of both beds and staff.[22]

Nationwide, at first sight it does not seem that there should have been problems with staff shortages. The numbers of medical staff increased from 1,497 in 1980 to 1,946 in 1991, an increase of 30 per cent. Of these staff 1,326 were senior health officers.[23] This increase more than kept pace with the increase in accident and emergency

22 Rickford, 1994, p. 20.
23 Department of Health, 1993a.

attenders. However, it raises the question as to whether medical staffing numbers in accident and emergency departments were adequate for the workload in 1980 and also the question of whether the medical 'skill mix', rather than just the numbers, is appropriate, given the heavy reliance on junior staff. Furthermore, the reduction in junior doctors' hours which occurred for some in 1994, while welcome and long overdue, means that the increase in staff has not led to a linear increase in the number of hours. Additionally, since 1992 there has been an 'unexplained' increase in emergency admissions to hospital, in some cases up by more than 20 per cent.[24] These may be patients who would previously have been attended by their GP.

We decided to investigate some of the reasons for the increase in attendance at accident and emergency departments and for increases in waiting times for treatment, utilising the insights of consultants who are well positioned to identify some of the factors involved.

In 1994 a questionnaire was sent to the clinical directors of 145 general accident and emergency departments in England and Wales. There were 119 replies, which is a response rate of 82 per cent.

We asked our respondents: *'Has there been any noticeable increase over the past three years in numbers of those patients using the department who are registered with a GP but are not able to receive treatment from the primary care services when they require it?'* In reply to this, 113 consultants expressed a view and three in five (61 per cent) agreed with the statement.

We also asked if there was an increase in patients who were not registered with a GP. A quarter of the consultants had seen such an increase and this could be a second factor in increased attendance.

The increase in attendance at accident and emergency departments by patients who are essentially self-referred may reflect at least two possible trends. First, there has been a growing and ever more widespread inability of the GP service to meet the primary health care needs of particular groups such as the unemployed and transients.[25] Secondly, increasing numbers of people may see accident and emergency departments as the appropriate place for the treatment of minor injuries and medical problems. This has resulted in the accident and emergency service fulfilling a very different role from that for which it was originally intended.

It was also suggested at the pilot stage of our study that GPs under

----

24 *Health Services Journal*, 1993.
25 Tomlinson, 1992, p. 13.

pressure were sending patients to accident and emergency units to a greater degree than they used to. We therefore asked respondents: *'Was there any increase in the number of direct GP referrals to A&E, as a proportion of new attenders?'* Out of the 119 units, fifty-six (48 per cent) had experienced such an increase.

Consultants finding an increase were asked to identify reasons for the increase in GP referrals. Those provided were as follows:

- GP fundholders were increasingly utilising accident and emergency facilities, such as X-radiography, for 'semi-urgent' cases, leading to speculation that this was a way of avoiding payment for these services, which fundholders would have to meet for 'non-urgent' patients. This was cited by 9 per cent of the sample.

- Non-fundholding GPs were perceived by 13.5 per cent of the sample as using accident and emergency departments as a means of circumventing booked admission waiting-lists for their patients, the result of bed shortages. Sending patients to an accident and emergency unit enables them to be seen by specialists in a clinic more quickly. In the words of one consultant, *'the hospital is always full with list admissions, so the GPs get fed-up and send "emergency" admissions to A&E'*. Another mentioned the *'difficulties in obtaining out-patient appointments and accessing specialists'* for non-fundholders.

- In the case of fundholders, this circumventing was, in the opinion of 8.5 per cent of the consultants, to avoid the costs of a list admission or referral for specialist consultation for their patients. A typical comment was that the accident and emergency department is seen by fundholders *'as a means of access to clinics without incurring expenses'* or *'a cheap option'*.

- GPs were perceived by 8.5 per cent of the sample to have less time for clinical diagnosis and treatment of patients as a result of changes in their contractual arrangements. They are perceived to be spending a greater amount of time on paperwork (in their role as purchasers), and in screening patients to meet the *Health of the Nation* targets.

- GPs were perceived by 7.5 per cent of the sample to be concerned about the increase in patient complaints, probably resulting from raised expectations about quality of treatment. This had resulted in an increasing willingness to refer their patients to accident and emergency units for a second or specialist opinion. As one consultant explained, this reflected *'changes in patient culture. Patients now want hospitals to deal with them rather than GPs.'*

- GPs were perceived by 5 per cent of the sample as being either unable to see patients 'out-of-hours' or as refusing to do so, instead referring their patients directly to accident and emergency – using the service, in the opinion of one consultant, *'as a 24-hour sink'*.

The results indicate a significant increase in direct GP referrals to the accident and emergency service and are frequently seen as relating directly to the structural changes in the NHS. The changes have meant that GPs, for a number of reasons, have an incentive to manipulate the admissions and specialist referral systems via the open access of accident and emergency departments. In addition, there is the increasingly important issue of emergency bed shortages throughout the country. This has obliged GPs to take radical action in order to get their patients requiring immediate admission into hospital.

As one consultant in the survey commented, *'because of emergency bed shortages, GPs are now making 999 calls (to be assured of getting their patients a hospital bed)'*. Supporting this, the Tomlinson Report[26] cited the London Ambulance Service, which said that there is a tendency for some GPs to tell their patients to ring 999 if their condition worsens.

REGIONAL DIFFERENCES IN ACCIDENT AND EMERGENCY UNITS

The Tomlinson Report argued that the significantly higher usage of the accident and emergency service in inner London (new attendances averaging 405 per 1,000 population, compared to an average for England of 234 per 1,000) was a direct result of the under-development of primary and community care. Tomlinson concluded that this resulted in accident and emergency services being used by many sections of the population in London as a 'primary care service'. This was due to the nature of the population in the inner cities and the particular difficulties face by GPs. If this picture of inner London painted by Tomlinson was true of all large cities, then we would expect to find an increase in new attenders in accident and emergency units in other large city areas rather than in suburban and provincial units. We identified thirty-six units as being in large cities and seventy-four as being suburban or provincial. In fact the proportion of patients not registered with a GP was 27 per cent in the units in large city centres and 26 per cent in other areas. This suggests that the causes of

26 Tomlinson, 1992.

increased attendance at accident and emergency units result from general changes in funding arrangements brought about by the NHS reforms rather than from non-registration with a GP.

SKILL MIX OF STAFF

The NHS Executive defines skill mix as 'the balance between trained and untrained, qualified and unqualified and supervisory staff within a service area, as well as between different staff groups'. The accident and emergency consultants were asked: *'Do you have the appropriate skill mix of medical, nursing and support staff to meet the workload in your department over any 24-hour period, including weekends?'*

Four out of five (81 per cent) of consultants stated that their departments did not have the appropriate skill mix to meet their workload. The other 19 per cent said they did have the right mix. Some of the latter believed that, although their skill mix was broadly correct, they lacked sufficient numbers of staff. Additionally, a number of consultants pointed out that the skill mix in their unit, which might be adequate in 'office hours' during weekdays, was often completely inadequate at nights and weekends. This related particularly to the frequent lack of senior medical cover in accident and emergency.

Among those eighty-six units that stated they did *not* have a balanced skill mix, the major problem identified was the lack of middle-grade staff; this was mentioned by fifty-nine (61 per cent) consultants. This is to be expected, given that the majority of accident and emergency units have only one consultant, and so frequently lack senior medical cover at certain times. Just under half (47 per cent) called for more senior house officers and two in five (41 per cent) called for more nursing staff.

A significant number of respondents identified a need for more senior nursing staff and support staff such as receptionists. This must reflect the perception, if not the reality, that resources are not keeping pace with the increasing workload and demands on the service. Incidentally, many consultants said they required more nursing staff trained in 'initial assessment' skills to enable patients to be assessed within five minutes of registering in the department. This partially reflects the distortion of clinical priorities as the units try to comply with the Patient's Charter standards. The setting of quality standards and performance indicators for the health service are the key objectives of both the Patient's Charter and the *Health of the Nation* strategy. The national charter standard most applicable to accident and emergency service is 'Immediate assessment upon arrival'; and indeed this was utilised as the only indicator of performance for these departments in the Department of Health's 'league tables' first published in June 1994. Hospitals and trusts are also required to set their own local quality standards.

We asked the consultants to comment specifically on their department's performance over the previous three years with regard to two further potential measures of quality and performance. The first of these was waiting times for treatment. To the average patient, this is more important than the Patient's Charter standard of waiting times for initial assessment. The other performance measure was the initial management of major trauma. A minority (38 per cent) of units reported some improvement in waiting times for treatment over the previous three years. The majority (62 per cent) experienced either an increase in waiting-times (33 per cent), or no change at all (29 per cent). Additionally a number of consultants pointed out that keeping waiting times the same over the previous three years had to be seen as an achievement given the extra workload, plus no improvement in staff numbers. Much more positively, 79 per cent of consultants believed there had been an improvement in the initial management of major trauma, with only 1 per cent believing there had been a deterioration. A number of consultants specifically attributed this improvement to the greater awareness of Advanced Trauma Life Support guidelines. Major trauma, however, represents only 1 per cent of all attenders at accident and emergency units.[27] These results would suggest that important developments have occurred in the management of major trauma since the initial report of the major trauma outcome study in 1992.

Consultants were asked about the other measures of quality they used in their own units. The two which were by far the most frequently mentioned, were initial waiting time for assessment, or – as it has come to be identified in practice – nursing triage (mentioned by 23 per cent of respondents); and the number of patient complaints (mentioned by 18 per cent of respondents).

One of the demands on consultants' time, which came as a direct result of the organisational changes, was the requirement for more information, particularly by purchasers. Although both *Working for Patients*[28] and *The Health of the Nation*[29] place a new emphasis on

27 Burdett-Smith, 1992.
28 Department of Health, 1989.
29 Department of Health, 1992.

information gathering, the majority of consultants (81 per cent) clearly regarded the task of collating data for contractual purposes as irrelevant or detracting from their role of meeting patient needs for treatment. This was mainly because of the time spent by clinicians on this task alone, a typical consultant's comment being, *'I am overwhelmed by paperwork.'*

The survey asked about the increased demand for information, in particular the collating of patient data, in support of the new contractual arrangements between purchasers and providers. The exact question was:

> *'Over the past three years, there has been an increase in the demand for information flow in support of the new contractual arrangements within the NHS. Have you found that the collating of this extra information required by purchasers has enhanced your response to local emergency service needs?'*

The results showed that only one in five (19 per cent) believed that it had helped care. Almost a half (48 per cent) said that it had hindered care, and the remaining 33 per cent said it had made no difference.

The survey was also concerned to examine the role of accident and emergency departments in contributing towards the *Health of the Nation* accident prevention targets. We asked: *'Has the expertise of your A&E department been utilised in any local accident prevention initiatives?'* The results show that fifty-six (47 per cent) of the consultants said that it had, while sixty-three (53 per cent) said that it had not. The majority of accident and emergency departments therefore had no input into accident prevention strategies. One consultant explained the comparative lack of involvement by the accident and emergency department in accident prevention initiatives as follows: *'These initiatives are rarely effective and we simply do not have the time.'* Another commented: *'The committees involved in accident prevention have no power to influence events.'*

In those departments that did play a role, it was largely confined to a consultant acting in an advisory capacity only. This was through local authority accident prevention committees or sitting on a district health authority Health of the Nation committee. This involvement usually related to accident data collection used to identify local road traffic accident black spots, advice concerning child accident prevention (i.e use of cycle helmets), or accidents in the home.

The final question in the accident and emergency survey was concerned with the consultants' perceptions of the major benefits and drawbacks of the structural changes in the NHS, with particular regard to their own accident and emergency department. The responses were more negative than positive. In terms of the benefits to their department, 107 of the 119 answered the question. The majority (64 per cent) of consultants could identify none. Of the 36 per cent of respondents who did identify benefits, the main one was that there was more autonomy for the consultants in running their departments. This was mentioned by 16 per cent. In addition 11 per cent mentioned that purchasers and the hospital trust were more aware of the contribution and significance of the accident and emergency department. In all, 7 per cent mentioned that the introduction of audit had forced a re-examination of work practices and one in twenty (5 per cent) mentioned an increase in staff.

In terms of the drawbacks of the structural changes within the NHS, fully 25 per cent said that they were spending less time in clinical responsibilities because of their increased administrative responsibilities. Almost a quarter mentioned that they were financially accountable without being given responsibility.

Many consultants recognised that the rhetoric of the reforms had made great play of the opportunities for greater local accountability and autonomy, yet after four years of the internal market this ideology meant nothing if it was under-resourced: *'Budgetary control is presented as a local advantage or empowerment, when in fact this is not the case...because [there is] no control over workload or resources.'*

A number mentioned the many kinds of information that 'purchasing agencies' expected from provider units in relation to the *Health of the Nation* targets; for example *'I can go a full day (10–11 hours) without time to see a single patient.'* Many of the accident and emergency departments in the survey had submitted audit data to the ongoing major trauma outcome study, and this may have stimulated improvements in trauma treatment. Many consultants identified a greater awareness of the requirement to have staff trained to the Advanced Trauma Life Support standard, the only internationally recognised standard of trauma resuscitation care. However, it must be conceded (although it was not specifically mentioned by many respondents) that as regards this particular quality measure, *The Health of the Nation* has had an impact. The key area handbook on accidents recommended that district health authorities should include in their contracts a specific timetable for the introduction of severity and trauma scores for all patients with serious injuries.

The quality measure most frequently cited by respondents was waiting time for initial assessment (Patient's Charter standard no. 5). Not coincidentally, this was one of only three charter standards that were selected to judge hospital performances in the Department of Health 'league tables' published in June 1994, and the only one in which the specific performance of accident and emergency departments was measured. The target is for a minimum of 80 per cent of attenders to be assessed by a trained nurse within five minutes of arriving in accident and emergency. Achievement of the target is needed for the trust to be awarded a star.

As one consultant put it: *'The pressure is on doctors and nurses to assess patients more quickly – this is not a quality standard.'* Many consultants stated that: *'nothing else seems to matter'*. Many also commented that the practicalities of meeting this standard meant tying-up well-qualified nurses to undertake the initial triage. This had the effect of taking high quality staff from the treatment areas, which in turn had the knock-on effect of increasing waiting times for treatment. As one consultant put it: *'The "immediate assessment" nurse replacing proper triage nursing, is a waste of skills and does nothing to improve patient care – It is only a cosmetic improvement.'*

Many of the consultants saw the increase in complaints as being due directly to expectations being raised beyond what was reasonably achievable, given the restrictions on resources. As one respondent put it: *'we are swamped with complaints most of which are resource issues and totally outside our control'*. Privacy is at a minimum in many units and a survey found that one in eight accident and emergency departments had no private consultation rooms because of insufficient space and limited resources for updating and expanding departments.[30]

The survey suggested that implementing major organisational changes without first piloting them had produced a series of unpredictable repercussions. In particular, there appeared to be a general consensus among the consultants that the power of non-clinicians had increased over what are essentially patient treatment decisions. This led to some dissatisfaction, as the following comments from consultants show:

'Power is now concentrated with Purchasers who have no knowledge of problems and are driven by market forces without paying attention to patient needs.'

'Clinical practice is being altered by management priorities.'

30 Rigge, 1993, p. 136.

'There are far too many managers, they hinder rather than help progress.'

'Managers are orientated entirely to business and not patients.'

PROPOSALS FOR IMPROVING ACCIDENT AND EMERGENCY SERVICES

We have seen some evidence that the merging of accident and emergency units has, in the opinion of some consultants, led to improvements in the treatment of major trauma. However, there was no evidence of a marked improvement in waiting time for treatment and, with the many closures of units, people were on average spending a greater time travelling to accident and emergency units. Improving the care that GPs are able to give would mean that fewer people would attend. As one consultant explained:

'Hospital closures have overloaded the system...the A&E is the last ditch for many people...everyone else is in a position to say NO...we are therefore prevented from giving the best care to more seriously ill patients. We are too stretched to teach (Juniors, & patients) effectively...the staff are disillusioned and the system is in disarray.'

So our survey showed that consultants had many ideas for improvements.

PROPOSALS FOR IMPROVING ACCIDENT RATES

A The figures for car accidents show that in Britain the rates have come down to a low level in comparison with other countries. It may be very difficult to make further improvements without changes in public preferences and transport policies. However, it is still possible to encourage driver safety by further reducing drinking and driving. We have seen data on the relative safety of different forms of travel. This suggests that improvements in the quality of public transport and a movement of people away from cars could have important effects in reducing the accident rates. An improvement in the quality and number of cycle lanes would reduce the danger of cars to cyclists and the increased use of cycle helmets would also reduce injuries.

B There are also a number of things that could be done to improve safety in the home. A reduction in cigarette smoking would reduce the number of fires in houses and the growth in the number of smoke alarms will promote early detection and damage limitation.[31]

C Improving children's education. We have detailed the case for better road safety instruction, which would help protect children from accidents.

D Improve the quality of care at accident and emergency units. Ensure that there is good quality emergency cover within easy reach of people's homes either by reopening some of the units closed since the reforms or by co-operation with local GPs. Improve the skill mix of staff at accident and emergency units.

E We should improve health and safety legislation and enforce it with more inspectors.

31 Travis, 1994.

CHAPTER TEN

AREAS OF HEALTH OUTSIDE THE GOVERNMENT'S TARGETS

No matter how efficiently you slice the cake, if it is
not big enough to start with someone goes hungry.
Orthopaedic surgeon who had had 30 per cent of
his operating sessions cancelled.

There are a number of areas of health outside the government's five targets of which we decided to monitor two:

1   Orthopaedics – a study of hip replacements and the views of consultants about the service.
2   Nephrology – a study of the treatment of kidney patients and the views of consultants about the service.

ORTHOPAEDIC SURGEONS AND THE NEW NHS

Hip replacement is an important life-enhancing operation and more than 400,000 are conducted annually worldwide.[1] There are questions about how the national total has been altered by the government's NHS changes. Furthermore, it is of interest to discover how orthopaedic consultants evaluate the NHS changes. There have been questions asked about cost, which were claimed to be between £3,800 and £9,406 per operation in 1994, with stays in hospital varying from five to twenty days. Press reports have also been critical of the estimate that one in five operations has to be repeated, at an extra cost of £25 million per annum.[2]

Methodology
We obtained national figures from a question in the House of Commons. At our request, Mildred Gordon, MP for Bow and Poplar, asked the Secretary of State for Health: *'How many hip replacement*

---

1 Goldie, 1993, p. 9.
2 Jones, 1995, p. 8.

operations have been carried out in each year for 1983–1993 in England, Scotland and Wales?'

In addition we drew a random sample of 190 orthopaedic surgeons from the *Medical Directory*. The first mailing was sent out on 30 March 1994, followed by two reminders. Eleven of those contacted could not respond for various reasons such as retirement. This left an effective sample size of 179 from which we received 141 replies, a response rate of 79 per cent. One consultant did not respond to the last three questions.

Results

The number of operations is tabulated as shown in Table 10.1.

Table 10.1   *Hip replacement in Britain (in thousands)*

Year	England	Scotland	Wales	
1983	36.2	2.7	1.8	(83/4)
1984	36.9	2.9	1.8	(84/5)
1985	36.5	3.1	1.9	(85/6)
1986	41.0	3.2	2.0	(86/7)
1987		3.5	1.7	(87/8)
1988–9	46.5	3.8 (1988)	2.2	
1989–90	50.8	3.6 (1989)	2.3	
1990–1	50.7	3.7 (1990)	1.9	
1991–2	55.6	3.7 (1991)	2.7	
1992–3		3.8 (1992)	2.9	
1993–4		3.9		

Note English figures include 'other arthroplasty operations', Scottish figures are just total hip replacement. Welsh figures are for 'total and partial hip replacement'.

The results show that in England the number of operations increased by 40 per cent between 1983 and 1989–90; in Wales they rose by 27 per cent and in Scotland by 33 per cent over the same period. Since 1990 the Scottish figures have shown only a slight rise while in England and Wales the increase has been more substantial. These differences are unlikely to be due to the needs of the population, and are probably due to accessibility or financial factors. The rate of hip replacement related to the population of pensionable age (women over 60, men over 65) in 1991–2 shows that in England it is 6.3 per thousand, in Wales it is 5.0

and in Scotland 4.1. The English have 50 per cent more operations than the Scots which, in part, will be due to the fact that the English figures include 'other arthroplasty operations'.

Let us now consider our survey results. The first question was: *'Has the waiting list for elective hip replacements increased or decreased over the past three years?'* The results are shown in Table 10.2.

Table 10.2   *Waiting lists*

	Number	Percentage	95% confidence
Increased	64	45.4%	37.0–54.0%
Remained the same	42	29.8%	22.4–38.1%
Decreased	35	24.8%	17.9–32.8%

The results show that for 45 per cent of consultants the waiting times had increased. Some said that the measurement of waiting times was not accurate. There are *'misdirected attempts to massage waiting times by intermittent "initiatives"'*. Another talked of *'invalid ratings, there is more to the quality of surgery than how long you wait for it'*. Another said that the increase in waiting lists was such that *'everybody now waits one year'*.

A second question was worded as follows: *'Some consultants have suggested to us that concern with waiting times has led to some urgent cases being deferred in favour of patients who have been waiting longer. Is this your experience?'* The answers are shown in Table 10.3.

Table 10.3   *Extent of making more needy cases wait longer*

	Number	Percentage	95% confidence
Happens often	37	26.2%	19.2–34.3%
Happens sometimes	59	41.9%	33.6–50.4%
Does not happen	45	31.9%	20.3–40.3%

The results show that over two-thirds of orthopaedic surgeons were at times faced with the situation in which a more urgent case was deferred in favour of someone who had been on the waiting list longer. For a quarter of these consultants this was a frequent occurrence. One consultant said he was *'trying to treat urgent cases when the management has negotiated unrealistic contracts and not given enough operating time despite reasoned arguments'*. Another called for a change in this situation. He said he wanted *'more concern about patients' problems than trying to beat deadlines and treating patients according to the length of time they have been waiting'*.

A further question was on fundholding and its effect on priority within the hospital service. We asked: *'Do patients of GP fundholders get priority?'* The results were as shown in Table 10.4.

Table 10.4   *Extent to which patients of fundholders get priority*

	Number	Percentage	95% confidence
Never	36	25.5%	18.6–33.6%
Sometimes	65	46.1%	33.7–54.7%
Often	40	28.4%	21.1–36.6%

The results show that almost three-quarters (74.6 per cent) had experienced fundholders getting priority treatment. Only a quarter of surgeons reported no priority being given to fundholders. This is similar to the answers of GPs, seven out of ten of whom (69 per cent) found priority was given to fundholders in their area.[3] Of course fundholders are limited by the size of their budget. One consultant told us that he had *'Patients coming from other areas who can't be seen because their fundholder has no money.'*

Delay because of financial constraints
The orthopaedic surgeons were asked: *'Were you constrained from carrying out elective operations until the end of April?'* In response to this thirty-six (26.3 per cent) said they were and 101 (73.7 per cent) said they were not. Four people did not respond to this question. One consultant said that he had *'30% of elective lists cancelled between November 1993 and April 1994.'*

Benefits of the NHS changes
We asked: *'What advantages have you found with the Government health changes?'* The results are included in Table 10.5.

3 Francome, 1994c.

Table 10.5   *Advantages of the NHS changes*

Advantages	Number	Percentage
None	77	55%
Increased cost awareness	14	10%
Improved efficiency/information	9	6%
Improved management	7	5%
Better staff performance	7	5%
More money available	4	3%
Better audit	4	3%
Other	13	9%
Total giving advantages	60	

The results show that the majority of consultants saw no benefits. Included in this number were a few people who made comments which were critical of the changes. One, for example, said '*[the] reforms provide employment for bureaucrats*'. Another said: '*All the suggested advantages are theoretical. We in orthopaedics worked flat out even before the reforms. We cannot improve without additional resources which are held back by petty officials in the purchasing department.*' A third put as an advantage, '*unscheduled half days*', which is presumably a wry reference to the cancelling of operating lists.

The major positive comment about the reforms by the surgeons was that there was increased cost awareness. Others mentioned improved management and the fact that their relationship with managers had improved. One of the consultants said the benefit of the changes was: '*Greater awareness of costing and quality of whatever we are doing confirms the underfunding of the NHS.*' Another said the reforms '*will eventually show that long waiting times are a result of insufficient orthopaedic surgeons not inefficiency*'.

Disadvantages of the changes
We asked our respondents: '*What disadvantages have you found with the Government health changes?*' The results can be tabulated as shown in Table 10.6.

Table 10.6   *Disadvantages of the NHS changes*

Disadvantages	Number	Percentage
Increased bureaucracy	71	51%
Inadequate resources for patient care	16	11%
Anxiety/low staff morale	15	11%
Economic factors override clinical needs	13	9%
Increasingly two-tier system (fundholding)	13	9%
Worse treatment or less freedom for patients	9	7%
Increased waiting lists	8	6%
Managers interfering or not communicating	8	6%
Unrealistic expectations (Patient's Charter)	7	5%
Other (e.g. chaos, pressure for more work)	17	12%
Total (average 1.3 reasons each)	177	

The results show that the surgeons mentioned in total three times as many disadvantages as advantages. The main one was the increase in bureaucracy. This was identified as a problem by seventy-one (50 per cent) of the total. Some comments were brief and blunt, for example, that there is an *'idiotic level of unimportant bureaucracy'*. Another commented: *'We now spend 30 per cent of our budget on management, office support and other non-clinical items. This is not an efficient way to deliver health care when money is tight.'* Another commented that there had been: *'The huge cost of increased administration ie numbers of managers and my own time involvement.'* A fourth talked of *'the enormous burgeoning of health service employees who consume resources and have no direct contact with patient care'*.

Sixteen consultants mentioned the lack of resources. Fifteen mentioned low morale and three of these said that the ethos within the hospitals had been undermined. Thirteen consultants talked of the problem of finance. One said there was *'increasing pressure on clinicians to make financial rather than clinical decisions'*. Others saw money being wasted: *'Vast sums of money are being wasted in management consultancy and restructuring.'*

Several consultants drew attention to the fact that the Patient's Charter had led to more complaints. Another, without mentioning the charter, talked of the *'encouragement of the more narrow minded patient to complain'*.

Nine doctors said that the reforms had led to worse treatment for the patients. One said *'quality and care are sacrificed for money and* numbers'. Another commented that 'Patients now have less choice as to where they are treated.'

Eight mentioned problems with managers. One spoke of the 'dangerous interference of managers'. Another commented more fully: 'We have poor quality managers with no understanding of medical practice managing services they know nothing about, selling services to people who do not know what they are buying.' Another commented that there was a problem with more bureaucracy: 'Money is spent not on direct patient care. Managers remain ignorant about the delivery of care but they still want to decide all the important issues.'

Several drew attention to the loss of the public service ethic. One such comment was: 'As an NHS service I did not mind sacrificing myself (hard work). As a business it is frustrating to see that health professionals have less say than managers.' Another commented: 'British surgery had a wisdom and ethic which was the envy of the world and it is currently being squandered.' Others spoke of the loss of morale and the fact that the hospitals had a depressed atmosphere.

Problems faced by orthopaedic surgeons

After the more general question about the effect of the reforms we asked about the problems faced at the level of the local hospital. We asked the consultants: 'What are the main problems you currently face?' Their response is shown in Table 10.7.

Table 10.7   Particular problems being experienced

Problems experienced	Number	Percentage
Staffing shortages	30	21%
Unrealistic workload	29	21%
Managers and bureaucracy	27	19%
Underfunding	16	11%
Waiting times	10	7%
Purchasers (including fundholders)	10	7%
Poor staff morale	9	6%
Bed shortages	9	6%
Patient's Charter and complaints	7	5%
Hospital buildings	4	3%
Other (e.g. litigation, poor information)	9	6%
Total problems mentioned	156	

The results show that 132 out of the 140 (94 per cent) mentioned problems. The major difficulty was staff shortages. Some of these mentioned the shortage of anaesthetists and nurses and others drew attention to the need for more consultants. One said there is an *'overwhelming amount of work because there were not enough surgeons'*. Another commented: *'I'm finding it difficult to start spinning a plate when I'm already running and juggling with three burning clubs in the air.'* Almost one in five mentioned problems with managers or administration. One said: *'Management is responding to central directives in a blind fashion without taking into account relevant clinical issues and longer term planning.'* Another spoke of the *'constant interruption of my clinical practice by blundering and bureaucratic stupidity'*. This surgeon went on to say that he had given up and was taking early retirement. A third said: *'We receive reams and reams of paper from the ever proliferating managers and their deputies. There is a tendency for managers to influence clinical decisions.'* A fourth pointed to the fact that managers' *'emphasis is on budgets and targets* without *consideration of quality of patient care'*.

Ten consultants mentioned problems with purchasers. One said there was a *'conflict of interest between various purchasers'*. Another said: *'"Purchasers" have a programme which is difficult to comprehend eg funding hospitals far away to operate on our patients.'* Another complained of *'interference particularly by purchasers who are after all only surrogates of patients'*. Several mentioned difficulty with fundholders. One said that they did not have enough finance while a different concern was with the *'lack of theatre space to respond to GP fundholders' demands'*. Nine mentioned bed shortages. One said: *'We waste time chasing beds.'*

Four mentioned problems with the Patient's Charter and the fact that people were more likely to complain these days. One said: *'Patients Charter, if we have to keep to this. What about a doctor's charter?'* A second said: *'Patients are encouraged by politicians to ask for what cannot be provided. Then dissatisfaction appears.'* A doctor from the Home Counties spoke of *'increasing patient expectations with decreasing facilities and support. Poor advice from the misinformed.'*

Four mentioned problems with hospital buildings. One spoke of the *'resiting of my hospital onto a smaller site with fewer beds and theatre sessions'*.

There were a few minor problems. Two mentioned litigation. This is a much smaller percentage than the result when we surveyed obstetricians.[4]

4 Francome *et al.*, 1993, p. 126.

Three mentioned problems with information. One, for example, complained of *'Totally untried new information technology which is worse than original manual systems.'*

Improving the quality of the service

We asked the orthopaedic surgeons: *'What changes would you like to see in the quality of care?'* The results show that 131 (94 per cent) made suggestions. The general theme of the comments was that there was a shortage of resources. The consultants would like an end to the main concentration on financial matters and feel that due attention should be given to the quality of patient care. The increase in expenditure on bureaucracy and management meant that there was less money available for the primary task of caring for patients. The managers were sometimes seen as intervening in medical matters which were not part of their responsibility. The actual results are tabulated in Table 10.8.

Table 10.8   *Proposals for improvements in care*

Proposal	Number	Percentage
Improve quality	34	26%
More staff	31	24%
More facilities	22	17%
Alter managers or bureaucracy	17	13%
Elimination of purchasing	14	11%
Better role for consultants	13	10%
Other	15	11%
Total	145	

The results show that the main concern was with quality. One said he would like to have *'the time to spend with explanations to ensure patients leave clinics satisfactorily'*. Another stated: *'The quality of care should be defined operationally. This would then protect clinicians and patients and expose the massive underfunding that needs to be addressed so that targets can be met.'* A third said: *'A standard of quality should be agreed on and then the costings worked out – not the other way round.'* Several said that values should be changed. A typical comment was *'forget numbers – we should treat sick people properly'*, and there was felt to be a need for *'a return to running a patient caring and orientated service rather than a bureaucratic machine governed by finance only'.*

Some doctors drew attention to the fact that patients were often treated at distant hospitals with total lack of planning for future care.

Sixteen consultants said they wanted changes in the level of bureaucracy. One said: *'Sack all the administration workers not in a post that was available pre-1990. Get more auxiliary staff with the money.'* Others echoed this point: *'We should spend the resources on care and remove the vast bureaucracy.'* A third talked of the *'vast waste on the financial side, accountants etc. Not much extra is going to patient care.'*

Some doctors said that they were maintaining standards but the presence of managers was making things more difficult: *'The quality of care is still excellent due to the dedication of staff but inefficient management has seriously reduced morale.'*

Fourteen consultants called for changes in the method of purchasing. One said there was a need for *'a return to patient needs rather than fundholder considerations'.*

Thirteen called for a better role for surgeons. One of these said: *'At the moment no one looks into the quality of life of the professionals or even their security of position.'* Two surgeons called for the overall change in the structure. One called for the district general hospital to be restored to the centre of activity. Another revived the idea put forward by the Liberal Democrats for there to be a specific health tax.

CONCLUSIONS

The figures provided by the government for the number of operations reveal little comparability and show once again the need to rationalise official data. Our survey results show that the reforms have failed to deliver in three imporant areas. First, a majority of consultants in our sample has been faced with an increase in waiting times and a quarter of them were asked to control the number of operations they conducted up to the end of the financial year. This issue is obviously of great importance. Evidence shows that those with adequate finance obtain immediate relief from pain, while those relying on the NHS suffer delays and in some cases miss opportunities through no fault of their own and then have an extended wait. In one case a hospital called the patient for immediate surgery when she was out shopping. As she was not back by 11 a.m., the bed was given to someone else and over a year later she had still not been recalled. Others have refused to go on holiday for fear of missing their appointment and were not admitted despite cancelling and losing their deposits.[5] There is a strong case for increasing resources so that all people are treated promptly. Finance is not infinite of course, and it would be useful to have some estimates of the number of operations needed by the population and use this as a basis for allocating resources.

Secondly, our evidence shows that two thirds of the consultants were faced with a situation where they had to give priority, not according to clinical need, but rather according to the length of time on the waiting list. Thirdly, three-quarters of consultants were faced with a situation where fundholders were given priority. Again, people were not being treated according to their clinical need but according to the kind of GP practice they attended.

Overall, from their answers to these questions and their comments, the position for the majority of consultants seems to have worsened with the changes. There are a substantial number who are clearly upset that resources that could be used for patient care are being diverted to other areas, particularly to management and bureaucracy.

INCREASING THE NUMBER OF KIDNEY AND OTHER TRANSPLANTS

This is another important area which the government did not make a priority. On 30 November 1994 4,874 people were waiting for a kidney transplant in this country. This is an increase from the figures of 4,640 in September 1993 and 3,847 on 31 December 1990.[6] In an attempt to reduce this list, in October 1994 the government decided to computerise the register of organ donors. This development has had a mixed reception. Some thought it was a small step forward while others said this would prove just as ineffectual as the existing donor card system.[7]

A more active approach is to assume people to be donors unless they opt out. The Belgians have such a system, which is modified to allow any objections of the donor's family to be accepted. Our initial research suggested that this system could work well here. A series of Gallup polls have shown that an opt-out system would have the support of the general public. However, our initial investigations indicated that the

5 Rigge, 1994.
6 UKTSSA, 1993.
7 Nuttall, 1994, p. 7.

government would not support this more active approach unless the medical practitioners in the area were in support of it. We therefore decided to find out the views of the doctors involved. We also sought to identify any other needs of consultants working in this area.

Methodology

In 1994 we sent questionnaires to all ninety-five nephrology consultants named in the *Medical Directory*. There were two reminders sent to non-respondents. The consultants were based in forty-two units in England and Wales. Six questionnaires were returned incomplete as the addressee had either recently died or retired from medical practice. This left an initial sample of eighty-nine. We received sixty-two completed questionnaires after three mailings. However, in six cases one nephrologist was nominated to complete the questionnaire after consultation with the whole unit. The questionnaires therefore represented the views of seventy-seven consultants, a response rate of 86.5 per cent. The responses came from thirty-eight units or 90.1 per cent of those contacted.

Results

The main question on the system of donation was as follows: *'The Kidney Patient's Association is recommending a change in the donor system to one where people opt out if they do not wish to donate. Would you support or oppose such a change in the law?'*

Eight consultants did not respond to this question, giving an effective sample size of sixty-nine. A total of forty-five (65 per cent) said they were in support, nine (13 per cent) said that they neither supported nor opposed and fifteen (22 per cent) said they were opposed to it. So a nearly two-thirds majority of consultants were in favour of such a change in the law and fewer than a quarter were opposed to it. However, consultants from two units said they were strongly against such an approach. They both felt that problems could arise if a mistake were made and a transplant occurred against the wishes of the donor's family.

Tom Sackville, the minister involved, has voiced similar concerns:[7]

> Britain has a voluntary tradition in terms of donating blood and organs for medicine and this should be maintained. Organ donation should be seen as a gift to help others rather than a requirement of the state.

7 Nuttall, 1994, p. 7.

He also said that the issue of organ donation needed to be handled sensitively, otherwise the whole area could be discredited.

There does, however, appear to be majority public support for such a change. At the request of the Kidney Patients' Association a Gallup Poll asked a random sample of 1,019 people a similar question on opting out: 'Would you approve or disapprove if the kidneys of anyone who had just died could be used unless they had "opted out", that is, stated that this must not be done?' The interviewing was carried out between 4 and 10 May 1994 and showed that three in five (59 per cent) would approve and just under a third (31 per cent) would disapprove. The other 10 per cent said that they did not know.[8] Hence there is majority support for the change, from both the professionals and the public.

We asked the sample of consultants: *'Do you ever have to refuse treatment to patients?'* In response 44 per cent of the seventy-seven responding said they sometimes had to. Those who responded positively were asked on what criteria they based their decision. All identified medical factors and some mentioned other criteria too. Several doctors pointed out that some patients would be unable to tolerate dialysis. The general feeling was that any decision would be based on general fitness and ability to withstand potential complications. Several said they would refuse treatment to patients with severe cardiovascular or neoplastic conditions. This decision would also be taken in cases where the quality of life would remain unacceptably low despite treatment. Amongst the non-medical reasons, fourteen said the age of the patient was relevant, eleven mentioned social factors and five economic considerations.

The responses showed that where the age of the patient and social factors were criteria in the refusal of treatment, they were never a reason on their own. They would be considered together with the medical condition of the patient. Treatment would only be refused if the patient were suffering from a severe or life-threatening condition. One consultant commented: *'We do not "refuse" to treat but sometimes agree that non-treatment is the best option.'*

The five units reporting that patients had been refused treatment for economic reasons expressed the hope that they would be accepted by other units.

Where refusal of treatment on the grounds of age was a factor, two consultants had an upper limit of 75 years, whilst two others set their limit at 80. However, one consultant pointed out: *'We have dialysis patients of ninety.'*

8 Gallup, 1994.

QUESTIONS ON TRANSPLANTS

Those carrying out transplants were asked the following question: *'How many transplants did you carry out last year?'* In the sample twenty-six consultants carried out 1,026 transplants, which was an average of thirty-nine each. The consultants also told us that 134 (13 per cent) of the transplants were from the patients' families. In 1991 nationally there were only eighty-four (4.8 per cent) such transplants. Clearly there has been a change in practice.[9]

We also asked: *'How many transplants would you have been able to carry out if the supply of donors was unlimited?'* In reply the consultants estimated that they would be able to treat 1,463 extra patients a year, an increase of 143 per cent.

DIALYSIS

In our sample thirty units carried out dialysis. We asked the consultants: *'How many patients do you currently treat?'* The results show that 3,631 patients (an average of 121 per unit) were treated by continuous ambulatory peritoneal dialysis. Haemodialysis was used for 3,608 patients (an average of 120 per unit). Only twenty-five units offered home haemodialysis, and 829 patients were treated by it (an average of thirty-three per unit).

We asked: *'How many patients could you treat if you had extra resources?'* Only five gave an exact figure in reply to this question. However, the comments indicated that the dialysis units were working to full capacity, in contrast to the transplant consultants who needed more organs.

Another question was: *'Do you feel that kidney disease is given high enough priority by the Government?'* In reply twenty (27 per cent) said it was and fifty-three (73 per cent) said it was not. Four did not respond to this question. Three pointed out that the same response would be given by most professionals, no matter which field of medicine they specialised in.

We asked all the consultants: *'Do you know of patients who have died through lack of resources?'* Only ten consultants were aware of patients who had died due to a shortage of facilities. However, two of these said, *'not in the last three years'*, and another qualified the reply by saying that the death in these circumstances was not in his unit. One consultant who was aware of patients dying who were awaiting

9 UKTSSA, 1993.

transfer to the renal unit argued: '*All patients who have renal failure should be eligible for dialysis treatment. The decision not to treat should be that of the patient/doctor.*'

We asked our sample: '*Do you have to close at any time for lack of staff?*' The results show that eleven of the thirty-eight units had found it necessary to close at some time. There were many reasons for closure, one of which was the lack of hospital-based staff. However, all related to a lack of resources.

We asked about changes the consultants would like the government to make. The responses show that the suggestions were in four main areas.

- The first was an improvement in financing to produce an increase in the number of units: '*We need an urgent increase in dialysis satellite centres and an increase in major renal centres (see European figures).*' Another identified the need for '*Realistic funding to allow capital expansion in busy units.*' A third said: '*There should be an appropriate financial commitment to the NHS – this may require an increase in taxation.*'
- The second point was a necessary increase in staff to service their units. One consultant drew attention to the conflict between the needs of the patients and the medical staff: '*We should not reduce junior doctors hours of work from 105 to 72 hours a week without putting in more junior doctors.*'
- Thirdly, more effort should be made to improve the availability of donors.
- Fourthly, there should be changes away from the market philosophy. Several were concerned about the competitive element that had been introduced into the NHS, which they felt contributed to inefficiency and undermined values. '*We need reductions in management numbers to reduce costs. In addition there should be a restoration of the old NHS where treatment was based on clinical need and not market forces.*' Another called for '*A return to co-operation rather than competition between health care providers. Dismantle the internal market mechanism of funding.*' However, there were several consultants who indicated that they were able to work within the reforms. One respondent said, '*The purchaser/provider situation for our unit is ensuring that all patients are treated.*'

Others, while not criticising the NHS changes overall, called for a change in the method of financing. Three called for central funding and in addition one said, '*There should be a recognition of paediatric renal services as a regional speciality that requires* central planning *and resources to avoid children being sent to adult units not equipped or experienced in the care of children.'*

In addition to these comments, one doctor felt there should be clearer instructions to purchasers and providers.

CONCLUSION

Two main issues were identified by the research: first, the lack of donors providing suitable organs for transplantation; and, secondly, the lack of facilities and funding for dialysis. One reason for the decline in the number of transplants is the cut in the number of deaths from road traffic accidents, which we looked at in the previous chapter. However, shortage of donors would not be a problem if donation were more readily acceptable. Several consultants pointed out that enough suitable donors die in intensive care each year to clear the waiting list as each donor could help two kidney patients.

This highlights the necessity for a change in the system of organ donation in this country. As the percentage of organs from live donors is less than 10 per cent it appears that cadaver donation is the only area in which improvement can be expected. The stumbling block has been how to find an acceptable system. In July 1994 the government announced an opt-in scheme which involves keeping the names of those willing to donate their organs after their death on a register held at Bristol.[10] It started on 6 October 1994. The idea is to target all new drivers when they apply for their licence. It is also theoretically possible to obtain a form from post offices, doctor's surgeries and hospitals. However, our research indicates there are problems with distribution. At the end of 1994 and the beginning of 1995 we visited three doctor's surgeries, six post offices and four chemists. All of these places were either unaware of the form or thought it was available elsewhere. We also telephoned the number given by the government to ask for a form at the beginning of November and two months later had still not received it. The system is clearly not yet working.

Furthermore, the problem with this opt-in system is that only those renewing their driving licence or applying for the first time are targeted. Many people who already carry a donor card and have a valid licence may be left off the register. Even once registered, the system requires doctors to ask the next of kin for their permission before carrying out the wishes of the donor. In this way the register will alert hospitals to

10 Anderson, 1994.

the fact that a person may be a possible donor but it does not solve the problem of relatives who may be reluctant to consider the option and give their consent at such a distressing moment.

We recommend two changes. In the short term, our recommendation is for all car tax renewal forms to carry information regarding the new register, complete with a form on which all drivers (and non-drivers) in the household could indicate their desire to be donors. This need not be a long-term requirement as after a year any current licence holder would have been given the chance to register, and new drivers would be able to register as they obtain their first licence. If the government is concerned about the tax holder filling in the form for family members without their knowledge, an acknowledgement card addressed to non-car tax registrants would solve this problem.

A better idea in the long term is to follow the example set by Belgium which has implemented a weakened presumed consent method which we feel meets the government's objections. This method has allowed Belgium to double the number of transplants performed each year. It works slightly differently from the normal method of presumed consent by allowing a veto to the family. Even with this veto the improvement is considerable because when a person is shown to be brain dead, it takes the hospital only five minutes to check the central register. Once they know that a person is a potential donor, they then inform the relatives – rather than having to ask them – that their loved one wished to donate his or her organs after death. Belgian doctors believe it is effective because the question is asked automatically and everyone expects to be asked. For this reason very few relatives have made use of the veto. In fact only 2 per cent of people have actually opted out of the system.[11]

In the area of dialysis, lack of funds appeared to be a much greater problem. One example is the case of the consultant who highlighted worries concerning the reduction in the hours worked by junior doctors. The single fact that a doctor is required to work even seventy-two hours per week (let alone 105), and while working has to make life and death decisions, illustrates the need for urgent action. The implication is that current funding is at a dangerously low level.

One of the worrying aspects of the lack of funds for dialysis is the possible knock-on effect it may have on transplantation. If people do not receive the best possible treatment whilst on dialysis, their chances of transplanting successfully may be reduced. In this area, there is plenty of scope for government action.

11 Channel 4, 1994.

RECOMMENDATIONS

A   There needs to be an increase in resources to support more hip replacements. They should be provided on the basis of clinical need rather than on the vagaries of funding being available.

B   There needs to be an improvement in official data to make them comparable between England, Scotland, Wales and Northern Ireland. Reasons for differences should be investigated with a view to improving care.

C   A greater number of transplants should be facilitated by changing the system of donation to one of modified opting out.

CHAPTER ELEVEN

IMPROVING THE HEALTH OF THE NATION

Every minute of every day a woman dies as a result of pregnancy or childbirth somewhere in the world.

We have seen that in many important respects British society has failed to improve the health of the nation and that Britain has fallen behind other countries. In this chapter we aim to analyse some other factors and make proposals for improvements. In its document *Working Together for Better Health*,[1] the government suggested that improvements in health will come about in three main ways. These are encouraging people to lead healthier and safer lives; ensuring better and safer environments in which people can live, work and play; and providing the right type of high quality local services. However, what this does not really consider is the role of the government in creating a social structure which improves health by reducing inequalities. We shall begin this chapter by collating the evidence in this area. We shall then outline a general theory of health. This will be followed by a discussion of other important factors related to health. There are important decisions to be made in respect of the long-term ill and of the elderly who need care and their carers. There are also concerns about environmental factors and health, inequalities relating to social classes and ethnic groups, as well as commercial interests and health.

INEQUALITIES AND HEALTH

In the early 1960s there were many who believed that a gradual movement was occurring towards equality. This was challenged by Richard Titmuss in his new introduction to Tawney's *Equality*.[2] He pointed out that the move towards equality occurred during the Second World War and that there was no necessary trend. At this time the philosophy of the Conservative Party was well to the left of what it became from 1979. Harold Macmillan talked of the need for full

---

1 Department of Health, 1993e.
2 Tawney, 1963.

employment and the welfare state. In 1938 in his book *The Middle Way*[3] he called for the nationalisation of the coal industry, and a subsequent Conservative Prime Minister, Ted Heath, actually nationalised Rolls Royce. However, with the implementation of New Right policies in the 1980s and 1990s inequalities increased.

In Britain in the 1970s and 1980s unskilled manual workers were found to have twice the death rates of those with professional occupations and their families.[4] Commenting on the data, Wilkinson suggested that the social class differences in death rates are neither fixed nor unalterable.[5]

Writing at the end of 1994, Peter Townsend commented:[6]

> This year has seen recurring reports of the swelling salaries and breathtaking pronouncements of rich people. Early this month Iain Valance, the chairman of British Telecom, described his salary – which with additions, is now in excess of £750,000 – as 'modest'. By comparison with what is going on at the top of Britain's hierarchy in the 75 largest non financial companies perhaps he was right.

He continued by noting that inequalities had not only increased, but that there had been a tendency for certain members of the government to stigmatise the poor rather than help them, as in the past. Peter Lilley said young ladies get pregnant to jump the housing list, a comment which had little relevance to young mothers. We have seen that three-quarters of them live with their parents and only one in ten young teenagers planned to become pregnant.[7]

Housing stock has also suffered with the move to the right. Iona Heath argued that social housing in Britain had a 150-year history of effectiveness as a health intervention. She pointed out that until 1951 central government's responsibility for housing was placed within the Ministry of Health.[8]

In contrast, government spending on housing fell from £13.1 billion in 1979 to £5.8 billion in 1992, while the sale of public housing realised £28 billion by the end of 1993. Shelter pointed out that the number of homeless people more than doubled between 1978 and 1989, when it was 126,680. In 1993 the figure had increased further, to

3 Macmillan, 1938.
4 Whitehead, 1992.
5 Wilkinson, 1994, p. 16.
6 Townsend, 1994, p. 1674.
7 Francome and Walsh, 1995, p. 17.
8 Heath, I., 1994, p. 1675.

139,110.[9] The 1991 Census identified 2,827 rough sleepers and 19,417 hostel dwellers, although these are thought to be gross underestimates. It was calculated that in inner city wards 30 per cent of young men had not been included in the 1991 Census.[10] It is therefore not surprising that Homeless Network estimated that three thousand people spent all or part of 1994 sleeping on London's streets.[11]

One factor related to homelessness for young people is that in 1988 benefit rates were reduced for 18–24-year-olds and general entitlement to income support was removed for most unemployed 16- and 17-year-olds. In 1991 the government commissioned a survey of 16- and 17-year-olds who had claimed special hardship allowance. There were 76,957 such claims in the first nine months of 1992. The children's charity Barnardo's published evidence commenting that these young people presented a sorry sight:[12]

> 45% had been forced to sleep 'rough' at some point, many were still homeless, half had no money, and a quarter of them said they had needed to beg, steal or sell drugs in order to survive. A quarter already had criminal convictions, and a quarter of the girls were pregnant.

Overall, Heath comments:[13]

> The consequent fall in the quantity and quality of local authority housing has led to growing social, economic and health disparities between local authority tenants and home owners...the lack of investment in decent affordable housing produces and sustains homelessness, which in turn damages health, increases the demand for health care, increases the costs of health care.

These comments come after a number of reports documenting the inequalities of income and in some cases their growth:
- There has been a great widening of income disparities. In 1983 the ratio of the income of the richest 20 per cent to the poorest 20 per cent was 4:1. It grew with an especially steep rise between 1985 and 1987 until in 1991 the ratio was over 5.7:1.[14] An official study confirmed these findings. It showed that after housing costs had been

9 Shelter, 1995.
10 Brown, P., 1995.
11 Heath, I., 1994, p. 1675.
12 Wilkinson, 1994.
13 Heath, I., 1994, p. 1676.
14 Wilkinson, 1994, p. 4.

taken into account, the group having the lowest 10 per cent of income suffered a 14 per cent decline in real income. In contrast, the top 10 per cent had a rise of over 20 per cent, due in part to a move away from direct to indirect taxation. So, whereas in 1979 only 9 per cent of the population received less than 50 per cent of the average income, the proportion had risen to 24 per cent by 1990–3.[15]

Wilkinson commented that health data reflect this inequality. In the years from 1975 to 1983 there was a reduction in the sum of the mortality indexes for the age groups up to 44 years from 410 to 310, a decline of around a quarter.[16] Over the next eight years, however, until 1990 the decline was much less marked and only fell to around 280 although it would have been expected to decline to around 230 if trends had continued. So the improvement in mortality was less than half that which might have been expected and is one factor in Britain falling behind other countries in mortality indicators. More recent developments since Wilkinson's work suggest that inequality will have increased further now. The imposition of 8 per cent VAT on fuel will fall proportionately more heavily on the poor than on others. Furthermore, there have been some well-publicised increases in income for bosses of privatised industries. At the end of 1994 British Gas reported a 75 per cent increase in salary for its chief executive, taking it to £475,000, while at about the same time the company cut the wages of its workforce and, in the words of a quality newspaper, was 'slashing the pipeline safety budget'.[17]

- Data from the European Community from 1975 to 1985 showed that of the twelve countries in the European Community Britain had increased its income inequality by far the highest amount. The data also show that France, the country which had moved the most towards equality had increased its life expectancy the most. Indeed, the six countries which had decreased inequality or maintained their position all had an increase in life expectancy greater than the other seven countries which had grown in inequality.[18]

- Data from eight OECD countries showed that the USA had the highest infant mortality rate as well as the highest percentage in relative poverty. The UK had the second highest percentage in relative poverty and the third highest infant mortality rate after the United States and Canada. Sweden, Norway, Switzerland and the

15 Department of Social Security, 1993.
16 Wilkinson, 1994, p. 4.
17 Rose, 1995.
18 O'Higgins and Jenkins, 1990.

Netherlands had much lower infant mortality rates and much less relative poverty.[19] One factor probably influencing the poor health performance in the United States is the growth in inequality during the 1970s and especially the 1980s as the country followed similar economic policies to Britain. In the United States differences in life expectancy between white and black people increased with widening income differentials.[20]

- A study of deprivation and mortality in Scotland between 1981 and 1991 found that there was an increase in inequality and deprivation. This was reflected in changes in mortality. The Standardised Mortality Ratio in Scotland declined by 22 per cent over the period. However, in the poorer areas the decline was over half this and so the gap between the rich and the poor was widening. In fact in poor groups there was an increase in mortality of the age group 20 to 29 of 29 per cent for men and 11 per cent for women.[21]

- In his report for 1990 the Chief Medical Officer drew attention to data indicating a rise in the national mortality rates in the age group 15–44 years from 1985. This correlated with the growth in inequality.[22]

- A study in England of a random sample of 300,000 people aged between 16 and 65 at the 1991 Census found that declining material circumstances such as insecurity of housing tenure and lack of access to a car were associated with increasing mortality risk. Unemployed men had a 24 per cent higher risk of death than employed men. For unemployed women there was an even higher risk (48 per cent), but the researchers suggested that non-working women often had the alternative category of housewife. Only 8 per cent of non-working women said they were unemployed compared to 51 per cent of non-working men. So the women in this category were possibly a special group.[23]

- There is evidence that respiratory and infectious diseases are specifically related to deprivation. An article in the British Medical Journal stated:[24]

Since 1987 the numbers of cases of tuberculosis in England and Wales have shown a steady increase, a similar rise to

....
19 Wennemo, 1993.
20 Davey Smith and Eggar, 1993.
21 McLoone and Boddy, 1994, p. 1465.
22 Department of Health, 1991.
23 Sloggart and Joshi, 1994, p. 1470.
24 Spence et al., 1993, p. 759.

that seen in the United States…poverty and deprivation are thought to have played a part in the rise in tuberculosis. In an analysis of the increase in incidence in England and Wales by age and sex we have shown that HIV is not yet implicated in the increase in the number of cases notified. The biggest rises have been seen in young females and in older men and women.

Liverpool had a rate of tuberculosis of 12.7 per 100,000. Ethnic minorities had a rate of 47.9 per 100,000. However, irrespective of ethnic group, research also indicated that the illness was far more common in deprived areas with a high proportion of council houses and a high rate of free school meals than in more affluent areas. The researchers were not clear why poverty led to tuberculosis. However, they suggest it may be related to poor nutrition, which leads to the immune system being more vulnerable. Overcrowding may also be important. One example given in the report was of a 21-year-old man who shared a two-bedroom house with his mother and six siblings. He had to share a bed with three siblings under the age of 10. All the family was infected and three developed the disease. The researchers suggest such overcrowding may be uncommon but it is more common among ethnic minorities than in the population as a whole. In general the increase in tuberculosis is likely to be due to an underlying deprivation amongst a segment of the population.[25]

- Research for the National Children's Home charity published in 1994 calculated that the basic social security benefit paid to more than 1.5 million families was only £5.46 a week. At this level it was not enough to pay for the diet prescribed for a child in a Victorian workhouse. They costed diets for Bethnal Green in 1876 and for the Poor Law orders in 1913 at £5.46 and £7.07 respectively. In 1913 the children had bread and milk for breakfast; beef, potatoes or vegetables and fresh fruit pudding for lunch; and a supper of seed cake and cocoa. This diet is much better than can be afforded by Britain's poor today. Tim White, the charity's chief executive, commented: 'It is appalling, as we approach the year 2000, that even an 1876 workhouse diet is too expensive for one in four of our children.'[26]

- Former Prime Minister Ted Heath commented on proposed government measures to cut money further to the poor in 1993:

---

25 Spence *et al.*, 1993, p. 760.
26 Brindle, 1994b.

Single parent families are having enough trouble surviving on £67 a week. By making life even more difficult for them, the Government will only be penalising children who are already likely to be substantially disadvantaged.[27]

In the introduction we considered the case of Japan and the fact that between 1970 and 1990 the people of that country gained on average three years greater life expectancy than Britain. In 1980 income inequalities in the two countries were similar. Since that time Japan's inequalities have declined to become the lowest of any country reporting to the World Bank. In contrast Britain's inequalities have increased substantially.[28] In fact a report by the Joseph Rowntree Foundation in February 1995 found that in Britain the gap between the rich and the poor was the widest since the war and that since 1977 the number of people with less than half the average national income had trebled. Britain's inequality has grown faster than that of any comparative country. The report called for collective investment to be placed before tax cuts.

In several other countries inequalities have narrowed. This applies to Spain, Ireland, Denmark and Italy. In these countries the effects of class differences on death rates can be expected to decrease. In contrast British inequalities and social class differences in death rates have increased. Regional data already show that increased inequalities in income distribution have been associated with increased differentials in Standard Mortality Rate.[29] When national data are published in future years there can be little doubt that the differences will be seen to be accentuated.[30]

THE GREAT BETRAYAL

This was the headline in the *Daily Telegraph* at the end of 1994 above an article about the plight of elderly people. It pointed to the example of May Campbell, who inherited £70,000 from her father but died old and penniless. The report commented:[31]

> She wasn't a spendthrift or unlucky, and she wasn't robbed. Her mistake lay in thinking that the National Health

27 Heath, E., 1993, p. 24.
28 Wilkinson, 1994, p. 22.
29 Phillimore *et al.*, 1994.
30 Wilkinson, 1994, p. 22.
31 Grice, 1994, p. 13.

Service to which she and her husband had contributed all their lives, would take care of her in her final illness. Instead her savings were systematically plundered to pay for nursing home fees in the last eight years of her life.

The report continued that Mrs Campbell came from a family that believed in self-sufficiency. They 'pulled themselves up by their own bootstraps' and her husband became a successful businessman. Before the NHS came into being they paid into the Bradford Hospital Fund. However, once the NHS was set up they paid their national contributions, believing that they had a contract which would look after them when they were in need. Mrs Campbell developed Alzheimer's disease and was looked after by her children until she needed permanent care. As she had more than £8,000 and needed nursing rather than medical care, the health service was entitled to ignore her. She ended her days in a nursing home costing £320 a week. By the time she died her whole capital, consisting of her inheritances from both her husband and her father, had been spent and her children were forced to sell her house to meet the bills. Her son said that she would have been terribly saddened to see her whole life's work come to nought. He said that the system was a confidence trick and his parents would have been better treated had they been poor:[31]

I listened to John Major talking about inheritance cascading down the generations and I felt that he was being economical with the truth. The other day I went to see my solicitor and put my own house in trust for my children so that the Government won't be able to demand that it is sold to pay for the fees if I have to go into a nursing home.

A similar article appeared in the *Observer*, which contained the same quote about wealth cascading through the generations. However, this article concentrated on the position of families, and especially women, in having to look after elderly relatives in the guise of community care. There are those who argue that the primary purpose of community care is to save money rather than to provide good care. Examples of poor practice are easy to find:[32]

- A middle-aged woman in Willesden, North London, has to look after her 81-year-old mother plus two aunts in their 70s virtually single handed. She thinks this saves the state about £1,500 a week.

31 Grice, 1994, p. 13.
32 Jones, 1994a.

- A woman recovering from a heart attack has been told she may have to wait a year for someone to come and lift her in the bath. In other places (e.g. Enfield) no help whatsoever may be available for bathing.
- 'My mother had to go into hospital earlier this year and after she came out, a social worker called for a while, but the visits suddenly stopped. When I asked about it, the social services department said that after six weeks they pass cases on to the community – what they meant was me!'

There has been a largely unannounced move within the NHS away from long-term care of the elderly. This has forced people either to be a burden on their family or to go into private nursing homes. There are around six million people looking after elderly or disabled relatives, and these carers are mainly middle-aged women. For 1.5 million this is a full-time job. In 1994 there were 168,000 places in private nursing homes, which was more than three times the number in 1987 and led Labour MP Malcolm Wicks to comment that 'wealth is cascading into private nursing homes'.[33]

This problem has led to a great amount of confusion about the role of the NHS in long-term care. Many elderly people are very concerned about being a burden to their relatives and have a fear of becoming penniless. This problem needs to be addressed to ensure that there is not a great deal more distress and worry among people who have contributed high amounts of insurance contributions to the NHS. The Department of Health wrote in the summer of 1994 that the issue should be solved locally. However, unless additional funds are provided this is clearly unsatisfactory.

The situation needs urgent attention. The *British Medical Journal* recommended that those who care for elderly or disabled relatives at home should have two weeks' paid holiday each year and a weekly allowance. The report 'Taking Care of the Carers' coincided with a report from Scope (formerly the Spastics Society) which showed that two-thirds of carers said that they did not get enough help from the state. Furthermore three-quarters of carers said that their health had suffered.[34]

It has been pointed out that carers within families save the country a great deal of money and therefore deserve support. However, we would argue that in the interests of greater social cohesion caring for people –

33 Jones, 1994a, p. 19.
34 Court, 1995, p. 617.

whether children, disabled or elderly – should be shared. Families on their own should not be left to fend for themselves. There is no shortage of labour; rather what is evident is the lack of political will to deal with this growing problem.

IMPROVING THE ENVIRONMENT

This is an important area and one which is omitted from the government's health strategy. A major problem is the level of pollutants from vehicle emissions. One of the generally accepted pollutants is lead. After reviewing the evidence from scores of studies, Markham argues that lead in petrol is responsible for restricted mental development in children.[35] A cautious review suggested that a doubling of body lead burden is associated with a mean deficit in full-scale IQ of around one to two IQ points.[36] Governments have taken some measures to deal with lead but there are several other pollutants causing concern. Carbon monoxide can reach seven times the recommended World Health Organization limits for long periods in London and it is known to aggravate chronic respiratory and cardiac disorders.[37] In Glasgow traffic pollution in the form of nitrogen dioxide has been recorded at levels twice the recommended limits for periods of over one month.[38] The fact that lung cancer deaths are higher in urban areas has led to suggestions that they are due to hydrocarbon emissions from cars and one estimate has suggested that cars are the cause of three thousand lung cancer deaths a year.[39]

One major problem in recent years has been the massive increase in car ownership. Parents have become very concerned about the number of cars on the road and are giving stricter supervision and restricting their children's mobility. A report by the Policy Studies Institute published in 1993 showed that over a twenty-year period there has been a slump in the proportion of children allowed to visit friends, cross roads or go home on their own.[40] The *Guardian* commented:[41]

> Now parents spend more time chauffeuring their able bodied children around, denying them the opportunity to

35 Markham, 1987, p. 2.
36 Pocock *et al.*, 1994.
37 Russell-Jones, 1987, p. 3.
38 BBC News, 10 April 1995.
39 Russell-Jones, 1987, p. 3.
40 Hillman, 1993.
41 Smithers, 1993.

use healthy forms of transport such as bicycles, the institute says. It claims the main reason for parents wanting to escort their children home from school is the danger of traffic... In Britain boys aged 11–15 make 13% of their journeys by bike and girls 4%. In the Netherlands, figures for the 12–14 age group are 61% and 60% respectively. The report points out that children's social and emotional development is being hampered by constant adult supervision, while the lifestyles of parents are also being restricted by the need to escort their offspring.

All is not doom and gloom, however. Under pressure from Friends of the Earth the 1992 Traffic Calming Act permits local authorities to control traffic in streets where children play.[42] If the numbers of cars and lorries can be reduced in favour of bicycles and public transport, improvements are possible in the overall health of society.

INCREASE IN ASTHMA

In the introduction we discussed the fact that the number of people affected by asthma had doubled and the probable link between this and poor air quality. On 12 March 1994 Friends of the Earth took out a full-page advertisement in the *Guardian* reporting that the government was about to announce a £20 million allocation for bigger and better roads. It commented that one in ten children suffers from asthma and that uncontrolled traffic growth will make matters worse. This campaign was successful in that the government abandoned investing such large amounts into new traffic schemes. Table 11.1 gives information about air quality in Britain in 1993.

Table 11.1   *Air quality in Britain 1993*

Worst	Best
Sheffield	Strath Vaich, Ross and Cromarty
Newcastle	Lullington Heath, Sussex
London	Ladybower, Derbyshire
Manchester	Cardiff
Belfast	Stevenage, Hertfordshire

Source Ryan and Reeves, 1994.

42 Ryan and Reeves, 1994.

The official data show that Sheffield had twenty-five days of poor air quality, when the concentration of nitrous oxide – largely from exhausts – soared to more than a hundred parts per million. Sheffield's scientists believe that the high level of pollution is due to many short car journeys.[42] A survey carried out in Manchester on 22 December 1994, when 66,000 cars entered the city between 7 a.m. and 10 a.m., revealed high levels of pollution. The nitrogen dioxide level was 170 parts per million, well above ninety-four for Glasgow, seventy-five for Liverpool and forty-eight for Birmingham. Carbon monoxide levels were also very high. Arnold Spencer, chairman of Manchester's Planning Committee, noted the effect that the pollutants were having on the health of people in the city. He called for:

- Government investment in the local rail network.
- Extensions to Manchester's tram system.
- An end to motorway extension.
- Banning of through traffic from central areas.

He might have added banning a second runway at Manchester Airport.

In London, one borough's report showed that nitrogen dioxide levels had exceeded World Health Organization limits several times during the summer. High levels of nitrogen dioxide pollution caused by car exhaust and causing asthma were recorded in Greenwich, Hackney, Tower Hamlets, Westminster, Bloomsbury, Southwark and the City.[43] Other European capitals are taking positive action to curb the motor car. For example, Athens launched a pilot scheme in April 1995 excluding all vehicles except mini-buses from 8 a.m. to 8 p.m. in the city centre. The proposal to reduce the number of cars is obviously important. Also relevant is the need for motorists to ensure that their cars are running efficiently and cleanly.

On 19 January 1995 the Environment Secretary announced a package of measures designed to improve the quality of air in British cities. Reports suggested that the proposals had been delayed for several months because of pressure from the Department of Trade, which was anxious to protect industry from restrictive legislation. The proposals included monitoring levels of pollution and controlling benzene and emissions of 2.3 butadiene, a petrol-derived carcinogen. The reactions to the proposals were mixed. In a news release, Friends of the Earth criticised the minister about the lack of legislation, saying,

....
42 Ryan and Reeves, 1994.
43 McHardy, 1995.

'unless he is willing to act on a national level, everything else will be ineffective'. The British Asthma Association and the British Lung Association also expressed deep concern. In contrast, the motoring organisations including the Freight Transport Association, were pleased with the announced delays. This divide shows that business interests are protected by government policies and that these are given priority over public health.[43]

CONTROLLING BUSINESS INTERESTS

Business interests conflict with good health.[44] Where this is the case they need to be controlled for the benefit of the health of the society.

One area where there are strong conflicts is children's health, as discussed in Chapter 5; see p. 105. Advertisers wish to sell more sweets, sugary soft drinks and crisps to children despite the fact that the average diet needs to move away from sugar and salt towards fruit and vegetables. We saw that one proposal was to limit advertising to children until 8 p.m. In fact this limit is probably too early. A more effective watershed would seem to be 9 p.m., a generally accepted dividing line. Commenting on the research into diet, Maggie Sanderson of the British Dietetic Association said:[45]

> At the end of the century, as at the beginning of the century, it is the children of the poor who are most at risk, albeit that the types of disease have changed. If we want to break this cycle of poverty and ill health, we need to influence children's diets now.

One point made by Lesley Doyal is that governments have placed few constraints on food producers but have concentrated on encouraging people to eat healthy diets.[46]

KEEPING AN OPEN MIND ABOUT ALTERNATIVES

One important area where there is active debate is on the question of alternative medicine. In recent years there has been an easing of the hostility towards what some prefer to call 'complementary' medicine. In 1980–1 it was estimated that there were about twelve practitioners

43 McHardy, 1995.
44 Doyal, 1985.
45 Nicholson-Lord, 1994.
46 Doyal, 1985, p. 92.

of alternative therapy per 100,000 population, with annual consultation rates of twenty to twenty-six per hundred population.[47] In 1983 the British Medical Association's Board of Science and Education commissioned a working party to assess the practice of complementary or alternative therapies. Its report identified the dissatisfaction of the general public with the increasingly technical approach to medicine, the fragmentation of care and the loss of bedside skills as factors which contributed towards their popularity. In 1989 the *British Medical Journal* reported that about one in eight Britons used complementary therapies such as herbal remedies, homoeopathy, acupuncture, hypnotherapy and spiritual healing.[48] Furthermore, a more positive approach occurred in 1993 when the BMA published *Complementary Medicine: New Approaches to Care*.[49]

A study of 4,600 patients in osteopathic clinics showed that a quarter were there with their GP's blessing and one in ten had been referred there.[50] Scottish evidence showed that one in ten Lothian GPs practised homoeopathy or referred to a homoeopath if necessary. This was according to a study based on answers from 304 GPs.[50]

A special article in the *British Medical Journal* considered the use of alternative medicine by cancer patients. The study was based on 415 patients who had cancer diagnosed over three months before. It found that over 16 per cent had used complementary therapies. More women (one in five) than men (one in eight) used such therapies. The authors suggested that clinicians should be conversant with the popular forms of complementary therapies and that they had psychological benefits. It suggested that there is great value in fostering a hopeful attitude in the management of cancer patients.[51] What is needed is further random controlled experiments to identify the effectiveness of different treatments, apart from their psychological benefits.

BRITAIN'S ROLE IN THE WORLD COMMUNITY

We have seen how inequality has been growing in Britain in recent years and in the world as a whole there has been a widening of income disparities. The number of absolute poor was calculated to have risen by about two-thirds in the fifteen years to 1993. Around two-thirds of

47 Fulder and Munroe, 1982.
48 Aldridge, 1989.
49 British Medical Association, 1993.
50 GP, 1994, p. 16.
51 Downer *et al.*, 1994, p. 87.

the population of sub-Saharan Africa lives in absolute poverty, as do about 1.25 billion people worldwide.[52] An editorial in the *British Medical Journal* pointed out that in the previous year there had been a net outflow of $19 billion from the forty poorest countries to the richest.[53] Most of this outflow is interest on overwhelmingly large foreign loans. Africa spends four times as much on servicing its debts as on providing health services to its 600 million people.[54] In 1985 one-fifth of Third World debt was estimated to be due to arms purchases. Economies have been distorted as cash crops are produced to attempt to service debts. Austerity measures designed to cut public spending have reduced expenditure on health and education.[55] This has meant that the attempted improvements in health with better vaccination coverage, rehydration therapy and community health initiatives have been largely negated. In fact in seven countries there was a rise in the mortality of children under the age of 5 years. In contrast with Western experience worldwide, the number of underweight children has risen from twenty-one million in 1980 to thirty million in 1989. Enrolment in schools in Africa fell by 7 per cent between 1980 and 1990.[55]

Childbirth is still a very dangerous activity for women in the poor countries. The World Health Organization states: 'Every minute of every day a woman dies as a result of pregnancy or childbirth somewhere in the world.'[56] An estimated 500,000 die as the result of pregnancy each year. One estimate is that women in the poorer communities of the world are two hundred times as likely to die in childbirth as are women in Western Europe. Furthermore those women undergo that risk more often. India, Pakistan and Bangladesh account for 28 per cent of the world's births and 46 per cent of its maternal deaths.

The World Health Organization document *Maternal Mortality* included the figures shown in Table 11.2.

....
52 Smith and Leaning, 1993.
53 Godlee, 1993.
54 Smith and Leaning, 1993.
55 Godlee, 1993, p. 1369.
56 Zahr and Royston, 1991, p. 3.

Table 11.2   *Estimates of maternal mortality*

UN region	Live births	Maternal mortality rate (100,000 births)	Maternal deaths (thousands)
World	128	390	500
Developed countries	18	30	6
Developing countries	110	450	494
Africa	23	640	150
Asia	74	420	308
Latin America	13	270	34
Oceania	0		2

Source Zahr and Royston, 1991, p. 3.

The main cause of death is puerperal sepsis (infection). This is often due to the introduction of foreign bodies into the genital tract. Other factors are obstructed labour, hypertensive disorders in pregnancy, and abortion. Abortion mortality is estimated to be 100 to 200,000 women a year.

There are numerous other health problems in the poorer countries. UNICEF reported as follows:[57]

> Carrots provide a rich source of vitamin A which is essential for healthy growth, protects sight and the body's immunity to disease. Every year a quarter of a million young children are permanently blinded because their diet lacks this vital nutrient. The first symptom of this is called night blindness.

It continued by pointing out that breast milk is a rich source of Vitamin A and that it helped to provide Vitamin A capsules to poor countries and also helped people grow their own foods. UNICEF has a health of the world target to eliminate Vitamin A blindness by the year 2000.[58]

The 1990 world summit for children set as a priority the meeting of basic needs – primary health care, primary education, housing, sanitation and nutrition. Its goals include reducing the mortality of children under 5 by a third to seventy per thousand – a modest target –

57 UNICEF, 1993.
58 UNICEF, 1994.

by the year 2000, halving maternal mortality and providing everyone with clean water and sanitation. This aim is supported by 150 countries.

It has been estimated that these improvements will cost an extra $25 billion. One suggestion is that two-thirds of it could come from redistributing spending within developing countries – by reducing military expenditure or redistributing expenditure to primary health care. Other money could come by improving the terms of trade along lines proposed by GATT.[59] A radical change in thinking would be needed for there to be noticeable improvement even by the year 2020.

There is a strong case for Britain to step up its commitment to help reduce world poverty. The United Nations Development Programme's *Human Development Report* recommends that one-fifth of overseas aid budgets should meet countries' basic needs – primary education and health care, drinking water, adequate sanitation, family planning and nutrition. In 1994 Britain designated only 6.6 per cent of its aid in this way. Furthermore the United Nations suggests countries should pay 0.7 per cent of their gross national product to help poor countries. Denmark and the Netherlands exceed the target but Britain was below half at 0.3 per cent in 1994.[60] To meet United Nations targets on primary care Britain needs to increase its budget by over six times. In fact the World Development Movement states that in the budget of 30 November 1994 the government announced that the aid budget would be frozen from 1996–7 and that, 'The freeze is set to take Britain's aid spending to below its previous lowest level of 0.27 per cent of GNP.' So although the government said that it was committed to the United Nations' 0.7 per cent target, the reality is that it has moved in the opposite direction.

Such decisions fly in the face of strong public support for help to the poor countries. The World Development Movement found that over half of those polled in June 1994 said that the peace dividend should be used to increase aid. Three in five said that 'helping poor people in poor countries' should be the most important reason for aid. Only 15 per cent said it should be winning contracts or jobs and only 2 per cent cited winning weapons contracts. However, Godlee[61] stressed the need to raise public awareness of the importance of action and to show people that helping those in poor countries is right, not only for moral reasons but also for practical ones. With the decline of the Cold War the future does not lie with armaments. We need to tackle poverty and

59 Godlee, 1993, p. 1370.
60 World Development Movement, 1994.
61 Godlee, 1993.

help to produce a healthy world. This will help to achieve social stability and benefit everyone. Areas of poverty are breeding grounds of illness.

Furthermore, the rich countries should be seriously considering their role in the sale of arms to poor countries. Developing countries spend about $38 per person on arms annually but only $12 on health. The annual budget of the World Health Organization amounts to about three hours of world expenditure on arms.[62] This could change and countries could begin to give much higher priority to health.

There are three other issues that are important.

• Population is an important area. Richard Smith, editor of the *British Medical Journal*, set out some of the problems in an editorial:[62]

> If population growth is not controlled then poverty will never be reversed, rapidly increasing energy consumption and environmental degradation will continue and leaders will still invest heavily in arms in order to fight for resources or defend their privileges.

One of the problems for people in developing countries is that they have poor access to means of birth control and so are unable to choose the size of their families. A study in 1987 reported that only one in five had good access to birth control and if everyone who wanted family planning could get it, then the birth rate in the poor countries would reduce by a third.[63] UNICEF reported that according to current trends sixty-one countries are set to double their populations in one generation from 1990 to 2025. The list includes Tanzania, Libya, Zaire, Ethiopia, Saudi Arabia and Uganda, all of which if present trends continue will increase their population by at least two and a half times in the thirty-five years.[64]

• There is a problem of energy consumption. World energy consumption grew from one terawatt in 1890 to 3.3 terawatts in 1950 and 13.7 terawatts in 1990. Poor people use less than a tenth of the energy of rich people. An increase in living standards combined with population growth may lead to a fourteen-fold increase in energy consumption by the year 2050.[65] One approach is that of the charity Intermediate Technology. Their view is that what is needed for development in many parts of the world is not labour-saving devices but rather levels of technology that use human energy,

62 Smith and Leaning, 1993.
63 Francome, 1990, p. 9.
64 UNICEF, 1993, p. 35.
65 Smith and Leaning, 1993.

which is available in abundance. In terms of health this would mean developing community health services for everyone rather than a few highly technical hospitals for the rich.[66]

• The world is still a very violent place with the health of great numbers of people being destroyed by violent conflicts. There are also many people who are concerned about the possibility that atomic and nuclear weapons will eventually fall into the hands of guerrilla groups who are opposed to the dominant societies. The *British Medical Journal* reprinted an important editorial from *The Economist*:[67]

> Did you stop worrying about nuclear obliteration when the cold war ended? Start again. To make an atom bomb, a terrorist or a would be proliferator would need to get hold of only 5 Kg of weapon grade plutonium or 15 Kg of weapon grade uranium, less than you would need to fill a fruit bowl. At present the world probably contains about 250 tonnes of this sort of plutonium and 1500 tonnes of the uranium. To lose one bomb's worth from this stock is the equivalent of losing a single word from three copies of the *Economist*...and more than half the world's stock of nuclear explosive material is inside the chaotic relic of the former Soviet Union.

So there is an urgent and strong need for the world to move as far away as possible from international or even civil confrontations.

SUMMARY OF RECOMMENDATIONS

Throughout this book we have considered the government's *Health of the Nation* targets. What has become clear is that they are very limited and that it is necessary to go beyond them. We shall begin our recommendations with the most important change, one which was omitted from the *Health of the Nation* targets, which is to reduce inequality.

A Reduce inequalities
The most fundamental change that will improve the health of the nation is to change government policy by moving towards greater

66 Francome 1990, p. 136.
67 Smith and Leaning, 1993.

equality. This would entail altering the tax system to more direct rather than indirect taxes and in other ways improve the income of the least well-off 20 per cent of the population. We have presented evidence that the percentage of the British population in both relative and absolute poverty has increased. We have also seen that other countries have been pursuing policies in a different direction and that their national health has benefited accordingly.

In 1980 Britain had a great opportunity. It was a wealthy country and was expecting a large amount of oil to come on stream with positive effects on the balance of payments. It had a chance to use this wealth to share out and create employment. There are clearly many jobs that need to be done, not least with the increasing number of elderly that need caring for. However, this did not happen – as we have seen – and Britain has fallen back in comparison to others. It is now more similar to the United States, which has much poorer health, than should be the case. There are those within the political spectrum who will suggest that what is needed is a Labour government and a movement towards socialism. However, there is no reason why a Conservative government could not create a caring society. Countries which have much greater equality and consequently better health are not necessarily hot-beds of socialism. It is not capitalism *per se* which is damaging British health, but rather the peculiar brand of New Right economics that has been so damaging to the social structures of Britain and the United States. This point was taken up by UNICEF in 1993. In its annual report *The Progress of Nations*[68] it suggested that there was a divergence between countries with an Anglo-American culture (including Canada, Australia and New Zealand) and those with a European culture (such as Germany, France and the Scandinavian and Benelux countries). The countries with an Anglo-American culture followed *laissez-faire* policies and experienced falls in health indices such as the social health of children as measured by such factors as infant mortality rates, spending on education and teenage suicide. In contrast the continental countries invested in people with policies of extensive training and a minimum wage. Their indices of child health have improved over the same period.[69]

Furthermore, taxes in Anglo-American countries became more regressive, as seen in the increase in value added tax and the reduction in income tax. In addition in Britain there have been cuts in state benefits, leading to increases in the percentage of children in poverty, as

68 UNICEF, 1993.
69 McKee, 1993, p. 1576.

defined by being 40 per cent or more below the median family income. By far the highest inequality is in the United States at 21 per cent. The other Anglo-American countries are at about 9 per cent, while France, Germany, the Netherlands and Sweden are all below 5 per cent. The UNICEF report mentioned other factors. The growth of privatisation and resulting redundancies led it to argue that people are insecure about their long-term employment. They have been working longer hours and spending less time with their children. Contact between parents and children has fallen since 1960. The report argued that the decision of the British government to opt out of the Social Chapter of the Maastricht Treaty exemplifies the difference between Britain and the rest of Europe. Commenting on the report, McKee states: 'UNICEF's reports are indictments of the *laissez-faire* policies pursued by the Anglo-American countries. Children are our future. If we fail to invest in them we will be the ultimate losers'.

What is clear from our analysis is that Britain needs a change of direction away from the divisive policies of the past few years towards building social cohesion.

B Health care fit for heroes
Health should be put high on the country's agenda. In 1995 the chairman of British Telecom went to a House of Commons committee investigating the pay of top executives. He made a joke that misfired about how he would find it relaxing to be a hospital doctor. In reply Edwin Boorman for the British Medical Association said, 'If he finds it relaxing to work flat out with just one or two hours sleep over a weekend he has missed his vocation.' His salary of £465,000 may be compared to the salary of the doctors, which is as low as £12,500. That means that for the same cost as one BT executive the health service could employ fifty-five junior doctors.[70] These kind of figures raise questions about what is valued in British society and how much more should be contributed towards improving health.

Having good health is arguably the most important factor in life. It is time to begin giving it much more priority. When considering the position before the NHS changes, we stressed the fact that sufficient funds were not available. There is other evidence to show that the NHS is still underfunded. A study by National Economic Research Associates, published in 1993, compared Britain to nine other industrialised countries. It found that Britain had the largest shortfall between what

70 Pilkington, 1995.

needs to be spent on health care this century and what will be spent if things do not change radically. Models developed by an independent health research consultancy on behalf of forty of the world's largest pharmaceutical companies found that Britain's shortfall would be equal to half its total expenditure. Taking into account the increased proportion of elderly and the demands of medical technology, the shortfall will reach over 100 per cent of total funding by the year 2000.[71] This report may be unduly pessimistic and one does not have to be a Marxist to see that pharmaceutical companies will benefit by the injection of more money into health care. However, there is no doubt that there are going to be increasing demands and more elderly people. Britain needs to begin planning now. Some have suggested a special health tax would have the support of the public.[72] We have seen that Britain spends less than the European average on health care and so proper funding is needed. However, not all technological and medical advances lead to more expense and in some areas treatment could become cheaper.[73] Furthermore, the market reforms cost an extra £1.7 billion which could have been ploughed back into patient care.[74] If this were carried out and there were commitment to cost saving in other areas, the health service could make much more efficient use of the money that is available. We could then begin providing the kind of health care of which we could justifiably be proud.

C Care for the elderly and disabled
We should assure all people that when they grow old or disabled they will be cared for and their families will be given adequate support. There is much room for improvement in meeting these targets.

D Unravelling the 1990 changes
In this book we have shown that the government has diverted resources away from major improvements in care and not set up the improved research and evidence-based service that was needed. The question now is what to do about it.

On Monday 6 March 1995 a man was struck by a hit-and-run van in Orpington. There was no intensive bed to be found in the London area and he was flown to Leeds where an operation began over ten hours after the accident. The surgeon who led the seven-hour operation

71 Appleby, 1993, p. 755.
72 Linton and Wintour, 1995.
73 Francome *et al.*, 1993.
74 NHS Consultants Association, 1995, p. 2.

said: 'We had to remove a very large blood clot. Ideally blood clots need to be dealt with within an hour or two. A delay of eight or nine hours, as in this case, is of deep concern.'[75]

The man died and the Prime Minister was questioned in Parliament. Such a series of events is so clearly regrettable that we would have expected to have heard him say so and admit that things needed to change. However, he did not do that and indeed a spokesman for the Department of Health said that there were enough intensive beds in the South East.[76] This was despite the fact that doctors reported that they know of at least nine cases where emergency patients were denied intensive care treatment in London and in other cases planned operations were cancelled. This single example shows the need for the government to stop trying to put the best gloss on the current situation. What is needed is, first, a clear recognition that things have gone wrong and, secondly, a determination to put them right.

There are some, even those towards the left of British politics, who argue that the internal market and fundholding should be allowed to continue. A reasoned article published by Andrew Coulson in 1995 in the *Fabian Review* argued that, although the 'reforms' created a two-tier system and 'paperwork and administrative and purchasing skills alien to GPs', a future government could not simply put the clock back ten years.[76] Although Coulson stated that probably the only achievement of the reforms was to undermine the entrenched power of the consultants, he noted that the system had showed some of the weaknesses of the previous system. These included variations in GPs' expenditure on drugs, the existence of (some) lazy, greedy, inefficient, incompetent or arrogant consultants and variations between hospitals and the opportunities and rationing so that 'free at the point of need' often meant 'free to those that were prepared to wait'.[77] He then argued that another 'administrative upheaval, without large extra financial resources' would raise expectations but take a long time to deliver. Coulson proposed that hospital trusts should be made to be more accountable to local people and that the major disadvantages of fundholding could be overcome by small practices clubbing together in consortia to purchase care, as has already happened in Birmingham and elsewhere.[78]

However, this kind of evidence is not persuasive. What is needed is for GPs and hospital consultants to concentrate as far as possible on

75 Mihill and Wainwright, 1995, p. 3.
76 Coulson, 1995, p. 13.
77 Coulson, 1995, p. 12.
78 Coulson, 1995, p. 13.

maintaining and improving the quality of care. Doctors should be doctors, not economists or business managers. One of the problems with the NHS reforms is that doctors have been taken away from their traditional roles and converted into managers and economists. One doctor put it to us: *'I trained at Guy's Hospital not the London School of Economics.'* Another said: *'If I'd wanted to work as a business manager I'd have gone to business school and applied for a job in Sainsbury's. But I wanted to be a doctor and so I went to medical school. Little did I know I would be expected to have done both.'*

While Enthoven's suggestion that a few GPs should be trained as managers is a good one, for the vast majority of medical people the primary consideration should be the best care of their patients. They need to keep up to date with developments and financial matters should be within the context of improved care. For these reasons the case against fundholding is very strong.

The problems with the internal market have been shown clearly by the case of a 10-year-old girl with leukaemia. She had one bone marrow transplant and two sets of consultants advised against a second one. The parents were in favour of continuing treatment, even though that treatment had only a small chance of success. In the new market situation the decision whether to fund the operations fell to the local area health authority. In March 1995 Cambridge Area Health Authority refused to fund the £75,000-worth of treatment. The parents' counsel argued it was 'unreasonable' for the health authority to refuse funding when doctors agreed she would have a 'significant' chance of her leukaemia going into remission, continuing: 'They have by refusing funding of this treatment, effectively taken the step whereby life is denied to this child'.[79] An administrator defended the decision on Channel 4 News on 9 March 1995 on the grounds that the money would be better spent on hip replacements. Her father had the decision overturned in court, which was itself overturned on appeal with legal costs greater than the cost of the treatment. The money for treatment was eventually provided by an anonymous donor. The whole process is unedifying and what is clear is that the decision on treatment should have been taken on the basis of what was in the girl's best interest. Treatment should be decided by doctors in conjunction with the patient and if appropriate his or her family. It should not be decided on the basis of cost, nor should it be decided in the last resort by managers.

The internal market was also attacked by a House of Lords select

79 Weale, 1995, p. 1.

committee in June 1995. Their report said that it was seriously damaging academic medicine and clinical research. It identified problems due to the closure of teaching hospitals, the decline in tertiary referrals, purchasing contracts and career blocks to academic medicine. The *British Medical Journal* reported:[80]

> Radical solutions are suggested to restore the flow of patients for research to the specialist hospitals now that more patients are treated locally. The peers recommend that specialist centres should advertise their superior outcomes, or else they should use research funding to lower their prices and maintain the number of patients needed for research or teaching.

E Improvements in data

In 1983, when we completed an analysis of the caesarean rates in Britain, we discovered that there were serious errors in government data.[81] Things do not seem to have improved. In July 1994 Trevor Sheldon of the University of York was quoted in the *British Medical Journal* as calling the lack of routinely collected data on health care process and outcome a national disgrace. He did point out that it had, however, protected us from the misuse of the figures that had occurred in the United States.[82] He continued, rightly, to stress the importance of randomised controlled trails where possible.

In 1994 one of us collected the latest caesarean rates for an update of the earlier book, *Caesarean Birth in Britain*. The results showed a sharp rise, which was in part due to government changes, and this led to a national debate on the issue.[83] The Royal College of Obstetricians and Gynaecologists initially challenged the figures before admitting that it had not analysed its own data, which were collected routinely.[84] This kind of situation shows that there is a strong need for improvements in data collection. Information should be collected by properly trained epidemiologists who will be able to interpret the results. By continuously investigating and monitoring the effectiveness of care, wherever possible by randomised controlled trials, the effectiveness of different kinds of treatment can be evaluated.

80 Warden, 1995b, p. 1556.
81 Boyd and Francome, 1983.
82 Sheldon, 1994.
83 Francome, 1994b.
84 Francome, 1994a.

F Removing ageism from research and treatment

A report on the elderly by the Medical Research Council in September 1994 criticised the fact that the elderly were being discriminated against in health care delivery. It followed cases of people in London and Brighton over the age of 65 who had been denied treatment. The report said that apart from the elderly being denied treatment, they were being excluded from trials which could lead to better care in the future. It called for there to be no age bar unless there were very strong grounds for exclusion.[85]

A GENERAL THEORY OF HEALTH

The Health of the Nation devoted one page only to what it referred to as 'variations' in health among different socioeconomic groups. These were claimed to result from 'a complex interplay of genetic, biological, social, environmental, cultural and psychological factors'. Virginia Bottomley provided the same list of factors in her message to a BMA conference on inequalities in health and suggested that 'there are no easy answers'.[86]

As pointed out by Davey Smith and Morris in an editorial in the *British Medical Journal* in 1994: 'it is inconceivable...that changes in genetic make up of different socioeconomic groups have occurred over the past 15 years to produce the increases in differences in mortality'.[87] Their view is that, while health-related behaviour is an appropriate target for health promotion activity, 'eating, smoking, drinking and participating in exercise do not occur in a social vacuum'. They suggest that the main agenda for making health improvements is in reducing inequalities through paying attention to child and family poverty, improved housing (which will create employment), the provision of nursery education and similar policies. As always, the health of the nation lies more in the hands of the Chancellor of the Exchequer than in those of the Secretary of State for Health.

In an attempt to bring some order to the various factors, we have constructed a general theory of health which is illustrated in Figure 11.1 on facing page. While we fully acknowledge that even this fairly complicated picture is in a number of respects an over-simplification, it at least provides a framework for discussing the relationship between

85 Mihill, 1994d.
86 European Public Health Alliance/BMA, 1994.
87 Davey Smith and Morris, 1994, p. 1454.

socioeconomic status and health and how this relationship may be mediated by other factors.

Figure 11.1 *A general framework for factors influencing health*

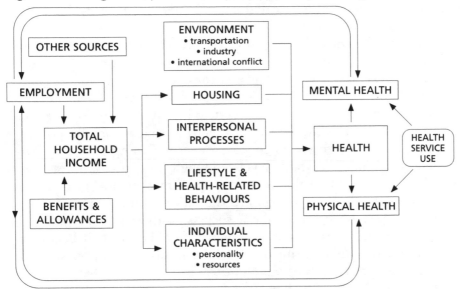

This general theory includes a combination of direct and indirect effects linking environmental variables, employment, household income, housing, interpersonal processes (including social comparisons, social support, and community and family relationships), health behaviour patterns and individual characteristics. These factors impact upon bodily systems, specifically the cardiovascular, pulmonary, musculo-skeletal, nervous and immune systems. In addition to health effects mediated by psychosocial and physical stressors, employment status and work-site conditions (when applicable) have direct effects on the health of people of economically active age.

Health care delivery often plays a role at a relatively late stage, when most of the damage has already been done. Its ability to make a major difference is therefore limited. Similarly, individual behavioural change is constrained by a host of factors which allow relatively little scope for health promotion and education programmes designed to produce informed, healthful choices.

Interpersonal processes within networks of relationships entail the giving, receiving and sharing of support of different kinds (informational, emotional and material). Interpersonal processes are also engaged in evaluating and comparing one's own position in society with that of others. This social comparison process is a core feature of the theory and is responsible for judging self-worth, setting aims and ambitions, and making changes to lifestyle and health behaviours.

The consequences of social comparison are profound and need to be considered in a socio-historical context. People of many walks of life, nationalities and cultures now share similar aspirations. Margaret Thatcher told Britons they could all expect to have houses, cars, holidays abroad and shares in the stock market. John Major even talked of a 'classless society'. Thus, at the end of the twentieth century, a rich person in a castle and a keeper at the gate share the same ambitions. The terrible flaw in the system is that in some societies such as Britain and the USA the rich are getting richer and the poor are getting poorer. There seems to be an ever-widening gap of relative deprivation. While everybody has been taught to expect a house, a car, a holiday abroad and a flutter on the stock market, for an increasing number of people these things are difficult – if not impossible – to obtain. Those who fail to make a success of their lives as judged by socially expected norms, and who will suffer the most ill health, are also those who are least amenable to the health promotion strategies embodied in *The Health of the Nation*. This is because they have little or no spare capacity and few or no resources to make the necessary changes.

Medical sociologist Peter Makara – who is director of the National Institute of Health Promotion in Budapest – describes the position very succinctly in relation to a typical factory worker in Hungary. The situation is perhaps more extreme than that which exists in Britain, but the principal features are essentially the same. Makara refers to the 'lifestyle' of the Hungarian factory worker, whose typical day goes something like this:[88]

> 5 am: get up, feed the pigs, eat breakfast; 6.30 am: travel by train for one-and-a-half hours to the factory; 8 am to 12 noon: work; 12 – 1 pm: eat meat and potatoes, drink beer; 1 – 6 pm: work; 6 to 7.30 pm: travel by train to home town; 7.30 pm: feed pigs, eat meat and potatoes; 9 – midnight: get drunk in the pub; 12 – 5 am: sleep.

Working a twelve-hour day, six days a week, fifty weeks of the year, and earning the equivalent of $300 a month is hardly a lifestyle which is conducive to making informed, healthy choices. It requires a huge

88 Personal communication, 1995.

amount of energy and commitment simply to keep going and pay the bills. Under such circumstances, not only are there limits to medicine, there are limits to prevention of illness and health promotion too.

While there may be no easy answers, there are ways forward if the government has the political will. One of the most obvious ways of improving the health of the nation involves reducing inequalities. This requires a policy which discourages further increases in income at the top end of the scale while increasing the higher rates of income tax, and which increases the income of the lowest income groups. By reducing the differentials between the richest and the poorest members of society, it will be possible to improve the health of the nation. Britain will then take its place among countries such as Japan and Italy, which have more equitable distributions of wealth and correspondingly better standards of health. See Figure 11.2.

Figure 11.2 *The effect of income distribution on life expectancy*

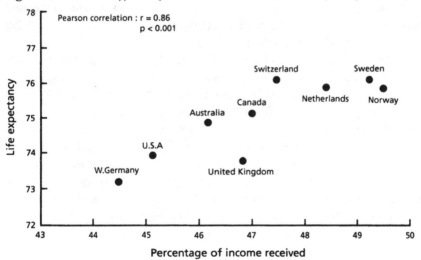

Source Adapted from Wilkinson, 1990, 1992.

Wilkinson[89] presented evidence that the relationship between income distribution and life expectancy is strong. Controlling for gross national product per head of population, a correlation of 0.90 was obtained between life expectancy at birth and the proportion of income going to the least well-off 70 per cent of the population. This contrasts with a relatively modest correlation of 0.38 in developed countries

89 Wilkinson, 1992.

between life expectancy and gross national product per head. Wilkinson suggested four possible explanations of these relationships between health and income distribution, the first two of which are concerned with potential intervening variables. First, more egalitarian countries are likely to have better public services which benefit health. As Wilkinson points out, however, medical services are unlikely to have a major impact on national mortality: 'Even the small proportion of deaths from conditions regarded as wholly amenable to medical treatment seem less influenced by differences in medical provision than they are by differences in socio-economic factors.'[90]

Secondly, Wilkinson suggested that ethnic minorities could be contributing to the health divide as a result of poorer health and discrimination in employment. However, the evidence of worse health among ethnic minorities is weak (when other factors are controlled) and also, during a time of strict controls of immigration, the relationship between life expectancy and income distribution has remained strong. It therefore seems highly unlikely that the observed relationship between health and income distribution is caused by variations introduced by the ethnic minorities.

Thirdly, there is the possibility that higher levels of mortality cause wider distributions of income across societies. This is also highly doubtful because the relationship is based upon life expectancy at birth for the total population: 'Children, pensioners, and those who are not economically active are unlikely to suffer any loss of income when ill.'[90]

Fourthly, there is the hypothesis that mortality is affected by income distribution. In this regard, the study of improvements in life expectancy in Japan and the contrasting deterioration in Britain are informative. Marmot and Davey Smith[91] found no explanation in changes of diet, health services or other aspects of life for the improvements in Japan. Japan's increasing, and Britain's decreasing, egalitarianism appear to be the most obvious and salient difference between the two populations. This is confirmed by the observation noted by Marmot and Davey Smith that mortality has fallen most rapidly among the upper classes in Britain and the lower classes in Japan. The evidence collated by Wilkinson suggests that if Britain were to adopt an income distribution like that of the most egalitarian countries, about two years could be added to the life expectancy of the British population.

---

90 Wilkinson, 1992, p. 167.
91 Marmot and Davey Smith, 1989.

What mechanisms could possibly be responsible for the effects of income distribution on a nation's health? Wilkinson suggests that 'social consequences of people's differing circumstances in terms of stress, self-esteem, and social relations may now be one of the most important influences on health'.[92] This position is endorsed by our current analysis of health. The relative judgement of one's own social and economic position appears to be a major determinant of well-being. Peter Townsend argued for a distinction between 'poverty' and 'deprivation' because the former tends to be judged in terms of abstract, absolute levels of income while the latter is relative to societal norms:[93]

> People can be said to be deprived if they lack the material standard of diet, clothing, housing, household facilities, working, environmental and locational conditions which are ordinarily available in their society, and do not participate in or have access to the forms of employment, occupation, education, recreation and family and social activities and relationships which are commonly experienced or accepted.

Townsend's concept includes social phenomena such as isolation, fear of going into the community, lack of community and social support, discrimination and lack of education and employment opportunities. The subjective aspects of deprivation are therefore a key characteristic which Townsend defines in the following terms: 'a difference between the summation of attitudes of individuals and the dispositions of organised representations of particular social groups'.[94]

The theory that people evaluate themselves by social comparison is a traditional concept in both sociology[95] and psychology.[96] However, previous discussions have tended to focus on comparisons with similar people – that is, people of similar background, occupation, gender, ethnic grouping and social position. This may be limiting. Clearly some of the most vivid comparisons are with those who have the most and least favourable positions with respect to any particular indicator – income, family situation and housing. This process may be particularly onerous and oppressive when comparisons are made with one's peers from childhood and youth if a significant majority of others have done

92 Wilkinson, 1992, p. 168.
93 Townsend, 1993, p. 94.
94 Townsend, 1993, p. 95.
95 Cooley, 1964.
96 Festinger, 1954.

relatively well. Given the tendency to make downward comparisons if at all possible – that is, comparisons with others who are less fortunate[97] – this propensity will lead to favourable comparisons for all except those who suffer the greatest deprivation levels. It therefore follows that feelings of low self-esteem, helplessness and hopelessness, all of which are predictors of poor health, will be greatest among those suffering the greatest deprivation. These feelings of relative deprivation reach their maximum in societies such as Britain and the United States which have the greatest inequalities in income distribution. The most effective and radical method of improving the health of the nation would be to reduce the currently high levels of inequality in British society. In addition to other merits – including social justice – egalitarian societies are healthier than inequalitarian ones.

Another positive argument for moving towards a more egalitarian society is that redistributing income actually does not cost any money. It is therefore the most cost-effective method for producing national health gain. It is also a vote winner because there will be many more winners than losers. Only greed within the richest classes can inhibit the necessary social reforms.

FOURTEEN MORE SUGGESTIONS TO IMPROVE HEALTH SUMMARISED FROM EARLIER CHAPTERS

1 The role of GPs as primary health care providers needs to be enhanced and strengthened. The time they spend on administration should be reduced to enable more time to be spent in caring for patients and keeping up to date with new developments.
2 The present inequalities in treatment should be eliminated so that people are treated according to clinical need.
3 Resources are needed to reduce waiting times so that treatment is delayed for clinical reasons only and not because of scarcity of resources.
4 Improvements in the primary care system are needed to remove the two-tier system and to restore trust between doctors and patients.
5 Reduce the risks of heart attacks by improving diet, taking more exercise and reducing people's weight. These changes should be made easier to achieve through the widespread availability of recognised healthier foods at affordable prices and improved accessibility to fitness centres and exercise programmes.

---

97 Wills, 1987.

6 Health education programmes in schools should promote good habits.

7 We have seen that the wide differences in heart disease and strokes according to ethnic group provide the possibility for useful research. More data on this issue need to be collected and possible differences in lifestyles should be analysed.

8 More research is needed to provide an in-depth analysis of the possible effects of alcohol on heart disease.

9 Improvements in diet, reductions in obesity, smoking and drinking, increased activity levels and improved screening are all factors. A comprehensive strategy is needed at societal level for the achievement of these changes. These should not rely solely on the provision of information and the delegation of responsibility to individual 'healthy choices'.

10 It is clear that there is a need for improvement in the treatment of cancer. It is important that, once cancer is diagnosed, treatment begins immediately, so once again we are looking for an injection of funds. The setting up of specialist regional centres and careful monitoring of all treatment are also important.

11 More epidemiological research is necessary to consider the reasons for national differences in incidence of different forms of cancer and to identify lifestyle factors which will reduce prevalence.

12 Creative new methods of preventing smoking and drinking in young people are needed. Cost-effective methods of helping smoking cessation within the NHS are also needed. Although helpful, increases in price are an inadequate mechanism for the reduction in smoking. A combination of education and a complete advertising ban will help ensure that young people are provided with consistent and reliable educational messages about smoking.

13 Improve transport safety by encouraging a move to public transport (which is safer), improving the environment for cyclists by providing more bicycle lanes, improving children's education and encouraging driver safety by further reducing drinking and driving.

14 Improve the quality of care at accident and emergency units. Ensure that there is good quality emergency cover within easy reach of people's homes either by reopening some of the units closed since the reforms or by co-operation with local GPs. Improve the skill mix of staff at accident and emergency units.

CONCLUDING REMARKS

This book has shown that the United Kingdom has fallen behind many other countries in terms of health. Many mistakes have been made and there has been a lack of political will and finance to improve matters. The changes we have recommended do not cover all the issues. However, if they are introduced there is no doubt that they will have important effects when implemented. It is possible that the British National Health Service once more could be the 'envy of the world'.

APPENDIX

Further details of the methodology of all the surveys may be obtained from the authors. However, as an example we give further details of the GPs' survey, including the questionnaire and covering letter for the first mailing.

THE METHODOLOGY OF THE TWO SURVEYS OF GENERAL PRACTITIONERS

The 1992 survey of General Practitioners

This survey was conducted in conjunction with the journal *General Practitioner* and the NHS Support Federation. A random sample of four hundred GPs was chosen. The first mailing was sent on 15 February and those not responding were sent a reminder on 13 March. The questionnaire asked about attitudes to the reforms and also about the way doctors planned to vote in the forthcoming elections. An article was published in *General Practitioner* on 3 April and a report was also published.[1] These reports were based on the first 253 questionnaires returned. In addition thirty-five people wrote back giving reasons why they could not fill in a questionnaire, such as that they were part-time, had retired from practice or were only recently appointed.

Following the publication of the article and the report, twenty-seven more questionnaires were received and one additional doctor reported back that he had retired. These replies have been included in this report and published for the first time. So the total number of questionnaires completed was 280 out of a possible 364 (400−36). This gives an overall response rate of 77 per cent which is very good.

The 1994 Survey of General Practitioners

A random sample of 396 was drawn from the mailing list of *General Practitioner* at the request of Jane Feinemann. The first mailing was sent out on 27 February 1994. Those not responding were sent reminders on 19 March and 3 August 1994. The questions were again about the effect of the NHS reforms. Several questions were identical to those asked in the 1992 survey. In all 306 (77 per cent) of people replied and there were two refusals. The respondents fell into three main groupings. These were fundholders (53), non-fundholders (198)

1 Francome, 1992a, 1992b.

and those (55) who could not complete a questionnaire. If we calculate the response rate based on the percentage of those who could respond, that is 251 divided by 341 (396−55), this gives a figure of 72 per cent. This is perfectly acceptable, but slightly disappointing in that it is below that obtained in 1992 with only two mailings. Possibly one of the reasons for the high response rate in 1992 was that doctors felt that their response might lead to a change away from the new reforms. One of our two refusals was based on the fact that no change was likely, as will be seen below. Another reason is that many who would have liked to have contributed were unable to do so. This can be seen from the following table.

Reasons for not completing the questionnaire	Number
Not been a GP long enough to comment	24
Left practice or on sabbatical	7
Working in a hospital	6
Not a General Practitioner	5
Locum or part-time	4
Retired	4
Maternity leave	2
Army doctor	2
Working abroad	1
Total	55

The major reason for not filling in the questionnaire was linked to length of service: *'I wish your survey well. I have not filled the questionnaire as I have only recently entered General Practice and have not been in position for three years.'* Another said: *'I've just a completed year as GP trainee after standard two years in hospital jobs. Not currently in full time practice.'* Similarly a third commented: *'I have only been in practice for 8 months as a GP trainee and therefore cannot really make any comparisons over a 3 year period.'*

Seven people had left their practice or were on sabbatical. A doctor from the West of England wrote:

'I am afraid I'm unable to complete the questionnaire as I have resigned from general practice. My resignation was due to ill health caused directly by the stress induced by "general practice" –

which has less and less to do with patient care and more to do with layers of administration. Perhaps this in some ways goes to answering your questions.' (1 March 1994)

Six people said they were not working as a GP. One rang me up at home to say that he could not respond as he worked in a hospital but would I please not let *General Practitioner* know as he still wished to receive the journal because it had many useful articles. I had a letter from East London which said, *'Dr X is not an NHS GP so the questions you asked are not applicable. Sorry we cannot be of help but hope you get a good response rate.'*

Four said they were locum or part-time. One said, *'I am unable to answer – I'm a retainer GP only doing two sessions and have insufficient experience.'*

Only two people wrote back refusing to answer; however, their comments are revealing. One of these stated: *'As a result of the Government Health Reforms I have no time to complete this questionnaire for which I have "been selected".'* The other said: *'I am not entirely convinced that your survey is the type of information that swings Government opinion since Virginia Bottomley et al are slow enough to listen to working parties commissioned by the Government.'*

Overall the response rate was good, especially considering that the results show that GPs have many forms to fill in.

The proportion of fundholders in the final sample was 21 per cent. Figures provided to me by the British Medical Association suggested that during 1993, 25 per cent of doctors were fundholders, rising to 34 per cent during 1994. This suggests that our sample contained a smaller than proportionate number of fundholders. This, however, was to be expected. There are two reasons why fundholders would be expected to have problems in replying. The first is that many of them had only recently taken charge of their own budgets and so were unable to monitor the changes. Secondly, the fundholders were more likely than other doctors to be short of time. We saw this in the survey as one of the factors in the time they had available to keep up to date with the latest literature. So for this reason they probably made up a disproportionate proportion of the non-responses.

Confidential Questionnaire

1 Over the past three years has the freedom of referral of your practice improved, remained the same or deteriorated?

   improved____   remained the same____   deteriorated____

2 Over the past three years have your waiting lists risen or stayed the same in the following areas?

Speciality	Risen	Same	Fallen
Overall			
General surgery			
Orthopaedics			
Gynaecology			
Urology			
ENT			
Ophthalmology			

3 How has your overall referral rate changed over the past three years?

   risen____   remained the same____   fallen____

4 Have any of your patients had to be returned to hospital because of too early discharge in the past year?

   none____   one____   two____   more than two____

5 Is day surgery increasing or decreasing pressure on you as a GP?

   increasing pressure____   remaining the same____   decreasing pressure____

6 Are the community services in your area coping well with the extra patients they are meant to care for?

   coping well____   coping moderately____   not coping well____

7   During the past three years has the amount of clerical work per patient increased or decreased?

increased____   remained the same____   decreased____

8   During the past three years has the amount of time you can spend with each patient increased or decreased?

increased____   remained the same____   decreased____

9   Has the average waiting time for an emergency ambulance to arrive (from the time the call was logged) increased or decreased?

increased____   remained the same____   decreased____

10 Is the policy of community care placing a strain on any of your patients?

yes____   no____   comment (if any)

. . . .

. . . .

11 The NHS was designed as a high quality service available to all irrespective of their ability to pay and free at the point of need. Do you agree these basic principles are an ideal we should still work towards?

agree____   neither agree nor disagree____   disagree____

12 Do you think that the recent reforms have enhanced these principles?

Please circle   yes   /   no

13 Are you a fundholder and if so are you first, second or third wave?

not fundholder____   first wave____   second wave____   third wave____

14 Are there differences in priority given to fundholders in your area?

Please circle   yes   /   no

15 Do you feel the system would be fairer if all doctors were either fundholders or non-fundholders?

Please circle   yes   /   no

16 Do you believe in the principles of fundholding?

Please circle   yes   /   no

Comment ....

....

17 Since the NHS changes have been introduced has your personal income increased or decreased (apart from inflation)?

increased___   remained the same___   decreased___

18 Do you feel that you are getting enough time to keep abreast of medical developments?

Please circle   yes   /   no

What improvements in patient care would you like to see? (if any)

....

....

....

....

....

19 *Fundholders only*
    a) Do you take cost into account before referral?

    Please circle   yes   /   no

    b) What has happened to any savings you have been able to make?

    ....

    ....

Thank you very much for your help.

27 February 1994

Dear

In April it will be three years since the Government Health reforms were introduced and I am co-operating with GP magazine to conduct a survey of a sample of General Practitioners. You have been selected to help with this and the questionnaire should take under five minutes to complete. We include a stamped addressed envelope for your reply.

I look forward to hearing your comments by March 10th. The results will be published in GP in April.

Yours sincerely

Dr Colin Francome

Reader in Medical Sociology

BIBLIOGRAPHY

Abel-Smith, B. (1964), *The Hospitals 1800–1948*, Heinemann Educational Books: London.

Abel-Smith, B. (1978), *National Health Service: The First Thirty Years*, HMSO: London.

ACSF Investigators (1992), 'AIDS and Sexual Behaviour in France', *Nature*, vol. 360, 3 December, p. 407.

Aldridge, D. (1982), 'Europe Looks at Complementary Therapy', *British Medical Journal*, vol. 299, pp. 1211–2.

Allen, I. (1995), *Doctor's and their Careers: A New Generation*, Policy Studies Institute: London.

Altman, D. (1986), *Aids and the New Puritanism*, Pluto Press: London.

Altman, L. K. (1994), 'Surgery is Found to Avert Strokes', *New York Times*, 1 October, p. 1, col. 5.

Anderson, P. (1994), 'Transplant Donors to Go on Computer', *Daily Express*, 4 July.

Andrews, G. and M. Teesson (1994), 'Smart Versus Dumb Treatment: Services for Mental Disorder', *Current Opinion in Psychiatry*, vol. 7, no. 2, pp. 181–5.

Anonymous (1987), 'Health Care Dilemmas', *Financial Times*, 9 December, p. 22, cols 1–2.

Anonymous (1993), 'Killings Prompt Plea to Re-open Hospital', *Hendon Times*, 8 July.

Anonymous (1994a), 'Doctors Talk of Painful Choices', *Doctor*, 29 September, p. 1.

Anonymous (1994b), 'GPs are Forced to Sink or Swim', *General Practitioner*, 21 October, p. 20.

Anonymous (1994c), 'The Lottery of Long Term Care', *British Medical Journal*, vol. 308, 19 March, p. 742.

Appleby, J. (1993), 'Economists Warn of Gap in Health Care Funding', *British Medical Journal*, vol. 307, 25 September, p. 755.

Appleby, J. (1994) 'Fundholding', *Health Services Journal*, 11 August.

Association of Metropolitan Authorities (1993), *Mental Health Services: Issues for Local Government*, Association of Metropolitan Authorities: London.

Austoker, J. (1994a), 'Cancer Prevention in Primary Care: Current Trends and Some Prospects for the Future: 1', *British Medical Journal*, vol. 309, pp. 449–52.

Austoker, J. (1994b), 'Diet and Cancer', *British Medical Journal*, vol. 308, 18 June, pp. 1610–14.

Austoker, J. (1994c), 'Melanoma: Prevention and Early Diagnosis', *British Medical Journal*, vol. 308, 25 June.

Austoker, J. (1994d), 'Reducing Alcohol Intake', *British Medical Journal*, vol. 308, 11 June, pp. 1549–52.

Austoker, J. (1994e), 'Screening and Self examination for Breast Cancer', *British Medical Journal*, vol. 309, 16 July, pp. 168–74.

Austoker, J. (1994f), 'Screening for Cervical Cancer', *British Medical Journal*, vol. 309, 23 July, pp. 241–8.

Austoker, J. (1994g) 'Screening for Colectoral Cancer', *British Medical Journal*, vol. 309, pp. 382–6.

Austoker, J. (1994h) 'Screening for Ovarian, Prostatic, and Testicular Cancers', *British Medical Journal*, vol. 309, 30 July, pp. 315–21.

Austoker, J., D. Sanders and G. Fowler (1994), 'Cancer Prevention in Primary Care: Smoking and Cancer: Smoking Cessation', *British Medical Journal*, vol. 308, pp. 1478–82.

Balarajan, R. and V. S. Raleigh (1994), 'Public Health and the 1991 Census', *British Medical Journal*, vol. 309, p. 287.

Beck, E., S. Lonsdale, S. Newman and D. Patterson (1993), *In the Best of Health*, Chapman and Hall: London and New York.

Beecham, L. (1994), 'Consultants Show Growing Frustration with the NHS', *British Medical Journal*, vol. 308, 18 June, p. 1587.

Beecham, L. (1995), 'British GPs Reject Out of Hours Offer', *British Medical Journal*, vol. 310, 17 June, p. 1553.

Benson, M. (1994), 'Doctors Forced into Rationing Care', *Observer*, 13 November, p. 24, col. 1.

Beral, V., C. Hermon, G. Reeves and R. Peto (1995), 'Sudden Fall in Breast Cancer Death Rates in England and Wales', *The Lancet*, vol. 345, 24 June, pp. 1642–3.

Black, D., J. N. Morris, C. Smyth and P. Townsend (1992), *The Black Report*, Penguin: Harmondsworth.

Blackwell-Smyth (1994), 'Has the Basic Medical Degree Become Obsolete?', *General Practitioner*, 16 September, p. 27.

Blane, D., G. Davey Smith and M. Bertley (1990), 'Social Class Differences in Years of Potential Life Lost: Size, Trends and Principal Causes', *British Medical Journal*, vol. 301, pp. 429–32.

Bogle, J. (1981), 'We Got it Wrong', *Daily Mail*, 7 September.

Bonita, R. (1994), 'The Monica Project Comes of Age', *British Medical Journal*, vol. 309, 17 September, pp. 684–5.

Boyd, C. and C. Francome (1983) *One Birth in Nine*, Maternity Alliance: London.

Bradlow, J. and A. Coulter (1993), 'Effect of Fundholding and Indicative

Prescribing Schemes on General Practitioners' Prescribing Costs', *British Medical Journal*, vol. 307, 6 November, pp. 1186–9.

Brearley, S. (1994), 'The Failure of Consultant Expansion', *British Medical Journal*, vol. 309, 12 November, p. 1245.

Brindle, D. (1993), 'Bottomley Steps into NHS Market to Aid Hospital Caught in Cash Trap', *Guardian*, 16 December, p. 11, col. 4.

Brindle, D. (1994a), 'Acute Care Beds Will Fall by a Third', *Guardian*, 14 February, p. 2, col. 7.

Brindle, D. (1994b), 'Basic Benefit "Will Not Buy Children a Workhouse Diet"', *Guardian*, 1 February, p. 5, col. 1.

Brindle, D. (1994c), 'Bottomley Speaks up for Lone Parents', *Guardian*, 27 May, p. 2, col. 4.

Brindle, D. (1994d), 'Killing Blamed on Care Breakdown', *Guardian*, 23 February.

Brindle, D. (1994e), 'NHS to Cut Back Managers by Renaming', *Guardian*, 22 October, p. 12, col. 3.

Brindle, D. (1994f), 'Patients Die through NHS Market Delays', *Guardian*, March, p. 1, col. 1.

Brindle, D. (1994g), '"Trusts First" NHS Chief Condemned', *Guardian*, 14 November, p. 2, col. 7.

Brindle, D. (1995a), 'AIDS Cases Total Passes 10,000', *Guardian*, 28 January, p. 8, col. 5.

Brindle, D. (1995b), 'More than 50 NHS Trusts Have Cumulative Deficit', *Guardian*, 23 January, p. 3, col. 1.

Brindle, D. (1995c), 'NHS Managers up 15 pc in Year', *Guardian*, 2 September, p. 4, col. 2.

Brindle, D. (1995d), 'Salaries of Health Chiefs "Could Pay 11,000 Nurses"', *Guardian*, 2 January, p. 3, col. 1.

Brindle, D. (1995e), 'Spending up £1bn on NHS Bureaucrats', *Guardian*, 28 February, p. 3, col. 7.

Brindle, D. (1995f), 'Surgeons Flouting NHS Rules on Private Patients', *Guardian*, 18 January, p. 7, col. 6.

British Medical Association (1993), *Complementary Medicine: New Approaches to Care*, Oxford University Press: Oxford.

Brough, G. (1994), 'NHS Deal in Donor Blood', *The Mail on Sunday*, 6 March, p. 1.

Brown, A. (1994), 'Thalidomide's Horrors Plague the Poor of Brazil', *Observer*, 23 October, p. A20.

Brown, G. W. (1984), 'Depression: A Sociological View', in *Health and Disease: A Reader*, N. Black, D. Boswell, A. Gray *et al.*, Open University Press: Milton Keynes.

Brown, P. (1995), 'One Million Missed in 1991 Census', *Guardian*, 6 January, p. 9, col. 5.

Bunker, J. P. (1970), 'Surgical Manpower: A Comparison of Operations and Surgeons in the United States and in England and Wales', *New England Journal of Medicine*, vol. 283, no. 3, pp. 135–44.

Burdett-Smith, P. (1992), 'Estimating Trauma Centre Workloads', *Journal of the Royal College of Surgeons of Edinburgh*, vol. 37, pp. 128–39.

Bury, J. (1984), *Teenage Pregnancy in Britain*, Birth Control Trust: London.

Caldicott, F. (1994), Letter to the Secretary of State for Health, *Psychiatric Bulletin*, vol. 18, pp. 385–6.

Cancer Research Campaign (1991), *Factsheet 6.3: Breast Cancer*, Cancer Research Campaign: Oxford.

Carr, S., D. J. Goldberg and S. T. Green (1994), 'Prostitution: Would Legalisation Help?', *British Medical Journal*, vol. 308, 19 February, p. 538.

Carstairs, G. (1962), *This Island Now*, Hogarth Press: London.

Caulfield, P. (1995), 'Next Time our Hospital May Be Too Far Away', *Hendon Times*, 20 April, p. 12, col. 4.

Channel 4 (1994), 'Dying for a Donor', 4 July.

Chouillet, A. M., C. M. J. Bell and J. G. Hiscox (1994), 'Management of Breast Cancer in Southeast England', *British Medical Journal*, vol. 308, pp. 168–71.

Coggon, D. and H. Inskip (1994), 'Current Issues in Cancer: Is There an Epidemic of Cancer?', *British Medical Journal*, vol. 308, p. 705.

Cook, R. (1988), *Life Begins at 40: In Defence of the NHS*, Fabian Society.

Cooley, H. (1964), *Human Nature and the Social Order*, Schocken Books: NY (originally published 1902).

Coulson, A. (1995), 'The Internal Market Can Work', *Fabian Review*, vol. 107, no. 1, February.

Court, C. (1995), 'Taking Care of the Carers', *British Medical Journal*, vol. 310, p. 617.

Davey Smith, G. and M. Eggar (1993), 'Socioeconomic Differentials in Wealth and Income', *British Medical Journal*, vol. 307, pp. 1085–6.

Davey Smith, G. and J. Morris (1994), 'Increasing Inequalities in the Health of the Nation', *British Medical Journal*, vol. 309, pp. 1453–4.

Davis, B. (1994), 'GP Facilitators and HIV Infection', *British Medical Journal*, vol. 308, 19 February, p. 538.

Dean, M. (1993), 'Targeting Teenage Single Mothers', *The Lancet*, vol. 342, 16 October, p. 978.

Dearnaley, D. P. (1994), 'Cancer of the Prostate', *British Medical Journal*, vol. 308, pp. 780–4.

Dennis, M. and P. Langhorne (1994), 'So Stroke Units Save Lives: Where Do We Go from Here?', *British Medical Journal*, vol. 309, p. 1273.

Dennis, N., P. Henriques and C. Slaughter (1956), *Coal is our Life*, Tavistock.

Department for Education (1987), *Sex Education*, Circular 11/87, Department for Education: London.

Department for Education (1994), *Sex Education*, Circular 5/94, Department for Education: London.

Department of Health (1989), *Working for Patients*, HMSO: London.

Department of Health (1991), *On the State of Public Health*, HMSO: London.

Department of Health (1992), *The Health of the Nation*, HMSO: London.

Department of Health (1993a), *Health and Personal Social Services Statistics for England*, HMSO: London.

Department of Health (1993b), *Health of the Nation Key Area Handbook – Accidents*, HMSO: London.

Department of Health (1993c), *Mental Illness: What Does It Mean?*, HMSO: London.

Department of Health (1993d), *The Health of the Nation: One Year On*, HMSO: London.

Department of Health (1993e), *Working Together for Better Health*, HMSO: London.

Department of Health (1994a), *The Government's Expenditure Plans. 1994–1995 to 1996–1997,* Department Report, HMSO: London.

Department of Health (1994b), *Working in Partnership*, HMSO: London.

Department of Social Security (1993), *Households Below Average Income: A Statistical Analysis 1979–91*, HMSO: London.

Department of Transport (1990), *Children and Roads – a Safer Way*, HMSO: London.

Department of Transport (1994a), *Road Accidents Great Britain 1993: The Casualty Report*, HMSO: London.

Department of Transport (1994b), *Transport Statistics Great Britain*, HMSO: London.

Dillner, L. (1994), 'Health Committee Critical of Community Care', *British Medical Journal*, vol. 308, p. 1062.

Dixon, C. (1994), 'Health Reforms Close 88 Casualty Units', *Independent on Sunday*, 14 August, p. 1, col. 2.

Doll, R., R. Peto, E. Hall, K. Wheatley and R. Gray (1994), 'Mortality in Relation to Consumption of Alcohol: 13 Years' Observation on Male British Doctors', *British Medical Journal*, vol. 309, pp. 911–18.

Downer, S. M., M. M. Cody, P. McClusky *et al.* (1994), 'Pursuit and Practice of Complementary Therapies by Cancer Patients Receiving Conventional Treatment', *British Medical Journal*, vol. 309, pp. 86–9.

Doyal, L. (1985), *The Political Economy of Health,* Pluto Press: London.

Dracup, K., D. K. Moser, M. Eisenberg *et al.* (1995), 'Causes of Delay in Seeking Treatment for Heart Attack Victims', *Social Science and Medicine*, vol. 40, no. 3, pp. 379–92.

Draper, P. (1994), 'Privatisation is a Reality', *British Medical Journal*, vol. 309, 17 September, p. 739.

Draper, P., J. Griffiths, J. Dennis and Popay (1980), 'Three Types of Health Education', *British Medical Journal*, 16 August, pp. 493–5.

Drife, Jo (1993), 'Deregulating Emergency Contraception', *British Medical Journal*, vol. 307, pp. 695–6.

Durkheim, E. (1964), *Suicide*, Free Press: Glencoe III (originally published 1897).

Dyar, O. (1994), 'London Scientists Blame NHS Reforms for Brain Drain', *British Medical Journal*, vol. 309, 30 July, p. 291.

Dyer, C. (1995), 'New Legal Threat on Thalidomide', *Guardian*, 20 January, p. 1.

Eames, M., Y. Ben-Shlomo and M. G. Marmot (1993), 'Social Deprivation and Premature Mortality: Regional Comparison Across England', *British Medical Journal*, vol. 307, pp. 1097–1102.

Eckstein, H. (1970), *The English Health Service*, Harvard University Press: Cambridge and Massachusetts, third printing.

Editorial (1994), 'Fatter and Fatter', *New York Times*, 21 November, p. A14, col. 1.

Enthoven, A. C. (1985), 'National Health Service: Some Reforms That Might Be Politically Feasible', *The Economist*, 22 June.

Enthoven, A. C. (1994), 'On the Ideal Market Structure for Third Party Purchasing of Health Care', *Social Science and Medicine*, vol. 39, no. 10, pp. 1413–24.

Esteve, J., A. Kricker, J. Ferlay and D. M. Parkin (1993), *Facts and Figures of Cancer in the European Community*, International Agency for Research on Cancer: Lyons, France.

European Public Health Alliance and BMA (1994), *Action on Social Inequalities and Health*, BMJ Publishing Group: London.

Evans, B., K. A. McLean, S. G. Dawson, S. A. Teece, R. A. Bond, K. D. MacRae and R. W. Thorp (1989), 'Trends in Sexual Behaviour and Risk Factors for HIV Infection among Homosexual Men 1984–7', *British Medical Journal*, vol. 298, 28 January, pp. 215–18.

Evans, M. (1994), 'Medicos Slammed over Schizo's Treatment', *Hendon Times*, 2 March, p. 3.

Evans, T. (1994), unheaded letter, *Guardian*, 31 January, sect. 1, p. 19.

Farrell, C. (1978), *My Mother Said*, Routledge: London.

Festinger, L. (1954), 'A Theory of Social Comparison Processes', *Human Relations*, vol. 7, pp. 117–40.

Field, J., A. Johnson, J. Wadsworth and K. Wellings (1994), 'The Facts of Homosexual Life', *Independent on Sunday*, Review, 23 January, p. 9, col. 2.

Fletcher, J. (1984), 'Homosexuality: Kick and Kickback', editorial in *Southern Medical Journal*, February.

Ford, R., A. Beadsmoore, P. Norton, A. Cooke and J. Repper (1993), 'Developing Case Management for the Long-term Mentally Ill', *Psychiatric Bulletin*, vol. 17, pp. 409–11.

Forwell, G. D. (1993), *Glasgow's Health: Old Problems – New Opportunities*, Department of Public Health: Glasgow.

Francome, C. (1976), *Youth and Society*, University of Kent: Canterbury.

Francome, C. (1979), 'More Teenage Sex', *Breaking Chains*, no. 11, p. 7.

Francome, C. (1980), 'Birth Control, a Way Forward', pamphlet to celebrate the centenary of Marie Stopes' birth, Marie Stopes: London.

Francome, C. (1983a), 'Teenage Pregnancy', *Novum*, April.

Francome, C. (1983b), 'Unwanted Pregnancies amongst Teenagers', *Journal of Biosocial Science*, vol. 15, pp. 139–43.

Francome, C. (1984), *Abortion Freedom*, Allen and Unwin: London and Boston.

Francome, C. (1986), *Abortion Practice in Britain and the United States*, Unwin Hyman: London and Boston.

Francome, C. (1990), *Sane New World*, Carla Publications: London.

Francome, C. (1991), *If You Ever Go Across the Sea to England*, Middlesex University: London.

Francome, C. (1992a), *GPs' Attitudes to the NHS Reforms*, London: NHS Federation.

Francome, C. (1992b), 'GPs Reveal Plans to Desert the Tories', *General Practitioner*, 3 April.

Francome, C. (1993), 'Sexual Behaviour', *British Medical Journal*, vol. 306, 16 January, p. 212.

Francome, C. (1994a), 'Caesarean Birth', *The Times*, December.

Francome, C. (1994b), *Caesarean Birth in Britain: 1994 Supplement*, NCT and Middlesex University Press.

Francome, C. (1994c), *Doctors to be Doctors*, Middlesex University and NHS Support Federation.

Francome, C. (1994d), *The Great Leap*, Department of Sociology and Social Policy, Middlesex University: London.

Francome, C. (1995), 'The Attitudes to the Closure of the Acute Beds and the Accident and Emergency Unit at Edgware Hospital', Middlesex University: London.

Francome, C., W. Savage, H. Churchill and H. Lewison (1993), *Caesarean Birth in Britain*, Middlesex University Press and National Childbirth Trust: London.

Francome, C. and J. Walsh (1995), *Young Teenage Pregnancy*, Middlesex University: London.

Francome, C. and R. Wharton (1973), *An International Social Index, New Internationalist*, September, pp. 19–21.

Friedman, M. and R. (1980), *Free to Choose*, Pelican: London.

Fulder, S. J. and R. E. Monro (1982), *The Status of Complementary Medicine in the UK*, Threshold Foundation: London.

Gallup (1994), 'Kidney Doning', Gallup Poll.

Garfield, S. (1994), *The End of Innocence*, Faber and Faber: London and Boston.

Garlick, R., B. Ineichan and Hudson (1993), 'The UPA Score and Teenage Pregnancy', *Public Health*, vol. 107, pp. 135–9.

Glass, D. (1940), *Population Policies and Movements in Europe*, Frank Cass: London.

Godlee, F. (1993), 'Third World Debt', *British Medical Journal*, vol. 307, 27 November.

Goldblatt, P. (1990), 'Social Class Mortality Differences', in *Bio-social Aspects of Social Class*, ed. N. M. Mascie-Taylor, Oxford University Press: Oxford.

Goldie, I. (1993), 'Effect of Total Hip Replacement on the Quality of Life', *Quality Assurance in Health Care*, vol. 5, no. 1, pp. 9–12.

Gournay, K. J. M. and J. I. Brooking (1994), 'Community Psychiatric Nurses in Primary Care', *British Journal of Psychiatry*, vol. 165, pp. 231–8.

GP (1994), 'GPs Refer to Osteopaths', *General Practitioner*, 16 September, p. 16.

Grice, E. (1994), 'The Great Betrayal', *Daily Telegraph*, 20 December, p. 13, col. 1.

Griffiths, R. (1988), *Community Care: Agenda for Change*, HMSO: London.

Groenbaek, M., A. Deis, T. I. A. Sorenson *et al.* (1994), 'Influence of Sex, Age, Body Mass Index, and Smoking on Alcohol Intake and Mortality', *British Medical Journal*, vol. 308, pp. 302–6.

Guppy, A. (1994), 'At What Blood Alcohol Concentrations Should Drink Driving be Illegal?', *British Medical Journal*, vol. 308, 23 April, pp. 1055–6.

Ham, C. (1994a), *Health Policy in Britain*, 3rd edition, Macmillan: London.

Ham, C. (1994b), 'Where Now for the NHS Reforms?', *British Medical Journal*, vol. 309, pp. 351–2.

Hann, M. and S. Ward (1994), 'NHS "on Verge of Collapse"', *British Medical Journal*, vol. 308, p. 17.

Harrington, J. M. (1994), 'Working Long Hours and Health', *British Medical Journal*, vol. 308, pp. 1581–2.

He, Y., T. H. Lam, L. S. Li *et al.* (1994), 'Passive Smoking at Work as a Risk

Factor for Coronary Heart Disease in Chinese Women Who Have Never Smoked', *British Medical Journal*, vol. 308, 5 February, pp. 380–4.

Headlines (1993), 'Leukaemia Linked to Smoking', *British Medical Journal*, vol. 307, 28 August, p. 532.

Headlines (1994a), 'A Third of New Cases of AIDS Are Occurring in Asia', *British Medical Journal*, vol. 309, p. 428.

Headlines (1994b), 'Britain Needs 30 Cancer Units', *British Medical Journal*, vol. 308, 23 April, p. 1058.

Headlines (1994c), 'BUPA Will Issue Guidelines on Best Practice', *British Medical Journal*, vol. 309, p. 8.

Headlines (1994d), 'Danish HIV Carriers Must Use Condoms', *British Medical Journal*, vol. 308, 4 June, p. 1456.

Health Education Authority (1990), *Young Adults' Health and Lifestyles: Sexual Behaviour*, Health Education Authority: London.

Health Service Journal (1993), article published on 11 November.

Heath, E. (1993), 'Tomorrow is a Better Day', *Guardian*, 18 November, p. 24, col. 3.

Heath, I. (1994), 'The Poor Man at His Gate', *British Medical Journal*, vol. 309, p. 1675–6.

Herlitz, C. (1993), 'Sexual Behaviour in the General Population of Sweden', *Social Science and Medicine*, vol. 36, no. 12, pp. 1535–40.

Hillman, M. ed., (1983), *Children, Transport and the Quality of Life*, Policy Studies Institute: London.

Hoffenberg, R., I. P. Todd and G. Pinker (1987), 'Crisis in the National Health Service', *British Medical Journal*, vol. 295, December, p. 1505.

Hollingshead, A. B. (1961), *Elmstown's Youth*, First Science Edition (originally published Wiley: New York, 1949).

Holloway, F. (1994), 'Supervision Registers: Recent Government Policy and Legislation', *Psychiatric Bulletin*, vol. 18, pp. 593–6.

Hoult, J. (1990), 'Dissemination in New South Wales of the Madison Model', in *Mental Health Care Delivery*, eds. I. M. Marks and R. Scott, Cambridge University Press: Cambridge.

Hoult, J. (1993), 'The Sydney Experience', in *Community Mental Health Care*, C. Dean and H. Freeman, Gaskell: London.

House of Commons Health Committee (1994), 'Better Off in the Community? The Care of People who are Seriously Mentally Ill', *British Medical Journal*, vol. 308, 23 April, p. 1062.

Hoyte, P. (1994), 'Complaints: The Escalating Problem', *Update*, 15 September, p. 307.

Hunt, L. (1993), 'Parents to Sue Guy's over £8,500 Operation', *Independent*, 5 July, p. 7, col. 1.

Hussain, L. M. and A. D. Redmond (1994), 'Are Pre-hospital Deaths from Accidental Injury Preventable?', *British Medical Journal*, vol. 308, 23 April, p. 1077.

Iliffe, S. (1994), 'Trends in Europe Health Care – Implications for Britain's NHS', in Iliffe, S. (ed.), *Health Care and the Common Market, Proceedings of the 8th International Association for Health Policy (Europe) conference*, IAHP/Medical World: London.

Iliffe, S., S. See Thai, M. Gould, M. Thorogood and M. Hillsdon (1994), 'Prescribing Exercise in General Practice', *British Medical Journal*, vol. 309, 20 August, pp. 494–5.

Irvine, D. (1993), 'Education General Practitioners', *British Medical Journal*, vol. 307, no. 6906, pp. 696–7.

Jackson, G. (1994), 'Coronary Artery Disease and Women', *British Medical Journal*, vol. 309, 3 September, pp. 555–6.

Jaehnig, W. (1979), *A Family Service for the Mentally Handicapped*, Fabian Society: London.

Jatoi, I. and M. Baum (1993), 'American and British Recommendations for Screening Mammography in Younger Women: A Cultural Divide', *British Medical Journal*, vol. 307, pp. 1481–3.

Jenkins, R. (1994), 'The Health of the Nation: Recent Government Policy and Legislation', *Psychiatric Bulletin*, vol. 18, pp. 324–7.

Johnson, A. M., J. Wadsworth, K. Wellings, S. Bradshaw and J. Field (1992), 'Surveying Sexual Attitudes', *Nature*, vol. 360, p. 410.

Jones, J. (1994a), 'Care the High Price to be Paid', *Observer*, 18 December, p. 19, col. 1.

Jones, J. (1994b), 'Changing the Habits of a Lifetime', *Observer*, 16 October, special supplement, Body Mechanics, p. 8.

Jones, J. (1994c), 'Claims Threaten to Bankrupt Hospitals', *Observer*, 27 February, sect. 1, p. 3.

Jones, J. (1994d), 'Junior Hospital Doctor Drops Dead after 86 Hour Week', *Observer*, 10 April, p. 1, col. 1.

Jones, J. (1994e), 'Kill or Cure Time for the NHS', *Observer*, 13 February, sect. 1, p. 4.

Jones, J. (1994f), 'Men Targeted for Shock Campaign in Cancer Battle', *Observer*, 31 July, p. A3, col. 1.

Jones, J. (1994g), 'Patients at Risk from Rookie Surgeons', *Observer*, 5 June, p. 14.

Jones, J. (1995), 'Sick Pay Price as Doctors Put Faith in Hunches', *Observer*, 5 February, p. 8, col. 5.

Karp, S. J. (1994), 'Clinical Oncology Information Network', *British Medical Journal*, vol. 307, 15 January, pp. 147–8.

Katz, I. (1994), 'The Bugging of an NHS Doctor', *Guardian*, 1 April, sect. 2, pp. 2–4.

Kemm, J. (1993), 'Alcohol and Heart Disease: The Implications of a U-shaped Curve', *British Medical Journal*, vol. 307, no. 6916, pp. 1373–4.

Kimberley, C. H. (1994), 'NHS Changes Rob us of our True Role', *General Practitioner*, 16 September, p. 24.

Kingdom, D. (1994), 'Care Programme Approach: Recent Government and Policy and Legislation', *Psychiatric Bulletin*, vol. 18, pp. 68–70.

Kinsey, A. C., W. B. Pomeroy and C. E. Martin (1948), *Sexual Behaviour in the Human Male*, Saunders: Philadelphia.

Kinsey, A. C., W. B. Pomeroy, C. E. Martin and P. H. Gebhard (1953), *Sexual Behaviour and the Human Female*, Saunders: Philadelphia.

Klein, Rudolph (1984), *The Politics of the National Health Service*, Longmans: London and New York.

Langhorne, P. (1994), 'Unexpected Cardiac Abnormalities in Lyme Disease', *British Medical Journal*, vol. 307, p. 736.

Langhorne, P., B. Williams, W. Gilchrist and K. Howie (1993), 'Do Stroke Units Save Lives?', *The Lancet*, vol. 342, pp. 395–8.

Law, M. R., N. J. Wald and S. G. Thompson (1994), 'By How Much Does Reduction in Serum Cholesterol Concentration Lower Risk of Ischaemic Heart Disease?', *British Medical Journal*, vol. 308, pp. 367–72.

Law, M. R., N. J. Wald, T. Wu, A. Hackshaw and A. Bailey (1994), 'Systematic Underestimation of Association between Serum Cholesterol Concentration and Ischaemic Heart Disease in Observational Studies: Data from the BUPA Study', *British Medical Journal*, vol. 308, 5 February, pp. 363–6.

Law, M., J. L. Tang and N. Wald (in press), 'An Analysis of the Effectiveness of Interventions Intended to Help People Stop Smoking', *Archives of Internal Medicine*.

Lawson, A. and D. L. Rhodes (1993), 'The Politics of Pregnancy: Adolescent Sexuality and Public Policy', Yale University Press: New Haven CT.

Lee, F. R. (1994), 'AIDS Toll on Elderly: Dying Grandchildren', *New York Times*, 21 November, p. 1, col. 2 and p. B6, col. 1.

Lees, Sue (1993), *Sugar and Spice*, Penguin: London.

Lelliott, P. (1994), *Monitoring Inner London Mental Illness Services*, Royal College of Psychiatrists: London.

Lelliott, P. and J. Wing (1994), 'A National Audit of New Long Stay Psychiatric Patients II: Impact on Services', *British Journal of Psychiatry*, vol. 165, pp. 170–8.

Lelliott, P., J. Wing and P. Clifford (1994), 'A National Audit of New Long

Stay Psychiatric Patients I: Method and Description of the Cohort', *British Journal of Psychiatry*, vol. 165, pp. 160–9.

Letters (1995), 'Reality Gap in the Health Service', *Guardian*, 28 January, p. 24, col. 5.

Levi, F., Lucchini and Vecchia (1994), 'Worldwide Patterns of Cancer Mortality 1985–9', *European Journal of Cancer Prevention*, vol. 3, pp. 109–43.

Lewis, D. (1994), 'Should Employee "Whistleblowers" be Given Greater Job Security', unpublished.

Lewontin, R. C. (1995), 'Sex, Lies and Social Science', *The New York Review of Books*, 20 April, pp. 24–9.

Liddell, A. (1994), 'Pensioner Calls for Official Enquiry after Wife's Death', *Hendon Times*, 27 January, p. 5.

Linton, M. and P. Wintour (1995), 'Voters' Yes to Higher Tax for NHS', *Guardian*, 13 April, p. 1, col. 1.

Llewelyn, J. (1994), 'Oral Squamous Cell Carcinoma', *British Medical Journal*, vol. 308, 4 June 1994, p. 1508.

Lonsdale, S. and N. Cicutti (1993), 'Mentally Ill Kill 40 in Two Years', *Observer*, 4 July.

Lowry, S. (1989), 'Housing and Health: Temperature and Humidity', *British Medical Journal*, vol. 300, pp. 32–4.

Lundberg, O. (1991), 'Causal Explanations for Class Inequality in Health: An Empirical Analysis', *Social Science and Medicine*, vol. 32, pp. 385–93.

Lundgren, J. D., C. Pedersen, N. Clumleck *et al.* 'Survival Differences in European Patients with AIDS, 1979–89', *British Medical Journal*, vol. 308, no. 23, pp. 1068–73.

McGeorge, P. (1993), in *Community Mental Health Care*, C. Dean and H. Freeman, Gaskell: London.

McHardy, A. (1995), 'Muted Welcome for Gummer Clean Air Package', *Guardian*, 20 January, p. 9.

McKee, M. (1993), 'Poor Children in Rich Countries', *British Medical Journal*, vol. 307, pp. 1575–6.

McKie, R. (1984), 'Doctors Who Do Not Care for the Sick', *Observer*, 2 December.

McKie, R. (1994), 'Body Mechanics', *Observer*, 16 October, special supplement, p. 8.

MacLeod, D. (1994), 'Young "Losing their Road Sense"', *Guardian*, 27 May.

McLoone, P. and F. A. Boddy (1994), 'Deprivation and Mortality in Scotland 1981 and 1991', *British Medical Journal*, vol. 309, 3 December, pp. 1465–70.

Macmillan, H. (1938), *The Middle Way*, Macmillan: London.

Mann, J. and M. E. Wilson (1993), 'AIDS: Global Lessons from a Global Epidemic', *British Medical Journal*, vol. 307, 18 December 1993, pp. 1574–5.

Markham, A. (1987), *The Perils of Vehicle Emissions*, Friends of the Earth: London.

Marks, D. F. (1993), *The Quit for Life Programme: An Easier Way to Stop Smoking and Not Start Again*, BPS Books: Leicester.

Marks, D. F. (1994), 'Psychology's Role in the Health of the Nation', *The Psychologist*, March, pp. 119–21.

Marks, D. F. (1995a), 'Alcohol Consumption and Mortality', *British Medical Journal*, vol. 310, pp. 325–6.

Marks, D. F. (1995b), 'Evaluating the Reforms: Balancing Act', *Health Services Journal*, 13 April, pp. 26–7.

Marks, I. M., J. Connolly, M. Muijen, I. Audini, G. McNamee and R. E. Lawrence (1994), 'Home-based Versus Hospital Based Care for People with Serious Mental Illness', *British Journal of Psychiatry*, vol. 165, pp. 179–94.

Marmot, M. G. and G. Davey Smith (1989), 'Why Are the Japanese Living Longer?', *British Medical Journal*, vol. 299, pp. 1547–51.

Marmot, M. G. and M. E. McDowall (1986), 'Mortality Decline and Widening Social Inequalities', *The Lancet*, vol. ii, pp. 274–6.

Marsh, D., G. B. Smith and B. L. Taylor (1994), 'Hidden Costs of Intensive Care', *British Medical Journal*, vol. 308, pp. 473–4.

MD (1994), 'Doing the Rounds', *Private Eye*, 22 April, p. 11.

Mead, M. (1944), *The American Troops and the British Community*, Hutchinson: London.

Meikle, J. (1994), 'Schools "May Ignore" Patten Sex Guidance', *Guardian*, 7 May, p. 3.

Mental Health Foundation (1994), *Creating Community Care*, Mental Health Foundation: London.

Mihill, C. (1993a), 'Doctors Fail to Refer Cancer Patients to Specialist Centres', *Guardian*, 1 December, p. 3, col. 6.

Mihill, C. (1993b), 'Night Surgery Set to Replace GP Home Visit', *Guardian*, 20 November, p. 10, col. 1.

Mihill, C. (1993c), 'Panic over Lone Parents a Travesty', *Guardian*, 13 December, sect. A, p. 7, col. 1.

Mihill, C. (1994a), 'Cervical Cancer Claims Fewer Lives', *Guardian*, 24 May, p. 4, col. 4.

Mihill, C. (1994b), 'Drinking Advice to be Reviewed', *Guardian*, 9 August.

Mihill, C. (1994c), 'New Deal not Protecting Doctors from Long Hours', *Guardian*, 17 March, p. 4, col. 1.

Mihill, C. (1994d), 'Sick Elderly "Denied some Treatments"', *Guardian*, 5 September, p. 4.

Mihill, C. (1994e), 'Women in UK Head Heart Deaths Table', *Guardian*, 12 July, p. 5, col. 1.

Mihill, C. (1995a), 'BUPA Signs Agreement to Treat Libyans', *Guardian*, 18 January, p. 5, col. 1.

Mihill, C. (1995b), 'Health Shake-up to End Cancer "Lottery"', *Guardian*, 25 April, p. 5, col. 1.

Mihill, C. (1995c), 'Hefty Proportion of Britons Is Too Fat', *Guardian*, 2 March, p. 3.

Mihill, C. (1995d), 'Sick "Denied Intensive Care Help"', *Guardian*, 10 March, p. 3, col. 1.

Mihill, C. and M. Wainwright (1995), 'Death of Patient in Helicopter Dash Sparks NHS Beds Row', *Guardian*, 10 March, p. 3.

Minerva (1993a), [Untitled], *British Medical Journal*, vol. 307, p. 456.

Minerva (1993b), [Untitled], *British Medical Journal*, vol. 307, p. 1572.

Minerva (1994), [Untitled], *British Medical Journal*, vol. 308, p. 546.

Moher, M. and N. Johnson (1994), 'Use of Aspirin by General Practitioners in Suspected Acute Myocardial Infarction', *British Medical Journal*, vol. 308, p. 760.

Morris, R. (1994), 'Cautious Welcome for Composition of Healthcare 2000', *The Times*, 8 August, p. 15.

Mosher, L. and L. Burti (1994), *Community Mental Health: A Practical Guide*, Naughton: New York.

Mutale, T. I. R. (1994), 'Link between Fundholding General Practitioners and Mental Health Professionals', *Psychiatric Bulletin*, vol. 18, pp. 603–5.

NHS Consultants Association (1995), *Health Policy Network in Practice: The NHS Market*, NHS Consultants Association/NHS Support Federation: London.

Nicholson-Lord, D. (1994), 'Junk-food Diet "Threatens Child Health"', *Independent*, 2 March, p. 8, col. 1.

Nuttall, N. (1994), 'Transplant Patients Say New Computer Donor Scheme is Useless', *The Times*, 7 October, p. 7, col. 1.

O'Higgins, M. and S. P. Jenkins (1990), 'Poverty in the EC', in *Analysing Poverty in the European Community*, eds. R. Tekkens and B. M. S. Praag, EUROSTAT: Luxembourg.

Onyett, S. (1992), *Case Management*, Chapman & Hall: London.

OPCS (1993), *1991 Birth Statistics*, HMSO: London.

OPCS (1994a), *1992 Birth Statistics*, HMSO: London, June.

OPCS (1994b), *Conceptions in England and Wales 1991*, OPCS Monitor FM1 94/1, 29 March.

OPCS (1994c), *Regional Trends 29*, HMSO: London.

OPCS (1994d) *Social Trends No. 24*, HMSO: London.

OPCS (1995), *Social Trends No. 25*, HMSO: London.

Oppenheim, C. (1993) *Poverty the Facts*, Child Poverty Action Group: London.

Pallister, D. (1986), 'Plastic Bag That May Save Thousands of Kidney Patients', *Guardian*, 24 March, p. 6, col. 1.

Pater, J. E. (1981), *The Making of the National Health Service*, King's Fund: London.

Phillimore P., A. Beattie and P. Townsend (1994), 'Widening Inequality of Health in Northern England 1981–91', *British Medical Journal*, vol. 308, pp. 1125–8.

Pilkington, E. (1995), 'BT Chief's Wish for Relaxing Life of Junior Doctor Angers Medical World', *Guardian*, 1 February, p. 1, col. 1.

Plummer, K. (1975), *Sexual Stigma*, Routledge and Kegan Paul: London.

Pocock, S. J., M. Smith and Baghurst (1994), 'Environmental Lead and Children's Intelligence: A Systematic Review of Epidemiological Evidence', *British Medical Journal*, vol. 309, pp. 1189–97.

Pope, N. and E. Campbell (1994), 'Perks General, Another NHS Scandal', *Today*, 16 March, p. 1, col. 1.

Radical Statistics Health Group (1987), *Facing the Figures*, London.

Rapp, A. (1993), 'Theory, Principle and Methods of Strength Model of Case Management', in *Case Management: Theory and Practice*, eds. M. Harris and H. Bergman, American Psychiatric Association: Washington DC.

Rickford, F. (1994), 'The Long Wait', *Nursing Times*, vol. 90, p. 20.

Rigge, M. (1993), 'Casualty Department's Compared', *WHICH? Way to Health*, August, pp. 136–9.

Rigge, M. (1994), 'Quality of Life of Long Wait Orthopaedic Patients before and after Admission: A Consumer Audit', *Quality in Health Care*, vol. 3, no. 3, pp. 59–63.

Ritchie, J. (1994), *Report of the Inquiry into the Care and Treatment of Christopher Clunis*, HMSO: London.

Robert, R. T., J. H. Gagnon, E. O. Laumann and G. Kolata (1994), *Sex in America*, Little, Brown and Company: London.

Rogers, L. and L. Thomas (1995), 'Young Dr Bottomley's 80-hour Week', *The Sunday Times*, 22 January, p. 3, col. 1.

Ronald, P. J. M., J. R. Robertson, R. Wyld and R. Weightman (1993), 'Heterosexual Transmission of HIV in Injecting Drug Users', *British Medical Journal*, vol. 307, 6 November, pp. 1184–5.

Rose, D. (1995), 'New Gas Blunders in the Pipeline', *Observer*, 1 January, p. 1, col. 1.

Rosenberg, K. and H. P. McEwan (1991), 'Teenage Pregnancy in Scotland: Trends and Risks', *Scottish Medical Journal*, vol. 36, pp. 172–4.

Royal College of Nursing (1993), *Waiting for a Bed*, Royal College of Nursing: London.

Russell-Jones, R. (1987), *The Health Effects of Vehicle Emissions*, Friends of the Earth: London.

Russell, M., C. Wilson, C. Taylor and C. Baker (1979), 'Effect of General Practitioner's Advice Against Smoking', *British Medical Journal*, vol. ii, pp. 31–5.

Ryan, S. and S. Reeves (1994), 'Revealed: The Most Polluted Parts of Britain', *The Sunday Times*, 10 July, p. 5, col. 1.

Salama, F., D. Beggs and E. Morgan (1994), 'Treatment of Oesophageal Cancer', *British Medical Journal*, vol. 309, 9 July, pp. 125–6.

Sandercock, P. (1993), 'Managing Stroke: The Way Forward', *British Medical Journal*, vol. 307, 20 November, p. 1297–8.

Savage, W. (1993), 'Money before Patients in the New NHS', *Guardian*, 5 March, p. 2.

Schroder, F. H. (1995), 'Detection of Prostate Cancer', *British Medical Journal*, vol. 310, pp. 140–1.

Sheldon, J. (1994), 'Public Service Ethos under Attack', *Guardian*, 31 January, sect. 1, p. 19.

Sheldon, J. (1995), 'The Netherlands Lags behind in Heart Operations', *British Medical Journal*, vol. 310, pp. 78–9.

Sheldon, T. (1994), 'Please Bypass the PORT', *British Medical Journal*, vol. 309, 16 July, p. 142.

Shelter (1995), *Homeless in London*, Shelter: London.

Shuttleworth, D. (1993), 'Sunbeds and the Pursuit of a Year Round Tan', *British Medical Journal*, vol. 307, 11 December, pp. 1508–9.

Sloggart, A. and H. Joshi (1994), 'Higher Mortality in Deprived Areas: Community or Personal Disadvantage', *British Medical Journal*, vol. 309, 3 December, pp. 1470–4.

Small, N. (1989), *Politics and Planning the National Health Service*, Open University Press: Milton Keynes.

Smith, D. I. (1992), 'The Vital Statistics of Sex', *Guardian*, 7 December, sect. 1, p. 20, col. 6.

Smith, R. (1993a), 'Doctors and Markets', *British Medical Journal*, vol. 307, pp. 216–7.

Smith, R. (1993b), 'New BMA Chairman Asks Government to Stop and Think', *British Medical Journal*, vol. 307, p. 83.

Smith, R. and J. Leaning (1993), 'Medicine and Global Survival', *British Medical Journal*, vol. 307, pp. 693–4.

Smith, T. (1988a), 'Listening to Consultants: Dr K the Cardiologist', *British Medical Journal*, vol. 296, January, pp. 45–7.

Smith, T. (1988b), 'Mr Q the Surgeon', *British Medical Journal*, vol. 296, pp. 123–5.

Smith, T. (1988c), 'New Year Message', *British Medical Journal*, vol. 296, no. 6614, p. 1.

Smithells, R. W. (1994), 'Thalidomide May Be a Mutagen', *British Medical Journal*, 13 August, p. 477.

Smithers, R. (1993), 'Safety Fears Prompt Parents to Limit Children's Mobility, Research Shows', *Guardian*, 17 July, p. 4, col. 3.

Social Services Committee (1986), *Fourth Report: Public Expenditure on the Social Services*, HMSO: London.

Socialist Health Association (1994), 'Community Care – Seamless or Full of Holes?', policy briefing, January, Socialist Health Association: London.

Spence, D. P. S., J. Hotchkiss, C. S. D. Williams and P. D. O. Davies (1993), 'Tuberculosis and Poverty', *British Medical Journal*, vol. 307, 25 September.

Stall, R. (1994), 'How to Lose the Fight against AIDS among Gay Men', *British Medical Journal*, vol. 309, pp. 685–6.

Stean, M. (1994), 'Patient Offered Gag as Anaesthetic Runs Out', *Evening Standard*, 21 March.

Stein, L. I. and M. A. Test (1980), 'Alternatives to Mental Hospital Treatment I: A Conceptual Model Treatment Programme and Clinical Evaluation', *Archives of General Psychiatry*, vol. 37, pp. 392–7.

Stiller, C. A. (1994), 'Population Based Survival Rates for Childhood Cancer in Britain 1980–91', *British Medical Journal*, vol. 309, pp. 1612–16.

Swift, P. G. F., J. L. Hearnshaw, J. L. Botha, G. Wright, N. T. Raymond and K. F. Jamieson (1993), 'A Decade of Diabetes: Keeping the Children out of Hospital', *British Medical Journal*, vol. 307, pp. 96–8.

Tatchell, P. (1994), *Safer Sexy*, Freedom Editions: London and New York.

Tawney, R. H. (1963), *Equality*.

Taylor, D. (1984), *Understanding the NHS in the 1980s*, Office of Health Economics: London.

Thatcher, M. (1995) *The Downing Street Years*, HarperCollins: London.

Thomas, S., C. Acton, J. Nixon, D. Battistutta, R. Pitt and R. Clark (1994), 'Effectiveness of Bicycle Helmets in Preventing Head Injury in Children: Case-control Study', *British Medical Journal*, vol. 308, pp. 173–6.

Thorogood, M., J. Mann, P. Appleby and K. McPherson (1994), 'Risk of Death from Cancer and Ischaemic Heart Disease in Meat and non Meat Eaters', *British Medical Journal*, vol. 308, pp. 1667–70.

Titmuss, R. M. (1950), *Problems of Social Policy*, HMSO: London.

Titmuss, R. M. (1968), *The Gift Relationship*, Penguin: London.

Tomlinson, B. (1992), *Report of the Inquiry into London's Health Service, Medical Education and Research*, HMSO: London.

Tonks, A. (1993), 'Patients with Cancer Wait Too Long', *British Medical Journal*, vol. 307, p. 757.

Towner, E. M. L., S. N. Jarvis, S. S. M. Walsh and A. Aynsley-Green (1994), 'Measuring Exposure to Injury Risk in Schoolchildren Aged 11–14', *British Medical Journal*, vol. 308, no. 6928, pp. 449–52.

Townsend, P. (1993), *The International Analysis of Poverty*, Harvester-Wheatsheaf: Hemel Hempstead.

Townsend, P. (1994), 'The Rich Man in His Castle', *British Medical Journal*, vol. 309, pp. 1674–5.

Townsend, P. and N. Davidson (eds.) (1992), *Inequalities in Health: The Black Report*, Penguin: London and New York.

Townsend, P., P. Phillimore and A. Beattie (1988), *Health and Deprivation: Inequality and the North*, Croom Helm.

Travis, A. (1994), 'Smoke Alarms Cut Fire Deaths', *Guardian*, 16 June.

Tudor Hart, J. (1994), 'NHS Reforms: A Conspiracy Exists', *British Medical Journal*, vol. 309, 17 September, p. 739.

Tunstall-Pedoe, H., K. Kuulasmaa, P. Amouyel *et al.* (1994), 'Myocardial Infarction and Coronary Deaths in the World Health Organization MONICA Project', *Circulation*, pp. 583–612.

UKTSSA (1993), *Renal Transplant Audit* and information from Julia Warren, United Kingdom Transport Support Services Authority: London.

UNICEF (1993), *The Progress of Nations*, UNICEF: London and New York.

UNICEF (1994), Personal communication – letter from Robert Smith.

Valkonen, T. (1989), 'Adult Education and Level of Education: A Comparison of Six Countries', in ed. A. J. Fox, *Inequalities in Health Within Europe*, Gower Press: Aldershot.

van Griensven, G. J. P., E. M. M. de Vroome, J. Goudsmit and R. A. Coutinho (1989), 'Changes in Sexual Behaviour and the Fall in Incidence of HIV Infection among Homosexual Men', *British Medical Journal*, vol. 298, pp. 218–21.

Venn, P. J. H. (1994), 'Trust Charged for Information', *British Medical Journal*, vol. 308, no. 6920, p. 63.

von Sternberg, P. L. (1994), 'Everything is Besheret?', *Shalom*, 15 March 1994, pp. 12–13.

Wallace, W. (1994), 'Why Academia and Labour Must Not Fail Each Other', *Guardian*, 1 September, p. 22, col. 7.

Ward, J. D. (1995), 'Reality Gap in the Health Service', *Guardian*, 28 January, p. 24, col. 3.

Warden, J. (1995a), 'Executives of NHS Trusts Beat the Pay Freeze', *British Medical Journal*, vol. 310, pp. 77–8.

Warden, J. (1995b), 'Peers Define Best and Worst of NHS Research', *British Medical Journal*, vol. 310, 17 June, pp. 1555–6.

Waterhouse, R. (1993), 'Study Shows No Evidence of Queue Jumping', *Independent*, 8 October.

Waterhouse, R. (1995), '£540m Plea for Mental Health', *Independent*, 17 March, p. 12, col. 8.

Weale, S. (1995), 'Dying Girl in Court Fight for Treatment', *Guardian*, 10 March, p. 1, col. 7.

Wennemo, I. (1993), 'Relative Poverty and Infant Mortality', *Sociology of Health and Illness*, vol. 15, pp. 429–46.

West, R. (1994), *Obesity*, Office of Health Economics: London.

Weston, C. F. M., W. J. Penney and D. G. Julian (1994), 'Guidelines for the Early Management of Patients with Myocardial Infarction', *British Medical Journal*, vol. 308, 19 March, pp. 767–71.

White, E. (1991), *Third Quinquennial Study of Community Psychiatric Nursing: Research Monograph*, Department of Nursing Studies, University of Manchester.

White, M. (1993), 'English Managers "up 262 per cent"', *Guardian*, 18 November, p. 3.

Whitehead, M. (1992), *The Health Divide*, Penguin: London and New York.

Wilkinson, P., K. Laji, R. Kulasgaram, L. Parsons, and A. D. Timmis (1994), 'Acute Myocardial Infarction in Women: Survival Analysis in First Six Months', *British Medical Journal*, vol. 309, 3 September, pp. 566–9.

Wilkinson, R. G. (1986), 'Income and Mortality', in *Class and Health: Research and Longitudinal Data*, ed. R. G. Wilkinson, Tavistock Press: London.

Wilkinson, R. G. (1989), 'Class Mortality Differentials and Trends in Poverty 1921–81', *Journal of Social Policy*, vol. 18, pp. 307–35.

Wilkinson, R. G. (1992), 'Income Distribution and Life Expectancy', *British Medical Journal*, vol. 304, pp. 165–8.

Wilkinson, R. G. (1994), *Unfair Shares*, Barnardo's: Ilford, Essex.

Williams, E. C., R. J. E. Kirkman and M. Elstein (1994), 'Profile of Young People's Advice Clinic in Reproductive Health, 1988–93', *British Medical Journal*, vol. 309, pp. 786–8.

Willis, P. (1977), *Learning to Labour*, Saxon House: Farnborough.

Wills, T. A. (1987), 'Help-seeking as a Coping Mechanism', in *Coping with Negative Life Events: Clinical and Social Psychological Perspectives*, eds. C. R. Snyder and C. E. Ford, Plenum: New York, pp. 19–50.

Wing, J. K. and G. W. Brown (1970), *Institutionalism and Schizophrenia*, Cambridge University Press: Cambridge.

World Development Movement (1994), *British Overseas Aid – Spending Trends*, WDM: London.

Wynand, P. M., M. van de Ven, F. T. Schut and F. F. H. Rutten (1994), 'Forming and Reforming the Market for Third Party Purchasing of Health Care', *Social Science and Medicine*, vol. 39, no. 10, pp. 1433–46.

Yates, D. W., M. Woodford and S. Hollis (1992), 'Preliminary Analysis of the Care of Injured Patients in 33 British Hospitals: First Report of the UK Major Trauma Outcome Study', *British Medical Journal*, vol. 305, pp. 737–40.

Yates, J. (1995), *Serving Two Masters*, Dispatches, Channel 4 Television: London and Cardiff.

Yudkin, P., L. Jones and G. Fowler (1994), 'Randomised Trial of Nicotine Patches in General Practice: Results at One Year', *British Medical Journal*, vol. 308, pp. 1476–7.

Zahr, C. A. and E. Royston (1991), *Maternal Mortality: A Global Factbook*, World Health Organization: Geneva.

INDEX